COOK CONTINENTALE

COOK CONTINENTALE

ELIZABETH CRAIG

OLIVER & BOYD

EDINBURGH AND LONDON

OLIVER AND BOYD LTD.
Tweeddale Court
Edinburgh 1

39A Welbeck Street
London, W.1

First published 1965

Printed in Great Britain by
Oliver and Boyd Ltd., Edinburgh

INTRODUCTION

Let me introduce you to *Cook Continentale*. It is a collection of recipes, from 15 different countries, which I have adapted to remind you of happy hours spent on holiday abroad. Some of them are for dishes I have enjoyed in many parts of Europe. Others have been given to me by acquaintances and friends who share my love for culinary adventures. . . .

To some people the scent of a flower will carry them back to magical hours on the Costa del Sol. To others the aroma of wine, or the flavour of a dish will waft them to sunny Italy, or to a bistro in Paris. Time was when you had to go abroad or patronise foreign restaurants to satisfy a taste for something different. Nowadays, with food pouring into Britain from all over Europe, you may prepare and serve Continental fare in your own homes.

I hope this book will help you.

Elizabeth Craig

Wethersfield Hall
Wethersfield
Braintree
Essex

ACKNOWLEDGMENTS

I wish to thank all those who kindly checked my copy to see that the foreign titles and the foreign references were correctly spelt, and also those who have kindly passed on to me some of their favourite recipes.

Austrian Embassy,
18 Belgrave Square,
London, S.W.1.

Mrs. F. Engel

Belgian Embassy,
103-5 Eaton Square,
London, S.W.1.

M. A. Cammaerts,
Attaché Agricole

Czechoslovak Embassy,
7 Kensington Palace, Gardens,
London, W.8.
    and
The Czechoslovak Woman,
Praha 3,
Jindrissak 5,
Czechoslavakia
    and
Pilsner Urquell Co. Ltd.,
Marlon House,
71-4 Mark Lane,
London, E.C.2.

Jaroslava Černá,
Public Relations Officer

Zdeňka Zimová,
Chief Editor

J. Dolezal,
Director

French Embassy,
22 Hans Place,
London, S.W.1.

C. Kerouedan,
Commercial Counsellor

Embassy of the Federal Republic
  of Germany,
Chesham Place,
London, S. W. 1.
    and
Deinhard & Co. Ltd.,
9 Idol Lane,
Great Tower Street,
London, E.C.3.

Dr. A. van Setten,
    and
W. Saeftel

A. J. Hasslacher,
    and
P. Hasslacher

Greek Centre Produce Display,
195-7 Regent Street,
London, W. 1.

Z. D. Alatzas

Royal Netherlands Embassy,
38 Hyde Park Gate,
London, S. W. 7.

Dr. L. W. Binkhorst,
Agricultural Attaché

Hungarian News and Information
Service
167 Kensington High Street,
London, W.8.

Lawrence Kirwan,
Director

Italian Institute for Foreign Trade,
31 Old Burlington Street,
London, W.1.

A. Giaroli
and
Dr. G. Zuccarello

Embassy of the Polish People's
Republic
15 Devonshire Street,
London, W.1.

S. Ungeheuer

Casa de Portugal,
20 Lower Regent Street,
London, S.W.1.
and
Evans Marshall & Co. Ltd.,
6 Idol Lane,
London, E.C.3.
and
Geo. G. Sandeman Sons & Co., Ltd.,
20 St. Swithin's Lane,
London, E.C.4.

Antonio Bento Franco Mendes
and
Jose da Rocha Ramos

Grendon E. Gooch

T. W. Sandeman

Spanish Embassy,
3 Hans Crescent,
London, S.W.1.

Señor Bozzano
Commercial Attaché

The Swiss Embassy,
18 Montagu Place,
Bryanston Square,
London, W.1.

J. Revilliod,
Cultural Counsellor

Turkish Embassy,
43 Belgrave Square,
London, S.W.1.

C. Vayisoğlu,
Commercial Counsellor

Gatwick Manor,
Nr. Crawley,
Sussex.

Nevvar Hickmet

Richard & William Teltcher Ltd.,
Town Hall Chambers,
374 Old Street,
London, E.C.1.

Richard Teltscher

CONTENTS

x

xi

xii

xiii

xiv

xv

AUSTRIA

Prost —— Good Health!

AUSTRIA

Every time I enjoy a Wiener Schnitzel, or make a Sachertorte, my thoughts wing back to Austria. Sometimes I find myself in Vienna, skimming up Himmel Strasse on my way to dine at Cobenzl to the lovely strains of Fledermaus.

I know no other country in Europe where food and wine have such romantic settings. There, dining and wining to Strauss and gipsy music is a feast in more senses than one.

The Austrian cuisine, though it has a distinct character of its own, is more than slightly influenced by all the other countries with which Austria has been associated throughout her checkered career. Many of the dishes you will enjoy when visiting this fascinating country are of foreign origin, but Austria has given to them a touch of her own.

You really have to adventure in Austria to become fully acquainted with her national fare. If you are as interested in food and wine as I am, try to plan your next visit to Vienna at Heurige time, when the Weinhauer (vineyard owners) open their gardens to the public, then make your way to Grinzing or Nussdorf, haunts of Beethoven and Schubert, and sample the new wine while you listen to the Schrammeln playing and singing old folk songs.

"Wein! Wein! nor du allein."

LEBER PASTETE (Liver Pâté)

*½ lb. finely minced lean pork, ½ lb. finely minced fat pork,
½ lb. raw turkey liver, ½ lb. raw calf's liver, 1½ teaspoons
salt, ½ teaspoon pepper, 2 large peeled truffles.*

Put the lean and the fat pork in a basin and mix well.
Put through a mincer. Wash, dry and slice livers. Add to
minced pork. Season with the salt and pepper. Chop truffle
peelings and add. Mix well, then pack into a basin. Cover
first with greaseproof paper then with foil. Place on a rack
in a large saucepan, containing enough cold water to come
to within an inch of the top of the basin. Cover pan. Bring
water to simmering point. Simmer gently for 8 hours.
Remove from stove. When water is lukewarm, remove foil
and paper from pâté, then rub pâté through a fine sieve. Chop
truffles. Stir into mixture, then place in 10 small earthenware
pots. Cover with a clean cloth. Stand for about an hour,
then examine the pots. If some are not evenly covered with
fat, remove fat from those that have too much and melt and
pour over others. Each pot of paste should be evenly covered.
Cover each pot with greaseproof paper and place again on
the rack in pan. Replace on stove. Cover and leave for 3
hours, seeing that the water barely simmers. Remove, and when
cold store in the refrigerator for at least 24 hours before serving.

To Serve: Turn out each pot on to a plate lined with a
lettuce leaf. Serve with potato salad and crisp toast and butter.

Note: Sometimes the paste is cooked in one large oblong
mould and served in slices.

YIELD: 10 servings.

WIENER ERDÄPFEL SUPPE* (Viennese Potato Soup)

*2 oz. butter, ½ cup chopped onion, 1 lb. minced lean beef,
3 teaspoons paprika, ¼ teaspoon dried marjoram, 1 teaspoon
salt, ¼ clove garlic, 2 tablespoons flour, 6 large peeled potatoes,
3¼ pints cold water.*

Melt butter in a large saucepan. Add onion. Fry slowly
until onion turns a pale yellow, stirring occasionally. Add

---

* Some Viennese cooks omit the meat and substitute rich beef stock
for the water.

beef. Fry for 5 minutes, stirring constantly, to prevent meat lumping. Add paprika, marjoram and salt. Bruise and mince garlic, and add. Cover. Simmer for 2 minutes. Sprinkle with a little of the flour. Cream remaining flour with water and stir into soup. Cut potatoes in dice, and add, with the water. Cover. Simmer very gently until potatoes are soft in about 20 minutes.

YIELD: 6-7 servings.

GEDÜNSTETER AAL (Stewed Eel with Wine Sauce)

1 medium-sized eel, salt as required, pepper to taste, 2 teaspoons minced parsley, ¼ pint white wine.

Wash and skin eel. With a sharp knife, cut in slices. Lay on a platter. Sprinkle with salt. Cover and stand for 30 minutes. Drain, then wipe with a clean cloth. Place, side by side, in a large frying pan. Season with pepper. Add parsley and wine. Simmer over moderate heat, turning the slices occasionally, until thoroughly cooked. (Do not let it cook too quickly or it will brown too much below before it is cooked through.) Serve, browned side up, on a heated platter, with boiled potatoes.

YIELD: 5 or 6 servings.

LEBERKNOEDEL (Liver Dumplings)

5 oz. minced calf's liver, 3 slices bread, 1 oz. butter, 1 dessert-spoon chopped onion, 1 tablespoon mixed parsley, 4 tablespoons flour, 1 egg, salt and pepper, pinch of marjoram if liked.

Wipe liver with a damp cloth before mincing. Remove crusts from bread. Crumble bread finely. Melt butter in a small frying pan. Add onion and parsley. Fry slowly for 2 or 3 minutes, stirring occasionally. Remove pan from stove. Stir in liver. Add flour. Stir till blended. Add breadcrumbs and egg. Season to taste with salt and freshly ground pepper, and flavour with marjoram if liked.

If wanted for garnishing clear soup, scoop out small balls with a rounded teaspoon and drop into boiling soup. Cover pan closely. Simmer gently over low heat for about 15 minutes. If required for serving with stewed meat, scoop

3

out into balls with a rounded soup spoon and drop into boiling stew. Cook as described for about 20 minutes. Serve round the meat.

YIELD: 4-5 servings.

TIROLER KNOEDEL (Tyrolean Dumplings)

4 handfuls bread cubes, 4 soupspoons ham cubes, 2 eggs, salt and pepper, chopped parsley to taste, clear stock as required.

Place bread cubes, cut quarter inch square, in a basin. Add ham cubes, cut the same size. Beat eggs. Stir into mixture. Season with salt and freshly ground black pepper. Stir in parsley to taste. Mix with clear stock to a paste that can be easily handled. Divide into 8-10 small portions. Shape each into a ball. Place quickly in clear boiling stock. Cover closely. Boil till they rise to the top in a few minutes. Drain thoroughly. Serve with any casserole or stew of meat, or with backhendl.

YIELD: 4-5 servings.

TIROLER LEBER (Tyrolean Liver)

1 lb. calf's liver, seasoned flour as required, 1 oz. butter, 1 tablespoon chopped onion, salt and pepper, 1 dessertspoon chopped capers, 1 dessertspoon vinegar, water as required, ½ gill soured cream or yoghurt.

Wipe liver with a damp cloth. Cut into thin slices. Dip in seasoned flour. Melt butter in a frying pan. Add liver. Fry over low heat till delicately browned on both sides and cooked through. Remove to a heated platter and keep hot. Add onion to fat in pan. Fry over moderate heat till soft. Stir in a tablespoon flour and salt and freshly ground black pepper to taste, then add capers, vinegar and enough water to make a thick sauce. Stir till boiling. Gradually add the soured cream or yoghurt, and heat till piping hot, stirring constantly. Do not allow to boil. Place liver in sauce. Reheat carefully, then dish up. Serve with boiled rice, dumplings or nockerln.

4

Nockerln: Sift 3 oz, flour into a basin. Dissolve 1 oz. butter or margarine in ½ pint milk, but do not allow to boil. As soon as butter has dissolved, remove pan from stove, and add 1 egg. Whisk until blended. Season to taste with salt. Stir in milk and butter, etc., then flour, until a stiff paste is obtained. Cut out small dumplings with the help of a teaspoon, dipping spoon frequently into boiling water. Place in a large pan of boiling salted water. Boil for about 2 minutes, then remove and taste one. (They need between 2 and 3 minutes' cooking, no more.) Drain in a colander or sieve. Rinse under cold water tap. Melt 1 heaped tablespoon butter or dripping in a frying pan. Add the nockerln. Heat carefully, shaking pan from time to time. Take care they do not brown. Serve with liver or goulash.

     YIELD: 4 servings.

GRETEL BEER, VIENNA.

WIENER SCHNITZEL (Fried Scallops of Veal)

6 scallops of veal, ½ inch thick, 1½ oz. flour, salt and pepper, 1 slightly beaten egg, 1 tablespoon milk or water, 1 cup sieved stale breadcrumbs, butter or cooking oil as required.

Trim scallops neatly. Flatten with a meat bat. Season flour with salt and pepper. Mix the egg with the milk or water. Season with a few grains of salt. Dip each scallop first in the flour, then shake off the surplus flour. Dip in egg, and lastly in the breadcrumbs. Chill. Heat enough butter or oil to cover the bottom of a large frying pan. Add scallops. Fry over moderate heat until brown below, then turn and fry on the other side, until golden brown. (They usually take about 5 minutes on each side.) Drain on absorbent paper. Arrange, overlapping, along the centre of a heated platter. If liked, garnish each on top with a curved fillet of anchovy. Garnish dish with sprigs of parsley and 6 wedges of lemon. Serve with green peas or a heart of lettuce salad and fried chips, or mashed potatoes.

     YIELD: 6 servings.

HASENBRATEN MIT RAHMSAUCE (Roast Hare with Cream Sauce)

1 saddle of hare, 1 medium-sized onion, 1 medium-sized carrot, 4 black peppercorns, 2 bay leaves, 1 piece root ginger, 1 sprig marjoram, 1 sprig thyme, 1 crushed clove garlic, ½ cup water, ½ pint red wine, bacon fat as required, 1 teaspoon flour, 1 cup soured cream, 1 tablespoon redcurrant jelly.

Trim saddle of hare, removing the flap. Lard, equal distance apart, with strips of bacon fat. Peel and slice onion. Trim and slice carrot. Place vegetables in a saucepan with the peppercorns, bay leaves, root ginger, marjoram, thyme and garlic. Add the water. Cover and simmer gently for 5 minutes. Add wine. Bring to boiling point. Remove from stove. Place hare in a deep container. Pour the marinade over. Cover and stand for 12 hours. Drain thoroughly through a strainer. Melt enough bacon fat to cover the base of a self-basting roasting tin. Add hare. Cover with lid. Roast in moderately hot oven, 375 °F (Mark 4-5), until meat is tender, basting occasionally with the marinade, in 1½-2 hours. Dish up. Keep hot. Blend the flour with the cream. Add to sauce. Simmer gently for 10 minutes, stirring constantly, adding a little more soured cream if required. Add red currant jelly. Stir till dissolved. Strain over the hare.

YIELD: 4 or 5 servings.

REHBRATEN MIT RAHMSAUCE (Roast Venison with Cream Sauce).

3-5 lb. loin of venison, salt and pepper, ¼ teaspoon grated nutmeg, 1 or 2 crushed juniper berries, 1 slice peeled onion, 1 slice trimmed carrot, 1 slice peeled celeriac, ½ oz. butter or bacon fat, 1 teaspoon French mustard, 1 bay leaf, 1 sprig thyme, 2 whole cloves, grated rind ½ lemon, ½ pint beef stock or water, ¼ pint red wine, ¼ pint soured cream.

Remove skin from meat, then lard neatly with tiny strips of bacon fat. Rub meat with salt and pepper, nutmeg and juniper berries. Prepare vegetables. Melt fat in a shallow saucepan. Add vegetables. Fry lightly, turning occasionally, for about 5 minutes, then add the venison. Fry till brown

6

below, then turn and fry on the other side. Transfer meat to a casserole. Arrange vegetables round. Add mustard, bay leaf, thyme, cloves and the lemon rind, then the stock or water flavoured with a beef cube. Cover closely. Cook in a slow oven, 325 °F (Mark 2-3), until meat is tender, allowing about 40 minutes per pound if 3 lb. in weight, and about 35 minutes if about 5 lb. (Add a little more stock or water during cooking if necessary.) Remove venison. Slice and arrange, overlapping on a heated platter. Cover and keep hot. Add wine to the casserole. Stir till blended, then add the soured cream. Stir till piping hot. Strain over the meat. Serve with boiled noodles, tossed in melted butter, or mashed potatoes, cranberry sauce, and häuptel salat.

YIELD: 6 or 8 servings.

GEDÜNSTETE KARTOFFELN (Casserole of Potatoes)

8 medium-sized peeled potatoes, 3 peeled onions, 3-4 oz. butter, salt and pepper to taste, 1½ tablespoons vinegar, white stock as required.

Cut potatoes and onions into very thin slices. Arrange a layer of potato in a buttered casserole. Cover with a layer of onion. Dab with butter. Season with salt and pepper. Repeat layers twice. Mix the vinegar with enough white stock, or water flavoured with chicken cubes, to come up to rim of casserole. Cover closely. (Some Austrians seal the lid to the casserole with a thick flour-and-water paste.) Bake for 1½-2 hours in a moderate oven, 350 °F (Mark 3-4). Serve with roast beef or lamb.

YIELD: 4 servings.

APFELSTRUDEL (Baked Apple Roll)

6 oz. flour, 1 beaten egg, warm water as required, 3 lb. cooking apples, 2 tablespoons Demarara sugar, 2 tablespoons grated hazelnuts, 2 tablespoons breadcrumbs, 2 tablespoons currants, 2 tablespoons sultanas, 1 tablespoon chopped minced candied peel, 1 dessertspoon ground cinnamon, grated rind of 1 lemon, grated rind of 1 orange, 1 oz. butter, melted, 2 oz. sifted icing sugar.

Sift flour into a warm basin. Mix to a soft paste with the egg, diluted with a tablespoon of warm water, and more water

7

as required. Turn on to a pastry board. Beat for 15 minutes. Flatten out a little with your hand, and lay a on well-floured cloth over a board. Stand for 10 minutes. Peel, core and cut apples into thin slices. Place in a basin. Add the sugar, nuts, breadcrumbs, currants, sultanas, candied peel, cinnamon and lemon and orange rind. Mix till thoroughly blended. Pull out the pastry, first on one side and then on another, until wafer-thin. Stand for 5 minutes. Pour apple mixture evenly over one end, then carefully lift up the end of the cloth and roll the pastry over the filling, away from you, on to a well-buttered baking sheet. Coat with a little of the melted butter. Bake in a hot oven, 450 °F (Mark 7-8), for 20 minutes until very delicately browned, basting occasionally with melted butter. Dust thickly with sifted icing sugar, vanilla-flavoured if possible. Cool. Serve on a long narrow platter, or wooden board, with thick cream.

YIELD: 6 or 8 servings.

KAISERSCHMARRN * (Emperor's Pancakes)

6 separated eggs, 2 oz. castor sugar, 6 oz. flour, 1 cup milk, 1 saltspoon salt, 2 oz. butter.

Beat egg yolks until smoothly blended. Beat in sugar, mixed with the flour, then milk and salt. Melt butter. Stir into mixture. Beat egg whites till stiff but not dry, and fold in. Melt 1 oz. butter in a large heavy frying pan. Pour in mixture. Fry for a few minutes over moderate heat until the base begins to brown lightly. (Be careful not to let pancake scorch.) Turn carefully and when brown below, tear it into irregular shaped pieces, called " schmarrn ", with two forks. Cook them very slowly a little longer. Arrange in a heated serving dish. Sprinkle with castor sugar.

To Vary: Stir 1 oz. cleaned currants or sultanas into the mixture before egg whites.

YIELD: 6 servings.

* This is the traditional sweet, associated with Emperor Joseph, who called at a peasant's house when hunting in the Tyrol and asked for a meal. The girl who was making the pancakes was so nervous, she broke a pancake, but her mistress quickly broke the remainder into small pieces, and served them as a speciality. The Emperor was so pleased with the cakes, that they were called after him for ever after.

SCHAUMKOCH (Chocolate Meringue Pudding)

7 egg whites, 12 oz. sifted icing sugar, 4 oz. plain chocolate.

Beat 6 egg whites until almost stiff. Add a little sugar at a time, beating constantly. After all the sugar has been added, beat for 10 minutes. (The success of this dish depends on the fluffiness of the meringue.) Melt chocolate in a small basin over hot water, but do not let it get hot. Beat in the remaining egg white. Gradually whisk into the meringue mixture, then beat for 10 minutes. Place in a deep, large, thinly buttered fireproof dish. Bake in a moderate oven, 350 °F (Mark 3-4), until well risen in about 30 minutes. Serve with cream.

YIELD: 6 servings.

INDIANERKRAPFEN (Indian Cream Buns)

6 oz. sifted icing sugar, 8 egg yolks, 2 tablespoons cold water, 5 oz. flour, 8 egg whites, whipped cream as required, chocolate icing.

Place icing sugar in a basin. Add egg yolks. Beat till light and frothy, in about 20 minutes, unless using an electric beater, when follow directions. Stir in the water, then sift in the flour. Beat till smoothly blended. Whisk egg whites till stiff, then lightly stir in 2 oz. sifted icing sugar. Fold into flour mixture. Moisten a sheet of greaseproof paper. Place it on a baking sheet. With a forcing pipe, press out round heaps, 2 inches in diameter, on to the paper. Shape carefully with a tablespoon. (Be sure to place them well apart, or they will run together.) Bake in a moderate oven, 350 °F (Mark 3-4), for about 15 minutes. (Do not let them brown.) Remove to a wire rack. Leave until quite cold. Cut in halves crosswise. Carefully scrape out a teaspoonful of sponge from half the buns. Fill hollows with whipped cream, sweetened and flavoured with vanilla essence. Cover each with a top. Coat top and sides with chocolate glacé icing.

GRETE SERENY, VIENNA.

LINZER BÄCKEREI (Austrian Shortbread Biscuits)

8 oz. flour, 5 oz. butter, 4 oz. castor sugar, 3 egg yolks, 1 beaten egg white, 2 tablespoons roughly chopped almonds.

Sift flour into a basin. Rub in butter. Stir in sugar and egg yolks. Turn on to a lightly floured board. Roll out thinly. Cut into small rounds anout 1½ inches across. Brush with egg white. Sprinkle with the almonds, mixed with equal quantity of castor sugar. Bake, on a lightly greased baking sheet, in a moderately hot oven, 350 °F (Mark 3-4), until light brown in 10-12 minutes.

LINZERTORTE

1½ cups coarsely chopped peeled almonds, 8 oz. butter, 8 oz. castor sugar, 2 eggs, 8 oz. flour, 1½ teaspoons ground cinnamon, ½ teaspoon ground cloves, 1 dessertspoon cocoa, ½ teaspoon baking powder, jam or jelly to taste.

Blanch and peel almonds and put through a mincer, fitted with a coarse blade. Chop the butter into pieces the size of peas. Place the almonds with the butter. Add sugar. Work and beat until butter is blended with the sugar. Stir in eggs. Sift flour with spices, cocoa and baking powder. Work it into the butter mixture with a wooden spoon, then knead to an elastic dough. Wrap dough in a towel. Chill in a refrigerator for at least 1 hour. Divide into two portions, one a little larger than the other. Roll out the larger to fit a 9-inch layer cake tin, well-greased with butter. Fill case with cherry, raspberry or strawberry jam or redcurrant jelly. Ornament the edges of the case with thumbs and forefingers. Roll out the other portion of dough into a round about 9 inches across. Cut into narrow strips. Arrange over the jam or jelly to form a lattice-work. Brush ends of strips with cold water and press lightly into sides of case. Bake in a moderate oven, 350 °F (Mark 3-4) for 30-40 minutes. Cool. Fill the openings in the lattice-work with more jam or jelly, using a piping syringe or a pointed teaspoon.

To Vary: Stir 2 tablespoons of chopped citron peel into the mixture before adding the flour.

PISCHINGER TORTE* (Chocolate Layer Cake)

10 Carlsbad Oblaten,† 5 oz. butter, 5 oz. castor sugar, 6 oz. chocolate, ½ teaspoon vanilla esssence, 5 oz. grated hazel nuts, 4 stiffly whipped egg whites, chocolate glacé icing.

Place a wafer on a large round platter. Beat butter till softened. Gradually beat in sugar. Beat till fluffy. Melt chocolate in a basin, standing in a saucepan of hot water. Beat into butter and sugar. Stir in vanilla essence and nuts. Fold in egg whites. Spread a thin layer over the wafer. Cover with another wafer. Continue spreading wafers and placing them on top of each other until you have a complete layer cake, placing the tenth wafer on top and leaving it uniced. Press cake lightly. Coat top and sides smoothly with chocolate icing. Decorate round sides with chopped walnuts and over the centre with chopped pistachio nuts and crystallized cherries or violets. Stand for 48 hours before cutting. If cut any sooner the layers will come apart.

Chocolate Icing: Mix 4½ oz. grated chocolate with 4½ oz. sifted icing sugar, 1 teaspoon vanilla essence, and about 4 tablespoons tepid water. Beat till blended, then use.

SACHERTORTE * (Viennese Layer Cake)

6 oz. butter, 6½ oz. plain chocolate, 6 oz. castor sugar, 8 egg yolks, 10 egg whites, 4 oz. sifted flour, 2 tablespoons apricot jam, chocolate icing.

Beat butter till creamy. Melt chocolate over hot water. Beat into butter with the sugar. When blended, add egg yolks, one at a time. Beat well, after each addition. Whisk egg whites till stiff. Fold a little flour and a little egg white alternately into butter mixture. Do not beat. Pour into a greased 8-9-inch cake tin, smoothly lined with greased paper. Bake in a slow oven, 275 °F (Mark ½) for about 1 hour, until dry in the centre, when tested with a very fine knitting needle or skewer. Remove from oven. Stand for a minute or two, then turn gently

---

* In some parts of Austria, the top of this cake is left undecorated.

† Creamy wafers about the size of a small dinnerplate, sold in many delicatessen shops and high-class grocery shops.

on to a rack. When quite cold, turn, base upwards, and with a very sharp knife, cut in three layers. Put layers together with jam, or fill layers with whipped cream, and then spread the jam thinly over the top and sides. Cover cake with chocolate icing.

Chocolate Icing: Pour ⅓ cup water into a saucepan. Add 8 oz. castor sugar. Stir till dissolved, then boil until the syrup forms a thin thread when a few drops are tossed. Melt 7 oz. plain chocolate in the top of a double boiler over boiling water. Gradually stir in the syrup. Stir constantly until the icing coats the back of a spoon, then use.

WITWENKUESSE (Widow's Kisses)

2 egg whites, 2½ oz. castor sugar, 2½ oz. chopped nuts, 1½ oz. chopped mixed peel, rice paper.

Whisk egg whites and sugar in a basin over steam until thick. Remove pan from stove. Whisk until cold. Fold in chopped nuts, almonds, hazel nuts or walnuts, or a mixture of all three, and peel. Arrange in small heaps on rounds of rice paper, placed on a baking sheet. Bake in a slow oven, 250 °F (Mark ½), until delicately tinged with colour.

GRETEL BEER, VIENNA.

* There are many versions of Sachertorte, the secret of which was long preserved by Madame Anna Sacher, its creator. Sometimes the cake is decorated on top after icing with toasted split almonds or with piping of whipped cream.

BELGIUM

Good Health !

" Gezondheid !" —— (Flemish Speaking)

" Santé !" ou " à la votre !" —— (French Speaking)

BELGIUM

If food is as important to you as scenery when you go on holiday, you will enjoy visiting Belgium. There, a high standard of cooking is met with wherever you happen to wander around the country or in the towns.

Naturally, owing to Belgium's geographical position, the Belgian cuisine is somewhat influenced by the Dutch and the French, but in spite of this, Belgium has a cuisine peculiarly her own, and some of her national dishes are so famous that you find them starred on menus in other parts of Europe.

Every time I visit Belgium I am impressed by the care taken in the cooking of vegetables and by the use of herbs in flavouring soups and stews. In Bruges, for example, I was taken aback when hop shoots, boiled in salted acidulated water, then drained, coated with seasoned melted butter, blended with cream, and garnished with poached eggs, were offered as a luncheon dish, and in Brussels I could not believe my eyes when I saw guests at a dinner party remove the outer leaves of heads of chicorée and eat the blades à la "croque-au-sel", with salt, like celery.

If you like Continental cakes as much as I do, you will revel in the patisserie of Belgium, which I first learned to like in Belgian cafés in London. One of the best places to sample them is in Brussels, when en fête on the 21st July for the Kermesse. You will never taste better patisserie anywhere else.

LE WATERZOIE DE POULET (Chicken Chowder)

1 boiling fowl, cold water as required, 1 celery stick, 2 trimmed leeks, 2 roots Hamburg parsley, 1 bouquet garni, 2 tablespoons chopped onion, salt to taste, 6 black peppercorns, 2 oz. butter, 2 oz. flour, juice of 1 lemon, 2 teaspoons minced parsley.

Divide fowl into joints suitable for serving. Place them in a strong shallow saucepan. Cover with cold water. Scald giblets and add. Chop celery and the white part of the leeks. Scrape and slice Hamburg parsley. Add vegetables to pan with the bouquet garni, onion, salt and peppercorns. Bring to boil. Cover and simmer gently until fowl is tender, in 2-2½ hours, time depending on age. Remove the chicken and bouquet garni. Pour vegetables and stock into a strainer. Remove peppercorns. Rub vegetables through a sieve. Remove crusts from 2 slices of toast. Place toast in a basin. Sprinkle with enough boiling chicken stock to moisten. Melt the butter in a shallow saucepan. Add flour. When frothy, stir in enough chicken stock to make a thin sauce. Add the vegetable purée and the toast. Bring to boil, stirring constantly. When the sauce is smooth, stir in the lemon juice, then add the chicken. Reheat. Dish up. Sprinkle with the parsley.

YIELD: 6 or 7 servings.

POTAGE AUX ENDIVES (Curly Endive Soup)

4 large crisp curly endives, 3 pints stock, 4 soupspoons of sago, 2 egg yolks, cream or milk as required, salt and pepper.

Wash endives thoroughly. Put into boiling salted water to cover. Boil until tender. Strain, then rub through a hair sieve. Pour the stock into a fairly large saucepan. Bring to boil. Add sago. Boil for 10 minutes, stirring constantly, then stir in the endive purée. Simmer very gently for 15 minutes, stirring occasionally, then skim thoroughly. Beat 2 egg yolks, and 2 or 3 tablespoons of cream or milk in a heated soup tureen. Pour in boiling soup. Season with salt and pepper as necessary. Serve at once.

YIELD: 4 servings.

MRS. F. ACKER,
103 EATON SQUARE,
LONDON, S.W.1.

BLANQUETTE DE VEAU (Stewed Veal)

2 lb. breast or neck of veal, 1 quart water, 6 cloves, 1 large peeled onion, 2 bay leaves, 2 sprigs thyme, 1 sprig parsley, 1 oz. butter, 1 oz. flour, juice of 1 lemon, salt and pepper to taste, 1 beaten egg yolk.

Wipe and cut meat up into fairly small pieces. Pour water into a saucepan. Stick the cloves into the onion, and add, with bay leaves, thyme and parsley. Bring to boil. Add meat. Cover and simmer gently until tender, in about 1½ hours. Remove meat. Rub the stock through a sieve. Melt butter in a saucepan. Add flour. Stir till frothy, then add about ¾ pint of the strained stock. Stir till smooth and boiling, then add lemon juice and salt and freshly ground black pepper to taste. Bring to boil, still stirring. Remove pan from stove. Stir a little of the stock into the egg yolk, then stir the egg yolk and stock gradually into remaining sauce. Arrange meat on a heated platter. Pour the sauce over. Garnish with finely chopped chives or parsley. The remainder of stock can be turned into soup.

YIELD: 5 or 6 servings.

BOUDINS DE NOEL (White Puddings)
(Generally served on Christmas Eve)

To make these famous sausages properly, you need sausage skins and the kind of funnel used when making sausages.

1 lb. very finely minced pork, 18 oz. green bacon, 2 oz. pig's liver, 1½ oz. onions, ½ oz. butter, 2 eggs, cream as required, salt and pepper.

Place the pork in a basin. Remove rind from bacon. Put bacon and liver through a mincer. Add to pork. Mix well. Peel and mince onions. Melt butter in a small saucepan. Add onion. Fry slowly till soft, but not coloured. Add to pork mixture with the eggs, cream to moisten, and salt and freshly ground black pepper to taste. Knead to a smooth paste, then fill the sausage skins rather loosely to avoid bursting. Tie securely. Half fill a large shallow saucepan with boiling water. Add the sausages. Bring to a full boil, then draw pan to side, and simmer gently for 12-15 minutes with lid on pan.

It is important that the "Boudins" should not boil all the time or the skins might burst. Remove from pan and leave until cold. When required, prick with a fork and grill and serve with mashed potatoes.

MRS. F. ACKER,
103 EATON SQUARE,
LONDON, S.W.1.

FOIE DE VEAU A LA WALLONNE (Stewed Calves' Liver à la Wallonne)

1½ lb. calves' liver, 2 rashers streaky bacon, 1 oz. butter, 1 large peeled onion, 1 tablespoon flour, 1 tablespoon chopped parsley, 1 sprig thyme, 1 bay leaf, salt and pepper, pinch of grated nutmeg, ¾ gill red wine, ½ pint cold water, ½ lb. prunes, soaked, 2 oz. cleaned sultanas.

Wash and dry liver. Cut into thin slices. Remove rind from bacon, and cut each rasher into 3 pieces. Place bacon in a frying pan. Add the butter. When dissolved, add the liver. Fry bacon and liver till slightly browned on both sides, then remove both to a shallow saucepan. Slice onion into fat remaining in frying pan. Fry slowly till lightly browned, then stir in the flour. Cook for a few minutes, stirring constantly, then sprinkle over the liver. Add parsley, thyme and bay leaf, salt, freshly ground black pepper, to taste, and nutmeg. Mix the wine with the water and pour into the pan. Cover. Simmer for about 45 minutes. Drain prunes, soaked for 12 hours, and add to liver with the sultanas. Cover and simmer gently for 30 minutes. Remove thyme and bay leaf. Dish up. Serve only with boiled potatoes.

YIELD: 6 servings.

POULETS SANS TÊTES (Stewed Beef Olives)

1½ lb. thinly sliced rump steak, 12 oz. minced lean pork, 1 tablespoon stale breadcrumbs, 1 egg, salt and pepper, 1 oz. butter, ½ pint beef stock, 1 sliced medium-sized onion, pinch of crushed thyme, 1 small bay leaf, strained juice 1 lemon, ¼ lb. sliced fried mushrooms, 1 teaspoon minced parsley.

Cut the steaks into pieces, 5 inches long and 3 inches wide. Mix the pork in a basin with the crumbs, egg and salt and

16

freshly ground black pepper to taste. Arrange beef slices on a board, covered with greaseproof paper. Season with salt and freshly ground black pepper. Spread on the mixture to within ½ inch of edges. Roll up so that the rolls are thicker at the centres than at the ends. Tie in place with cotton. Melt butter in a shallow saucepan. Add the stock, onion, thyme, and bay leaf. Cover. Simmer gently for 1½ hours. Dish up olives. Untie and keep hot. Thicken the sauce with cornflour creamed with stock. Stir till boiling. Add lemon juice, mushrooms and parsley. Stir again till boiling. Pour sauce over the olives. Serve with potato purée and green peas.

YIELD: 6 or 7 servings.

RAGOÛT D'AGNEAU BRABANÇONNE (Stewed Lamb Brabançonne)

8 trimmed lamb chops, 2 lb. chicory, 1 tablespoon chopped onion, 1 clove garlic, 1 bay leaf, 1 sprig parsley, ½ teaspoon powdered thyme, ½ teaspoon powdered cloves, salt and pepper, 1 cup beef consommé.

Choose chump chops. Place in a frying pan. Brown rapidly on both sides. Remove to a plate. Wash and dry chicory, and place in the bottom of a buttered casserole. Add vegetables, herbs, cloves, salt and freshly ground black pepper to taste, and consommé. Place chops on centre of vegetables. Cover. Simmer over low heat for 30 minutes. Remove meat and vegetables to a heated platter. Cover and keep warm in oven. Boil sauce down till reduced by a half. Pour over meat. Serve with plain boiled potatoes.

YIELD: 4 servings.

POULARDE RUBENS (Capons, Rubens Style)

1 fat capon, salt and pepper, 2 oz. butter, ½ cup cognac, 1 cup white wine, ½ cup cream, juice of ½ lemon, 1 egg yolk.

Wash and dry capon. Season the inside with salt and freshly ground black pepper. Melt butter in a large shallow saucepan. Add bird. Fry, turning frequently, until evenly browned, then cover and cook gently for 20 minutes. Add the cognac and white wine. Cover and simmer gently for 30 minutes. Remove capon from pan to a board. Joint it neatly. Arrange on a heated meat platter and keep warm. Add cream to saucepan. Simmer until reduced to half its quantity. Season if necessary. Strain in the lemon juice, then stir in the egg yolk. Cook, stirring constantly, until thickened, but do not allow to boil. Add 1 oz. of unsalted butter. Stir till smoothly blended. Pour over the capon. Garnish with asparagus tips. Serve at once.

Note: When asparagus is in season, trim off ends of stalks, leaving tips 2-3 inches long. Boil in salted water for about 10 minutes. Drain and moisten with a little of the chicken sauce, before adding the butter to the remainder of the sauce and coating the capon.

YIELD: 6-8 servings.

MRS. F. ACKER,
103 EATON SQUARE,
LONDON, S.W.1.

CELERIS AU LARD (Celery with Bacon)

1 lb. celery heads, ½ lb. potatoes, 3 or 4 rashers of fat bacon, melted butter as required, dash of vinegar.

Trim celery. Wash thoroughly. Divide into stems, and cut stems 2-3 inches long. Cook till tender in boiling salted water to cover. Peel and dice potatoes. Cook in boiling salted water till tender. Strain and place in a hot shallow fireproof dish. Strain and place celery on top. Grill or bake bacon till crisp. Coat celery freely with melted butter, flavoured with the vinegar. Garnish with the bacon rashers.

Note: If preferred, the celery and potatoes can be cooked together, then drained and placed mixed in base of dish, instead of in layers. Remove rinds from bacon before cooking.

Poireaux au Lard: Follow above recipe, substituting leeks for celery.

YIELD: 3 or 4 servings.

PURÉE DE MARRONS (Chestnut Purée)

2 lb. chestnuts, salt and pepper, butter as required, milk as required.

Make a slit on the thick side of each chestnut. Place in a saucepan. Cover with boiling water. Cover and simmer until tender. Drain quickly, then place in another saucepan. Cover with cold water. Replace on stove. Peel each one as you remove it from the pan. Pound nuts well, then rub through a sieve into a saucepan. Add salt and pepper to taste, 1 oz. butter, and a tablespoon or two of milk. Beat till smoothly blended, adding a little more butter or a little more milk as required to make a smooth purée. Serve in a heated vegetable dish with grilled or roast chicken or turkey, or with roast pork.

YIELD: 4 servings.

CHICOREE " COLESLAW " (Chicory Coleslaw)

3 fat chicory heads, 1 small tin mandarin sections, 1 level teaspoon French mustard, 1 dessertspoon brown sugar, 2 dessertspoons apple vinegar, pinch of cayenne pepper, generous pinch of salt, 1 pot yoghurt, 1 teaspoon lemon juice.

Slice chicory thinly crosswise. Drain mandarin sections thoroughly. Mix with the chicory. Stir remaining ingredients together. Place the salad in a serving dish. Sprinkle with the dressing. Chill and serve with cold ham, tongue or salt beef.

YIELD: 4 servings.

PAIN PERDU (Lost Bread)

4 fairly thick slices of bread, 1 cup milk, 1 well-beaten egg, 1 cup castor sugar, pinch of salt, a few drops brandy, rum or vanilla essence, butter as required.

Use stale bread, either from a plain or bun loaf. Heat the milk, mixed with the egg, sugar, salt, brandy, rum or vanilla essence. When nearly at boiling point, turn into a shallow dish. Remove crusts from bread, and place bread in the liquid. Soak for a few minutes, turning occasionally. Meanwhile, melt enough butter to cover the base of a large frying pan. Fry bread on both sides until golden brown. Keep each hot as prepared, then when all are ready, place them on a large heated oblong platter. Sprinkle with light brown sugar. Serve at once.

YIELD: 4 servings.

MRS. F. ACKER,
103 EATON SQUARE,
LONDON, S.W.1.

TARTE BELGE (Belgian Tart)

8 oz. butter, 2 oz. castor sugar, 2 tablespoons olive oil, ¼ teaspoon vanilla essence, 1 beaten egg, 1 lb. flour, 1 teaspoon baking powder, ¼ teaspoon salt, apricot or raspberry jam.

Beat butter till softened. Gradually beat in sugar. When fluffy, beat in the oil and vanilla essence. When thoroughly blended, stir in the egg, and then the flour, sifted with the baking powder and salt. Knead to a dough of the texture of shortbread. Brush an 8-inch cake tin evenly with melted butter, then with a coarse grater, grate the dough into the tin, covering base completely. Spread evenly with slightly warmed apricot or raspberry jam, then cover with the remainder of the mixture, grated as before. Bake in a slow oven, 300° F (Mark 1-2), for about 1½ hours, until pale gold. Sprinkle at once with sifted icing sugar. Leave until cold before turning out of tin. Serve, cut in wedges.

YIELD: 6 or 7 servings.

GALETTES DE NOUVEL-AN * (New Year Wafers)

1 lb. flour, pinch of salt, 8 oz. unsalted butter, 10 oz. castor sugar, 1 beaten egg, brandy or rum.

Sift flour and salt into a basin. Rub in the butter. Stir in sugar, then add egg. Mix well, adding while mixing a small glass of brandy or rum. Cover dough. Stand in a cool place for 24 hours. Heat a waffle iron. Divide the dough into small suitable pieces. Roll each out lightly, a little smaller than the waffle iron. Bake, pressed well down, for 2 minutes on each side, until golden brown. Remove with a flat knife or spatula. Leave on a wire rack until quite cold before serving or storing.

* These wafers are best kept for about a week before serving. Store them in an air-tight tin.

CZECHOSLOVAK
SOCIALIST REPUBLIC

Na Zdravi!——Here's Health!

CZECHOSLOVAK SOCIALIST REPUBLIC

What impresses me most of all about the Czechoslovakian cuisine is the excellance of its delicatessen, its infinite variety of dumplings, and the number of ways in which yeast is used to supply the Czechs with all kinds of delicious buns and cakes. If you wish to recapture the delights of holidaying in this fertile land, where the beef and the lamb are as good as the pork and the poultry, and the hams need no recommendation, for they are renowned throughout the world, I hope that with the help of this book and the Czechoslovakian imports you will be able to do so.

Czechoslovakia is celebrated for her pickled and preserved meats and sausages, and the housewives are famous for their sauces. Sometimes cream sauces are used for coating many of their dumplings. They are always made with unsalted butter and usually thickened with egg yolk or cream. When it comes to dressing boiled vegetables, often a little of the vegetable water is thickened with cream or egg yolks and used for coating instead of melted butter or white sauce.

I am told that fashions in food are changing in Czechoslovakia, and that the Czechs have become more calorie and vitamin-conscious, but this is not so at Christmas time. At this festive season, the Czechoslovakian board groans with the most delectable food you can ever hope to taste.

KULAJDA (Cream of Mushrooms)

8 oz. cultivated mushrooms, 1 pint boiling water, 1 teaspoon caraway seeds, 2 oz. plain flour, 1 quart soured cream, 4 large diced potatoes, 2 well-beaten eggs, a few drops vinegar, salt and pepper, 1 dessertspoon chopped dill.

Slice mushrooms. Place in a saucepan. Add the water and caraway seeds. Cover and simmer for 30 minutes. Sift flour into a small basin. Gradually beat in the cream. When smoothly blended, stir into soup, then add the potatoes. Bring quickly to boiling point. Cover. Simmer gently for about 15 minutes. Remove pan from stove. Stir in the eggs, vinegar, salt and pepper to taste, and the dill. Cook, stirring constantly, until thickened, but do not allow to boil.

YIELD: 6 or 7 servings.

MOZEČKOVÁ POLÉVKA (Brain Soup)

1 oz. diced carrot, 1 oz. diced turnip, 1 oz. diced potato, 3 pints water, 2 oz. butter, 2 oz. flour, 1 calf's brain, 1 tablespoon chopped onion, 1 beaten egg yolk, salt and pepper, 1 teaspoon chopped parsley.

Place the diced vegetables and the water in a saucepan. Cover and simmer gently until tender. Melt half the butter in another pan. Add flour. When frothy, stir in sieved soup. Stir till boiling. Melt remainder of butter in a small shallow saucepan. Add brain, blanched and skinned, and onion. Fry lightly, turning brain occasionally, for about 5 minutes. Remove brain and chop. Add to soup with the onion. Stir in egg yolk, salt and pepper to taste, and parsley. Stir till piping hot but do not allow to boil. Serve in a heated soup tureen.

YIELD: 6 servings.

MARINOVANÁ RYBA (Soused Fish)

3 lb. carp, perch, or pike, 1 pint wine vinegar, ¾ teaspoon salt, 3 chopped celery sticks, 2 roots Hamburg parsley, 1 large peeled onion, 3 cloves garlic, 4 black peppercorns, 4 allspice berries, 3 whole cloves, 1 bay leaf, nut of root ginger, 6 snippets lemon rind, ½ teaspoon salt.

Wipe and cut fish in equal portions. Bring vinegar and salt to a boil. Pour over the portions. Leave for a minute or two, then remove fish to a shallow saucepan. Drain the vinegar into another saucepan. Add the celery, Hamburg parsley, trimmed and cut in slices, onion, sliced, peeled cloves of garlic, peppercorns and allspice berries. Remove heads from cloves. Add cloves with bay leaf, ginger, lemon rind and salt to vinegar. Cover and simmer for 30 minutes. Pour over fish. (If the vinegar does not cover fish, add more as required.) Cover and simmer very gently for 30 minutes. Cool slightly, then carefully remove fish and arrange on a platter. Strain the stock over. Garnish with finely shaved lemon rind and sprigs of parsley. Cover and chill. Serve as a fish course, with salad.

YIELD: 6 servings.

TATARSKÝ BIFTEK* (Tartar Beefsteak)

1 lb. fillet steak, 1 egg yolk, 1 clove garlic, 1 medium-sized onion, 1 red pepper, 1 tablespoon caraway seeds, French mustard, paprika and salt to taste.

Wipe the steak and carefully remove any fat and membrane. Mince finely. Place in a mound on a round platter. Make a hollow in the centre. Break egg yolk into hollow. Sprinkle meat with the garlic, crushed with salt. Garnish round the base with rings of onion and red pepper, and caraway seeds. Serve with French mustard, paprika and salt to taste.

YIELD: 4 servings.

TELECÍ ŘÍZEK (Stuffed Scallops of Veal)

4 scallops of veal, salt and pepper, 2 oz. butter, 1 egg, 2 oz. chopped ham, 2 tablespoons green peas, 1 tablespoon milk, 2 tablespoons seasoned flour, beaten egg and crumbs, 4 oz. frying fat.

Wipe scallops with a damp cloth. Beat each lightly with a meat bat. Season with salt and pepper. Melt butter in a

---

* In Czechoslovakia, this steak is presented as a spread for black bread to which guests help themselves and choose whatever garnish they prefer.

small saucepan. Beat egg. Stir in ham, peas and milk. Pour quickly into pan. Stir till nearly scrambled, then season and finish cooking. Remove from stove. Stand until cool. Divide mixture between the 4 scallops, spreading it to within about ½ inch of the edges. Fold each scallop in half. Secure with a cocktail stick. Dip carefully in seasoned flour. " Egg and crumb." Heat fat in a frying pan. Add scallops. Fry till brown below. Turn with a palette knife. Fry till brown below. Serve with potato chips or straws and buttered green peas, French beans, or creamed spinach.

YIELD: 4 servings.

PEČENÁ HUSA SE ZELÍM (Roast Goose with Sauer-kraut)

1 goose (10-12 lb.), 1 teaspoon salt, pepper to taste, sauerkraut stuffing, knedliky (dumplings).

Wash and dry goose. If any fat has been left inside, remove it. Rub inside with salt and sprinkle with pepper. Stuff goose. Sew up opening. Season outside with salt and pepper. (If stuffing neck, fold the skin back and skewer it to back.) Truss. If bird is fat, prick skin well with a sharp fork. Weigh. Place on a rack in an open roasting tin, back downwards. Bake in a slow oven, 325 °F (Mark 2-3), allowing 10-20 minutes per pound. It is not necessary to baste it. Roast till skin is very crisp. When ready, dish up. Arrange knedliky round bird. Serve at once. In Czechoslovakia and in all other mid-European countries, the goose is carved across the breast in slices 1-1½ inches wide, instead of lengthwise.

Sauerkraut Stuffing: Melt 1 tablespoon goose fat in a large frying pan or shallow saucepan. Add 2 tablespoons minced onion. Fry slowly until a light brown. Rinse 2 lb. sauerkraut. Drain thoroughly. Place in pan. Add ¼ teaspoon freshly ground black pepper and ¼ teaspoon caraway seeds if liked. Stir till boiling. Grate in 1 large potato, 5½ ozs. in weight, or use two if necessary. Cook, stirring constantly, until the sauerkraut thickens, then gradually stir in a little white wine

24

or water, but not more than $\frac{3}{4}$ cup as the stuffing must not be too moist.

BRAMBORÁK * (Potato Pancakes)

2 lb. 2 oz. grated raw potatoes, 3¼ oz. flour, 1 teaspoon salt, 1 clove garlic, pepper to taste, ½ teaspoon crushed marjoram, if liked, oil for frying.

Peel and wash potatoes. Grate finely. Stand until they are covered with their own water. Drain thoroughly. Add a little less milk than there was water. Add flour mixed with the salt, garlic, pepper and marjoram. Mix well. Heat enough oil to cover the base of a large frying pan. Drop batter from a tablespoon on to pan. Spread thinly, with the back of spoon, into a round. Fry till brown below, then turn and brown on the other side. Serve piping hot with a lettuce or other green salad at tea time.

YIELD: 6-8 servings.

HALUŚKY (Mushroom and Noodle Pie)

8 oz. small noodles, 2 oz. butter or margarine, 2 tablespoons chopped onion, 2 teaspoons chopped parsley, 12 oz. sliced mushrooms, salt and pepper, 2 eggs, 1 cup milk.

Throw the noodles into a saucepan of boiling salted water. Boil till soft in about 10 minutes. Drain. Rinse under the cold water tap, then drain again. Melt the fat in a frying pan. Add onion. Fry slowly till soft, then add parsley and mushrooms. Cook over low heat for 2 or 3 minutes, stirring frequently, then stir into the noodles. Season. Pour into a shallow greased fireproof dish. Bake in a moderate oven, 360 °F (Mark 3-4), for 5 minutes. Beat eggs. Gradually stir in milk. Pour over the noodle mixture. Continue to bake until golden brown. Serve as a luncheon or supper dish with a salad.

YIELD: 4 servings.

* These pancakes are a speciality of Prague. At one famous snack bar they are fried in a giant skillet, 18 at a time, and served piping hot. They lose their taste when cold.

JABLKOVEC (Apple Layer Pudding)

10 oz. bread rolls, 1¼ pints milk, 3 oz. butter, ¾ oz. bread-crumbs, 1 lb. apples, 2 oz. castor sugar, ground cinnamon, about 1½ oz. sultanas, 1 oz. almonds, 1 egg.

Cut rolls into slices. Soak them in the milk. Smear a shallow baking tin with 1 oz. butter. Sprinkle with the crumbs. Drain slices of rolls. Arrange one-third in prepared tin. Peel, core and slices apples. Place one-third of the slices on top of the rolls. Sprinkle with half the sugar and ground cinnamon to taste, then with half the almonds and sultanas. Cover with half remaining rolls. Melt remaining butter. Sprinkle a little over the rolls. Cover with remaining apples, flavoured with a little cinnamon, sugar, sultanas and almonds, then with remaining slices of rolls. Sprinkle with remaining butter. Beat the egg. Stir in milk drained from rolls. Strain evenly over the puddings. Bake in a moderate oven 350 °F (Mark 3-4), for about 45 minutes. Serve with cream.

YIELD: 5 servings.

OVOCNÉ KNEDLÍKY (Fruit Dumplings)

2 large potatoes, 6 oz. flour, 2 oz. fine semolina, 1 egg, about ½ cup milk, fruit filling, 2 oz. butter, 2 oz. cottage cheese, 1 oz. castor sugar.

Boil the potatoes the day before you require them, then grate them into the flour sifted with the semolina and a pinch of salt. Make a hollow in the centre. Break in the egg, then stir in enough milk to make a stiff dough. Turn on to a floured board. Roll out into a fairly thin square. Cut in squares. Lay a ripe apricot or plum in the centre of each square, and mould each up into a ball. Place in a large pan of boiling slightly salted water. Cover closely. Cook steadily for 5-7 minutes. Serve at once, sprinkled with melted butter, cottage cheese and sugar.

YIELD: 5 or 6 servings.

BUCHTY (Poppyseed Buns)

1 oz. baker's yeast, 2 oz. castor sugar, 1 lb. plain flour, ½ pint tepid milk, grated rind ½ lemon, ½ teaspoon vanilla essence, ½ teaspoon salt, 2 egg yolks, 2 oz. butter, poppyseed filling, 3 oz. vegetable fat.

Mix the yeast and a little of the sugar to a paste in a cup. Stir in 2 tablespoons flour and 4 tablespoons of the milk. Mix with a wooden spoon until into a thick batter. Stand in a warm place until mixture forms into a " sponge ". Sift the remainder of the flour into a warm basin. Make a hole in the centre. Add remaining sugar, lemon rind, vanilla essence, and salt. Beat egg yolks. Stir in yeast mixture and the remainder of the milk, and the butter, heated only until melted. Pour into centre of the flour. Beat well with a large wooden spoon until bubbles form on top of the dough. Cover with a cloth. Stand in a warm place for 45 minutes to 1 hour until the mixture is double its size. Turn on to a floured pastry board. Divide into 2½ dozen equal-sized pieces. With floured hands, pat each out into a flat oblong. Place a heaped teaspoon of the filling in the centre of each. Press the edges of the dough together and neaten each again into an oblong. Grease a large baking tin lavishly with fat. Place buns, equal distance apart, in tin and slip a little fat between each one. Stand in a warm place until well risen in about 30 minutes, then bake in a moderately hot oven, 375 °F (Mark 4-5), for about 45 minutes until golden, when they will have risen and joined together. Remove tin from oven. Sprinkle buns with vanilla sugar and separate them gently.

Poppyseed Filling: Pour ½ pint milk into a small saucepan. Heat slightly then add 5 oz. ground poppyseeds. Bring to boil. Simmer, stirring frequently, until thick. Remove from stove. Add 3 oz. castor sugar, ½ teaspoon grated lemon rind, ¼ teaspoon ground cinnamon, and a few drops vanilla essence. Mix well. Use when cold.

To Vary: Fill buns with sweetened apple purée, flavoured with ground cloves or cinnamon if liked, or with cherry, greengage or plum jam.

MEDVĚDÍ PRACKY (PRACNY) (Bear's Paws)

12 oz. flour, 8 oz. castor sugar, 5 oz. ground almonds, 2 tablespoons cocoa, grated rind ½ lemon, 1 saltspoon ground cinnamon, 9 oz. butter, 1 egg yolk, vanilla icing sugar.

Sift flour into a basin. Stir in sugar, almonds, cocoa, lemon rind and cinnamon. Rub in butter. Add egg yolk. Work to a dough. Fill small tins up to the edge with the dough, choosing tins if possible that are grooved. Press out flat in tins. Bake in a moderate oven, 350 °F (Mark 3-4), until pale gold, in about 17 minutes. Cool on a wire rack. Sprinkle grooved sides with vanilla icing sugar.

VÁNOČKA (Christmas Plait)

1 lb. flour, 4 oz. castor sugar, pinch of salt, 1 oz. baker's yeast, ½ pint tepid milk, 2 separated eggs, 3 oz. butter, ½ teaspoon vanilla essence, 1 oz. cleaned sultanas, 1 oz. chopped peeled almonds, 1 lemon.

Sift the flour, sugar and salt, about half a teaspoon, into a large basin. Make a hollow in the centre. Crumble in the yeast. Add 4 tablespoons milk and about a dessertspoon of extra castor sugar. Work this with a little of the flour round the hollow into a thin batter with a wooden spoon. Cover with a cloth. Stand in a warm place until the batter in centre forms a sponge. Gradually stir in remainder of the milk, kept warm, mixed with the beaten egg yolks, then melt the butter. Stir into batter with the vanilla essence, sultanas and almonds. Grate in the lemon rind. When mixed to a stiff elastic dough, cover and leave in a warm place to rise. Turn the dough twice, at regular intervals, until well-risen in 1-2 hours. Divide into 8 equal portions. Shape each with your hands into a long roll.

To plait rolls, place 4 side by side, and start plaiting the middle two, then plait alternately with the outer and inner. There is an art in doing this, which I have not learned from the Czechs, so to prevent the rolls slipping, I weight down the ends before starting to plait. Place on a greased baking tin, covered with greased paper. Make a plait now from 3 rolls and lay on top of the first. Lastly, divide the eighth roll into

2 thin ones and twist them round and round together. Place on the top of the other plaits, and tuck the ends well under each end of the Vanochka. Secure the twisted plait at each end with cocktail sticks to prevent it slipping while rising and baking. Leave in a warm place to rise for about 15 minutes. Whisk egg whites till frothy. Brush carefully over the plait. Sprinkle with a handful of chopped almonds. Bake in a moderately hot oven, 400 °F (Mark 5-6), for 45 minutes to 1 hour. Dredge with sifted icing sugar. Cool on a wire rack. Serve sliced and buttered.

VÁNOČNI KOLÀČ (Christmas Cake)

3 eggs, 3 tablespoons castor sugar, 3 tablespoons sifted flour, nut cream, 4 peeled dessert apples or 3 seeded oranges, chocolate icing.

Separate yolks and whites of eggs. Whisk egg whites to a froth. Gradually beat in sugar. When stiff, beat in egg yolks, then fold in the flour. Bake in a dry cake tin, 9 inches across, in a slow oven, 300 °F (Mark 1-2), till puffy and golden, in about an hour. Invert on a wire rack for about 1 hour. If it does not slide out on to rack during that time, run a knife round the cake to help to ease it out. When quite cold, place on a large round serving plate. Cover with the nut cream, smoothing it with a palette knife. Stand in a cool place until the cream has partly solidified, then dent the cream all round the edge with the thin end of a wooden spoon. Peel, core and divide each apple into eighths. Stew gently for 3 or 4 minutes in sweetened water to cover, then drain thoroughly. If oranges are preferred, peel and divide oranges into sections. Arrange either apples or oranges in overlapping slices over the inside edge of the cream so that you have a wreath of fruit. Pour the chocolate icing into the centre. Strew lightly with chopped nuts. Stand in a cool place until required.

Nut Cream: Grind 2 oz. hazelnuts or walnuts. Pour ¾ gill boiling milk over the nuts. Stand till cool. Cream 2 oz. unsalted butter with 2 oz. sifted icing sugar. Add nut mixture and 1 tablespoon strong black coffee. Beat thoroughly till smoothly blended.

29

Chocolate Icing: Place 2 oz. butter, 4 oz. sifted icing sugar, 1 tablespoon cocoa and 1 egg in a basin. Beat over hot water until thickened and the mixture turns glossy. Pour, while still warm, on to the centre of the cake.

Note: This cake can be partly made a day or two before Christmas but do not arrange the fruit or pour the chocolate icing in the centre until shortly before cake is required. It is better if chilled in a refrigerator for two hours before serving.

FRANCE

A Votre Santé —— Good Health

FRANCE

There is no country in the world in which you can have such a wonderful gastronomic adventure as France. Go where you please, choose what you like, and you will never be disappointed.

The French housewife has much to teach us. She takes infinite pains with everything she prepares for the table. In the north, much of the food owes its flavour to the butter and cream used in its preparation. You have to go to the Midi, Provence, or the Basque country to be able to enjoy rich spicy food, flavoured freely with garlic and herbs, and frequently wine. Some of the Provençale housewives use only olive oil for frying. Others fry meat, to be made into a casserole or stew, both in butter and olive oil. Olive oil is also generally used in the south for salad dressings. In the north, a more lightly flavoured oil is preferred, usually arachide.

If you wish to entertain à la Française, keep a stock of inexpensive wine strictly for culinary use, as well as some miniature bottles of sweet liqueurs for flavouring fruit salads, and other sweets. When planning a luncheon or dinner from régionale fare, it is a good idea to pay it the compliment of serving it with wine from the same district.

To welcome your guests in the French manner, offer lightly chilled champagne as an apéritif instead of cocktails, but have Chambery Gaudin tawny port and sherry in the background. In this way you will not spoil their palate for the meal you have provided.

DODINE DE CANETON AU VOUVRAY * (Duck Pâté)

1 duck, about 5 lb. in weight, salt and pepper, cognac as required, 2 lb. 2 oz. pork sausage meat, 2 or 3 chicken livers, ½ bottle Vouvray, ¼ pint Madeira, 2 or 3 whole cloves, 1 blade mace, 6 black peppercorns, 1 peeled clove of garlic.

Clean and bone duck, leaving the skin intact. Season the inside with salt and cayenne pepper to taste, then sprinkle it with a dessertspoon of cognac. Place sausage meat in a basin. Wash, dry and soak the livers in a tablespoon of cognac mixed with the wines and spices, for 5 or 6 hours, then drain livers. Chop and add to sausage meat. Mix lightly till blended. Stuff the hollows in the flesh with the sausage meat mixture, then spread the remainder over the flesh. Return to skin and draw it over so that the stuffing is practically enclosed, then place it in an oval buttered fireproof dish. Cover with buttered aliminium foil. Stand dish in a baking tin containing warm water coming half way up the sides. Bake in a slow oven, 275-300 °F (Mark ½-1), for about 3 hours. Remove from oven. Take off foil. Cool slightly, then fill up dish with liquefied aspic jelly, flavoured with Madeira to taste. Chill. Serve as a first course, cut in slices, with French bread or crisp toast and butter.

Charles Barrier,
Restaurant de Nègre,
Tours.

PATE DE LIEVRE (Hare Pâté)

½ young hare, 8 oz. veal cutlet, 8 oz. pork sausage meat, 2 small bay leaves, salt and black pepper, ¼ teaspoon ground cloves, 1 saltspoon grated nutmeg, pinch of crushed herbs, thin salt bacon as required, ¼ cup water, ¼ cup port wine, 1 cup brandy.

Use the best joints of the hare with the heart and liver. Scald, then remove the flesh from the bones. Cut flesh into

* The pâté was garnished on top with an edible duck's head. As M. Barrier did not let me into the secret of how it was made, I would simply garnish the top with a spray of flowers, made with slices of truffle nestling in foliage of cucumber rind. Set the garnish in place with a very little liquefied aspic.

strips about 3 inches long and ¾ inch wide, then cut veal up in the same way. Chop heart and liver, Stir into the sausage meat. Season this forcemeat with salt and black pepper to taste, cloves, nutmeg and herbs. Place a layer of wafer-thin slices of lean bacon in the bottom of a fireproof dish. Sprinkle with a little freshly ground black pepper. Place 1 bay leaf on top. Cover with a layer of sausage meat, then with a layer of strips of hare. Cover with half the strips of veal. Fill up dish in this way. Press firmly down so that the dish is closely packed. Cover with a layer of wafer-thin slices of lean bacon. Sprinkle with freshly ground black pepper. Place remaining bay leaf and a sprig of thyme, if available, on top. Mix the water with the port wine and brandy, and pour over, piercing filling here and there so that the liquid will moisten it all. Cover tightly with foil, then seal edges with a flour-and-water paste. Bake in a slow oven, 300 °F (Mark 1-2), for 3 hours. Leave in the dish until required. The pâté is always better prepared and cooked at least 24 hours before serving. Serve, cut in slices, allowing 1 slice per person with a heaped table-spoon of potato salad, if liked, on the side. Serve with French bread and butter.

QUICHE LORRAINE * (Savoury Flan)

4 oz. flour, a few grains of salt, 4 oz. butter, ½ egg yolk, about 1 tablespoon cold water, 4 oz. diced cooked ham, 2 sliced medium-sized onions, butter as required, 4 eggs, salt and cayenne pepper, grating of nutmeg, 2 cups hot milk.

Sift flour and salt into a basin. Rub in butter. Mix to a dough with egg yolk and water. Chill in refrigerator for 1 hour. Line a greased flan ring, 9 inches across, placed on a greased baking sheet, smoothly with the pastry. Prick the base with a fork. Crimp edges. Place the ham over the base. Fry onions slowly in melted butter as required, until soft but not brown. Arrange over the ham. Break the eggs into a sauce-pan. Beat well with the salt and cayenne pepper to taste,

* This is a classical regional dish, but its filling, and also the pastry case, varies according to taste. Sometimes flaky or puff pastry is used when making case, sometimes the filling is flavoured with cheese, as you will see in the second recipe.

and nutmeg. Gradually stir in the milk. Beat over low heat until custard begins to thicken, then pour into case. Bake in a moderately hot oven, 375 °F (Mark 4-5), for about 30 minutes, until the custard is set and golden. Serve hot, cut in wedges.

YIELD: 4-6 servings.

QUICHE LORRAINE (Cheese Flan)

Make case as described but with flaky or puff pastry. Slice 4-6 oz. Gruyère cheese very thinly and place over the base and along inside edge of case. Beat 2 eggs lightly. Stir in ¼ pint thick cream, salt and pepper to taste, and 4 oz. lean bacon or ham, cut into small pieces. Pour this over the cheese. Bake in a moderately hot oven, 400 °F (Mark 5-6), for about 40 minutes.

BOUILLABAISSE * (Fish Soup)

¾ lb. John Dory, ¾ lb. mackerel, ½ lb. whiting, ¼ pint shelled cooked mussels, ¼ lb. chopped onion, ½ bay leaf, 1 peeled clove garlic, 1 whole clove, 1 sprig parsley, pinch of saffron, 2 pints cold water, ½ pint white wine, ½ gill olive oil, salt and pepper.

Cut the John Dory, mackerel and whiting into small chunks. Put whiting, with the mussels, in a basin. Place onion in a small saucepan. Add bay leaf, garlic, clove, parsley, and cold water to cover. Cover and simmer gently for 20 minutes. Add saffron, the 2 pints cold water, wine, olive oil, and ½ teaspoon salt. Bring quickly to boil. Place John Dory and mackerel in pan. Simmer for 10 minutes, then add the whiting and mussels. Season with pepper, and salt if necessary. Simmer for 5 minutes. Place slices of stale French bread in a heated soup tureen. Strain three-quarters of the soup over. Serve fish in a heated deep dish. Pour remainder of soup over. Garnish with chopped parsley. The fish may be served as a separate course, or with the soup as preferred.

YIELD: 6 servings.

FROM MARSEILLES.

* This traditional soup has many versions. In some parts of France, lobster is substituted for the mussels. In Provence, rascasse, a spiny shellfish, similar to lobster, is added in place of mussels or lobster.

SOUPE A L'OIGNON (Onion Soup)

2½ oz. butter, ¾ lb. minced onion, ½ oz. flour, 2½ pints cold water, salt and pepper.

Melt butter in a saucepan. When it starts to smoke, add onion. Fry over low heat, stirring occasionally, till evenly browned, but take care it does not burn. Add the flour. Stir till lightly browned, then add water, a little at a time, whisking constantly, until into a thick cream. Stir in remaining water. Bring quickly to boil. Cover and simmer gently for 20 minutes. Strain into a fresh saucepan. Reheat. Serve with fried croûtons and grated Parmesan cheese, both handed round separately.

YIELD: 4 servings.

SOUPE DE POISSON VENETIENNE (Venetian Fish Soup)

2 oz. butter, 2 oz. flour, 2 pints fish stock, ¼ pint cream, ½ gill white wine, chopped parsley, salt and pepper.

Melt butter in a saucepan over low heat. Add flour. Mix well. When frothy, cook for 10 minutes, stirring constantly. Gradually stir in the stock. When boiling, cover and simmer very gently for 1 hour, thinning with water if it becomes too thick. Rub through a fine strainer into another saucepan. Stir in cream, wine and parsley. Season to taste. Stir till piping hot, but do not allow to boil.

YIELD: 4 servings.

Note: Use sole or turbot bones for the stock. Add 3 pints cold water, a pinch of sage and saffron, 1 slice medium-sized onion and a bay leaf. Cover and simmer gently until reduced to fully 2 pints, then strain before using.

CARLO AVOGADRI,
HEAD CHEF,
BRISTOL RESTAURANT,
PALACE STREET.
LONDON, S.W.1.

HOMARD THERMIDOR (Lobster Thermidor)

2 small boiled lobsters, 1 oz. butter, ½ teaspoon minced shallot, dash of cayenne pepper, ½ glass dry white wine, ¼ pint Béchamel sauce, pinch of crushed herbs, sprinkling of brandy, ¼ pint cream, salt and pepper, 4 dessertspoons grated Gruyère cheese, grated Parmesan cheese to taste.

Remove all meat from shells and large claws of lobsters. Cut the meat into dice, and mince the coral if there is any. Melt butter in a saucepan. Add shallot. Cook over low heat until soft, but not brown. Stir in cayenne pepper, white wine, mixed with the Béchamel sauce, and the herbs. Sprinkle with the brandy. Set a match to it. When the flame dies out, stir in the cream, salt and pepper to taste, Gruyère cheese and the lobster. Divide equally between the shells. Sprinkle with grated Parmesan cheese, or substitute sieved breadcrumbs, then sprinkle with melted butter. Brown under the grill.

In some parts of France, ½ lb. cubed champignons or a chopped truffle is added with the Gruyère cheese, and in others, 2 eggs are beaten in before mixture in shells.

YIELD: 4 servings.

MOULES, LE SOURD (Mussels with Rice)

1 sliced peeled onion, ½ gill dry white wine, ½ glass French vermouth, pepper to taste, 1½-2 lb. mussels, butter as required, 2 oz. Patna rice.

Place onion in a thick shallow saucepan. Add the white wine and the vermouth, and salt and pepper to taste. Scrub and clean mussels and place them in pan. Add a knob of butter. Cover. Cook over rapid heat, shaking pan occasionally, for 5 minutes, until the shells open, then remove mussels to a dish. Strain the juice through a piece of linen into a basin, then shell mussels, and keep in a warm place. Melt 1 oz. butter in a small saucepan. Add rice. Fry slowly, shaking occasionally, until the butter is absorbed, then stir in the juice from the basin, and cook until rice is tender, in about 20 minutes, adding a little more white wine if required. Pile rice on a hot platter. Garnish with the mussels, preheated in melted butter. Serve with Muscadet.

YIELD: 3 servings.

FROM MONSIEUR LE SOURD, CALAIS.

SCAMPI EN PAPILLOTE (Scampi with Smoked Salmon)

1 lb. scampi, flour as required, 2 oz. butter, 4 chopped peeled tomatoes, 1 chopped clove garlic, 2 oz. sliced mushrooms, 4 slices smoked salmon.

Dip the scampi in flour. Melt the butter in a saucepan. Add scampi. Fry for 5 minutes, turning occasionally. In another saucepan melt enough butter only to cover the base. Add tomato, garlic and mushrooms. Fry for 2 or 3 minutes. Spread a sheet of oiled greaseproof paper on a pastry board. Pile the scampi on the centre. Cover with the smoked salmon slices. Garnish with tomato and mushroom mixture. Fold paper and twist ends. Bake in a moderate oven, 350 °F (Mark 3-4), for 10 minutes.

YIELD: 4 servings.

CARLO AVOGADRI,
HEAD CHEF,
BRISTOL RESTAURANT,
PALACE STREET,
LONDON, S.W.1.

TRUITES AUX AMANDES (Fried Trout with Almonds)

2 cleaned fresh trout, ½ teaspoon salt, ¼ teaspoon freshly ground pepper, flour, 1 oz. butter, juice of ½ lemon, parsley sprigs, blanched almonds as required, slices of lemon.

Leave heads on fish. Rinse trout and dry thoroughly. Mix the salt and pepper with the flour, then roll each trout evenly in the flour. Shake lightly. Melt half the butter in a frying pan, large enough to take both fish. When sizzling hot, place fish in pan. Cook over moderate heat until brown below, in about 4 minutes, then turn. Fry on the other side till cooked through. (Sometimes they are baked in the oven, when they can be weighted to keep their shape while baking.) Dish up. Keep hot. Add remaining butter to pan. Stir in lemon juice. Heat but do not allow to boil, then strain over fish. Sprinkle generously along the tops with shaved fresh almonds, lightly fried in butter till delicately coloured. Garnish dish with butterflies of lemon and sprigs of parsley.

YIELD: 2 servings.

FROM ORLEANS.

ALOUETTES SANS TETES (Stewed Veal Olives)

4 long thin fillets of veal, 2 tablespoons minced boiled ham, 2 tablespoons minced raw pork, 1 teaspoon minced parsley, 1 beaten egg, salt and pepper, 1 oz. butter, 2 tablespoons arachide oil, 2 chopped medium-sized onions, 3 chopped peeled tomatoes, dash of grated nutmeg, 2 coffee cups red wine, 1 minced clove of garlic, 1 cup boiled green peas, 8 oz. spaghetti.

Have fillets cut to the same shape and size. Mix the ham with the pork, parsley, egg and salt and pepper. Divide in 4 equal portions. Place each on the middle of a fillet. Roll up tightly. Tie with cotton. Melt butter. Add oil. When hot and blended, add veal rolls. Fry till evenly browned all over. Add onions, tomatoes, nutmeg, wine, garlic, and a minced shallot if liked. Season to taste with pepper and salt. Cover. Simmer very gently for 1½ hours, then dish up rolls, and untie. Add green peas and the spaghetti, boiled in salted water and thoroughly drained, to the gravy. Bring to boil. Pour over rolls.

YIELD: 6 servings.

MARCELLE CAP D'AIL.

CASSOULET DE CASTELNAUDARY

2 lb. haricot beans, 6 oz. fresh pork rind, 1 bouquet garni, salt, 1½ lb. shoulder of mutton, 1 chopped medium-sized onion, 8 peeled tomatoes, ¼ teaspoon crushed garlic, 1 lb. confit d'oie, 1 lb. French sausages, breadcrumbs as required.

Rinse beans and soak over night in plenty of cold water. When ready to make cassoulet, drain off water and place beans in a large saucepan. Cut pork rind into inch cubes and add with the bouquet garni (1 bay leaf, 1 sprig celery, parsley and thyme, tied in a muslin bag). Cover with cold water to the depth of at least 1 inch above the beans. Add a very little salt. Bring to boil, then simmer for about 2 hours until tender. Cut the mutton into 2 inch pieces. Season to taste. Fry in a little hot fat, tossing occasionally, until an even golden brown, then remove pan from stove. Add onion. Fry for a minute or two till browned, then add tomatoes, chopped, and garlic. Transfer meat mixture to a casserole. Simmer for a few minutes, then add beans, confit d'oie, and cover. Place on the middle shelf of a slow oven, heated to 250 °F (Mark $\frac{1}{4}$-$\frac{1}{2}$). Simmer constantly for at least 1 hour. Keep checking on simmering. If it stops, increase oven heat a little. Now fry the sausages, using Toulouse sausages if possible, cut in thick slices. Add to cassoulet, stirring gently with a wooden spoon. Remove muslin bag. When mixture in blended, sprinkle with breadcrumbs and return to oven. Serve when the crumbs are brown.

YIELD: 8-10 servings.

M. MARIUS DUTREY,
MAITRE CHEF,
THE WESTBURY HOTEL, LONDON.

ESCALOPES DE VEAU MEDICIS (Scallops of Veal à la Creme)

4 scallops of veal, salt and pepper, squeeze of lemon juice, 2 oz. butter, 3 oz. chopped mushrooms, 1 tablespoon cognac, 1 tablespoon port wine, $\frac{1}{2}$ cup cream.

Beat scallops of veal out thinly. Season with salt and freshly ground black pepper. Flavour with the lemon juice. Melt butter in a large frying pan. Add scallops. Fry for about 2 minutes on each side, till cooked through and lightly browned. Remove to a heated platter. Keep hot. Fry mushrooms in remaining butter for a moment or two, then stir in the cognac and port wine, and then the cream. When piping hot, season with salt and freshly ground black pepper to taste. Spoon over the scallops. Serve with new potatoes or potato purée.

YIELD: 4 servings.

FROM M. LOUIS JEUDI,
BON LABOUREUR,
CHENONCEAUX, VAL DE LOIRE.

SAUTE DE BOEUF MINUTE * (Casserole of Rump Steak)

2 oz. butter, 1 medium-sized peeled onion, 1 peeled clove of garlic, 1 bay leaf, 1 lb. rump steak, French mustard as required, ½ gill dry sherry or white wine, salt and pepper.

To make this, as Marcel of La Surprise prepares it, you need a casserole with a metal base, otherwise you will have to use a shallow saucepan. Melt the butter. Slice in the onion and garlic and add bay leaf. Cover and simmer gently for 3 minutes, then remove lid and add meat prepared in this way. Cut off any pieces of fat or gristle from steak, then cut steak into small cubes, about ½ inch square. Coat with French mustard to taste, then roll in about 2 oz. flour. *Do not season flour.* Fry over low heat, turning constantly, until evenly browned all over. Add sherry or wine. Boil quickly till reduced by half its quantity. Add a dessertspoon of chopped parsley and minced shallot. Season to taste. Serve with plain boiled potatoes.

YIELD: 3 or 4 servings.

MARCEL CACCIARDA,
LA SURPRISE,
LONDON.

TOURNEDOS BEARNAISE * (Grilled Steak with Béarnaise Sauce)

4 slices fillet steak, fully 1 inch thick, olive oil or melted butter, 4 slices of bread, salt and pepper, Béarnaise sauce.

Trim each steak into rounds. Tie a strip of streaky bacon around each. Brush steak and grill rack with oil or melted butter. Place steaks on rack. Switch on grill if electric, or light if gas. When red hot, cook steaks for about 5 minutes on one side, then turn and cook for 5 minutes on second side, seasoning to taste with salt and pepper when nearly ready. Cut slices of bread into rounds a fraction larger than the steaks. Melt unsalted butter in a thick frying pan until you have enough to cover the base. Heat till butter foams. Place

* This recipe was handed to my mother by my grandmother who was head-cook to the late Duke of Orleans.

rounds of bread in pan. Cover and cook for a few minutes, then remove lid and fry till golden brown below. Turn and brown on the other side in the same way. Drain on absorbent paper. Top each croûte with a tournedos. Garnish with sprigs of parsley. Place a teaspoonful of Béarnaise sauce on top of each. Serve remaining sauce in a heated sauceboat.

YIELD: 4 servings.

Béarnaise Sauce: Place a small peeled shallot, 1 teaspoon chopped onion, 1 teaspoon parsley, 1 tablespoon tarragon vinegar, 1 teaspoon salt, and pepper to taste, into a small saucepan. Boil rapidly until reduced to 1 teaspoonful. Strain into a basin, lowered into a saucepan, half full of water, nearly boiling. Drop an egg yolk into the vinegar. Add $\frac{1}{2}$ teaspoon butter. Beat lightly till blended. Gradually add 2 oz. butter, about a teaspoon at a time, stirring constantly. Cook slowly until thick, still stirring. Add 1 teaspoon finely minced parsley.

FROM BÉARN, PYRENEES.

Le Tournedos des Gardes Flambé au Vieux Marc de Touraine: Fry a fillet of steak in melted butter for about 3 minutes on each side. Season with salt and freshly ground black pepper to taste. Sprinkle with Marc. Set alight. Transfer to a heated plate. Pour about 2 tablespoons cream into frying pan. Stir only till blended, then pour over steak. Garnish with watercress and a grilled tomato. Serve with creamed spinach and Pommes Dauphines.

FROM TOURS.

TRIPE A LA MODE DE CAEN (Casserole of Tripe)

2 b. tripe, 1-2 cow heels, salt and pepper, 2 bay leaves, 2 sprigs thyme, 2 sprigs parsley, 4 large peeled onions, 4 cloves, 4 sliced leeks, 2 sliced carrots, 1 pint cider or dry white wine, $\frac{1}{2}$ glass brandy.

Wash tripe thoroughly, then blanch it. Cut into small pieces. Cut cow heels into joints. Place tripe and cow heels in a strong casserole. Add salt and freshly ground black pepper

* Béarn is famous as the birthplace of King Henry IV, who was a great gourmet.

to taste, bay leaves, thyme, parsley, and the onions, each speared with a clove. Sprinkle with the leek and the carrot. Add cider or wine and brandy. Cover closely. Stew very gently until tender, in 5 or 6 hours. Leave overnight. Carefully skim off fat. Remove bones and herbs. Reheat and serve with boiled or mashed potatoes.

Note: If a metal-based casserole is not available, cook in a stewing pan.

YIELD: 6 servings.

CANETON AU MUSCADET (Stewed Duckling Muscadet)

1 duckling, (about 4 lb.,) butter as required, dash of brandy, ¼ pint Muscadet, salt and pepper.

Divide duck into neat joints. Melt 1 oz. butter in a large saucepan. Add joints. Fry slowly, turning frequently, till well-browned. Remove joints to a plate. Pour the brandy and wine into the saucepan. Simmer till reduced to two-thirds its quantity, then replace joints. Season to taste with salt and pepper. Add 4 teaspoons melted butter to the sauce. Cook slowly, closely covered, for about 20 minutes, until tender, stirring occasionally. (When ready, the joints should be slightly rose-coloured.) Serve with black or green grapes, heated in butter, or slices of apple, fried in butter, and with small new buttered turnips.

YIELD: 4 servings.

FROM M. PIERRE LESERRE, CHEF-PROPRIÉTAIRE, MON RÊVE, BASSE-GOULAINE, NANTES.

COQ AU VIN (Cockerel with Red Wine)

1 cockerel, salt and black pepper, garlic powder to taste, 2 tablespoons fine olive oil, 2 oz. butter, 16 small peeled onions, 4 oz. streaky bacon, 13 small carrots, pinch of castor, sugar, 2 tablespoons brandy (optional), 1½ oz. flour, ¾ bottle red Burgundy, 1½ gills chicken stock, 8-10 oz. champignons, fleurons of puff pastry.

Carve bird into 8 joints. Mix salt and freshly ground black pepper, and garlic powder, in equal quantity. Dip

42

joints in seasoning and shake. Heat olive oil and butter in a wide heavy saucepan. Add the joints. Fry, turning frequently, till golden brown all over. Drain, and remove joints to a platter. Cover and place in a low oven. Rinse onions. Blanch bacon. Remove rinds, then cut bacon in dice. Trim carrots. Cut in slices. Place onions, bacon and carrots in saucepan. Add sugar. Fry slowly till the vegetables are lightly browned, and the liquid caramelises. Drain bacon and vegetables, letting liquid drip back into pan. Place bacon and vegetables aside. Return joints to saucepan. (Sprinkle brandy over, if used. Set a match to it. Leave till flames die out.) Sprinkle joints evenly with the flour, and cook, stirring them round and round, for 3 or 4 minutes. Simmer wine in another saucepan for 15-20 minutes, till reduced to about one-third of the original quantity. Add chicken stock, made from the giblets, and the bacon and vegetables, finely chopped, and a bouquet garni. Season with salt and freshly ground black pepper to taste. Cover pan with a tightly fitting lid. Bring to boil. Transfer to a casserole. Cover closely. Bake in a moderate oven, 350 °F (Mark 3-4), until tender, in 40-45 minutes. When nearly ready, slice and fry bottled or tinned champignons slowly in a little butter for a minute or two. (If using fresh, allow a minute longer.)

To serve, arrange joints down the centre of a heated platter. Strain sauce over. Pile champignons, onion and carrot, alternately round the sides. Garnish with baked fleurons of puff pastry, or with triangles of fried bread, points upwards.

YIELD: 4 servings.

FROM JACQUELINE KÉROUÈDAN.

CREPES DE VOLAILLE GRATINEES (Chicken Pancakes au Gratin)

About 1 lb. boiled chicken, ½ lb. mushroom, Béchamel sauce as required, seasoning to taste, ½ pint Mornay sauce, 12 unsweetened pancakes.

Weigh chicken, free from bones, then cut into dice. (If preparing filling from a freshly boiled chicken, one about 3 lb. in weight is sufficient.) Dice mushrooms. Place chicken in the top of a double boiler. Add equal quantity of Béchamel

43

sauce. Season with salt and freshly ground black pepper to taste. Cover and cook over boiling water, till thick, stirring occasionally. Prepare Mornay sauce and keep hot over boiling water. Make 12 thin unsweetened pancakes, about the size of a dessert plate. Lay them out flat on a large platter. Divide chicken filling equally between them. Roll up. Place side by side in a shallow buttered fireproof dish or on a metal plate. Coat with the Mornay sauce. Bake in a hot oven, 450 °F (Mark 7-8) for 5 minutes, until golden brown.

Béchamel Sauce: Melt 1 oz. butter. Stir in 2 tablespoons flour. When blended, add ½ cup chicken stock, and 1½ cups scalded milk. Stir till thick and boiling. Season with salt and freshly ground pepper.

YIELD: 6 servings.

Mornay Sauce: Melt 1 oz. butter. Stir in 2 tablespoons flour. When blended, add 1½ cups scalded milk. Stir till smooth and boiling. Add ⅓ cup grated Cheddar or Gruyère cheese and ¼ cup grated Parmesan cheese. Stir till thick and smooth. Season with salt and pepper. Yield: ½ pint sauce.

> M. A. GAUDIN,
> L'ESCARGOT BIENVENU,
> LONDON.

ESCAUTON DE VOLAILLE SARTHOISE* (Casserole of Chicken Breasts, Ricordeau)

2 chicken breasts with wings, ½ oz. seasoned flour, butter as required, 2 artichoke bases, 1 large firm tomato, 2 slices truffle, 1 tablespoon port wine.

Wipe breasts with a damp cloth. Dip in seasoned flour, then shake gently. Melt 2 oz. butter in a frying pan. When butter starts to sizzle add breasts. Fry, turning occasionally, over moderate heat, until evenly browned all over. Transfer to a casserole with remaining butter. Cover. Bake in a slow oven, 300 °F (Mark 1-2), until tender, in about 45 minutes, turning once or twice, and adding more butter if required.

* M. Ricordeau suggests drinking Bourgueil, a local red wine, with a faint aroma of raspberries, with this delicious dish.

When nearly ready, boil artichokes till tender, if fresh, or drain canned thoroughly. Reheat in melted butter. When breasts are ready, arrange on a flat heated oval platter. Garnish on either side with an artichoke base, topped, with half a tomato, skin side upwards, brushed with melted butter, seasoned and lightly grilled. Arrange two little groups of buttered new potatoes, green peas and small fried onions, alternately round chicken. Add the port wine to the casserole. Heat quickly. Strain over breasts. Garnish each on centre with a slice of truffle.

Buttered New Potatoes: Fry about a dozen small round new scraped potatoes, or potato balls, lightly in butter until golden brown, then cover and continue to cook, but over low heat, until tender, tossing frequently.

Buttered Green Peas: Toss ½ pint boiled green peas gently in melted butter until coated. Season with pepper.

Fried Onions: Peel 12 small onions of uniform size. Melt 1 oz. butter. Add 1 tablespoon castor sugar. Fry onions over moderate heat, shaking gently occasionally until delicately browned, then sprinkle with ½ cup chicken consommé, or water flavoured with a chicken cube. Boil rapidly, spooning the liquid over the onions until onions are glazed.

YIELD: 2 servings.

FROM M. RICORDEAU, CHEF-PROPRIÉTAIRE, LOUÉ, NEAR LE MANS.

ASPERGES VINAIGRETTE (**Asparagus with Vinaigrette Sauce**)

1 large bundle thick asparagus stalks, 3 tablespoons olive oil, 1 tablespoon tarragon vinegar, 1 teaspoon finely chopped chervil, 1 teaspoon finely chopped parsley, 1 teaspoon finely chopped tarragon, salt and pepper.

Choose a bundle of at least 20 thick stalks. Boil asparagus, prepared in the usual way, with stalks all the same length, till tender, in 15-25 minutes, time depending on freshness and thickness. Place carefully on a rack and leave until quite cold. Arrange on a flat serving platter, with stalks lying all

45

the same way. Chill. Mix the olive oil with the vinegar, herbs, and salt and freshly ground black pepper to taste. Stir till blended. Pour into a sauceboat. Serve with asparagus.
YIELD: 4 servings.

FROM M. PIERRE LESERRE, CHEF-PROPRIÉTAIRE,
MON RÉVE, BASSE-GOULAINE, NANTES.

RATATOUILLE (Provencale Vegetable Dish)

4 firm tomatoes, 2 medium-sized aubergines, 1 courgette, 2 large peeled onions, 1 green pepper, 1 red pepper, 4 tablespoons olive oil, 1 peeled clove of garlic, salt and pepper, grated Parmesan cheese.

Peel tomatoes, aubergines and courgette. Slice quarter inch thick, then slice onions to match. Slit peppers and carefully remove seeds. Slice peppers thinly. Heat oil slowly in a saucepan. Add onion, peppers, and garlic, thinly sliced. Cover and stew until nearly soft, then add slices of tomato, aubergine and courgette. Simmer slowly until soft, but not reduced to a purée. Season with salt and freshly ground black pepper to taste. Drain well. Transfer to a shallow greased fireproof dish. Sprinkle with grated Parmesan cheese to taste. Brown lightly under the grill. Serve as a separate course or as an accompaniment.
YIELD: 6 servings.

CREPES SUZETTE * (Pancakes Suzette)

10 oz. flour, 1 teaspoon salt, 2 cups milk, 3 eggs, 1 cup water, 1 tablespoon strained orange juice, 1 dessertspoon olive oil, Cointreau sauce.

Sift flour and salt into a basin. Slowly stir in the milk. When smoothly blended, add eggs, water, orange juice and oil, stirring constantly. Beat well. Stand for 15-20 minutes. Melt enough butter to cover the base of a small frying pan. Pour

* When pancakes are wanted for 2 persons, adapt quantities and cook them at the table. Drop the number of pancakes required into the hot syrup. Turn them gently in the syrup, then sprinkle with the Cointreau and light it.

in enough batter to cover the base thinly, moving the pan from side to side until evenly coated. Fry till lightly browned below, then turn and brown on the other side. Fold in four. Place in a fairly deep heated dish. Cover with a clean cloth. When all the pancakes are ready (there should be about 2 dozen), pour juice of 2 oranges and half a lemon into a small frying pan. Add 2 tablespoons castor sugar. Stir over heat until sugar is dissolved, then add the Cointreau. Lift. Reheat. Pour over pancakes. Light with a match, and serve aflame.

YIELD: 6 servings.

PETITS BABAS AU RHUM (Rum Babas)

3 oz. flour, pinch of salt, 1 oz. baker's yeast, 1 teaspoon castor sugar, ½ gill warm milk, 1 large egg, 2 oz. seedless raisins, ½ gill rum, 1½ oz. butter, rum syrup.

Sift flour and salt into a large basin, and warm slightly at side of stove or in a warming cupboard. Cream the yeast with the sugar. Add milk. Beat egg, and stir into mixture. Make a well in the centre of the flour. Pour in milky liquid. Gradually work in the flour, then beat with your hand for two of three minutes. Cover. Allow to rise in a warm place for 45 minutes. Place raisins in a small basin. Add the rum. When dough has doubled its bulk, strain rum from raisins, and add raisins to dough, with the butter, beaten till softened. Continue beating till the dough leaves the side of the bowl in about 5 minutes. Grease 12 small baba tins or muffin tins with melted unsalted butter, then fill half full with the dough. Cover and allow to rise in a warm place until double their size. Bake cakes in a moderately hot oven, 400 °F (Mark 5-6), for about 15 minutes. Turn the tins upside down on a wire rack. Cover them with a folded towel. Stand for 5 minutes, then remove carefully and place on rack. Spear each cake with a fork. Dip cakes in the syrup. Cool on a wire rack. Reheat syrup. Repeat this dipping process three times until all the syrup is absorbed. Serve hot or cold, garnished with sweetened whipped cream, and glacé cherries and angelica.

Rum Syrup: Place 4 oz. castor sugar in a saucepan. Add 1 cup water. Stir till sugar is dissolved, then boil to a syrup. Remove from stove. Add rum, drained from the raisins.

47

Petits Babas Armagnac

Take a jar of prunes preserved in Armagnac. Drain off Armagnac. Dip cakes in the liqueur when hot. Cool on a wire rack. Reheat liqueur. Repeat this process three times until all the liqueur is absorbed. Top each with whipped cream, and garnish with a prune.

YIELD: 6 servings.

TARTE AUX MARRONS GLACES (Marron Glacé Flan)

1 baked flan case, 8 inches across, crème patissière, marrons glacés as required.

Make flan case with pâté sablé, a light crumbly French pastry equivalent to shortcrust. Bake and leave until cold. Fill with the crème patissière. Arrange marrons glacés to taste on top of filling. Paint them with the syrup, boiled down until thickened, and flavoured with rum.

Pâté Sablé: Sift 8 oz. flour with ¼ teaspoon salt and ¼ teaspoon ground cinnamon into a basin. Make a well in the centre. Beat 5 oz. butter till softened. Place in well. Add 1 egg and 1 egg yolk, and 3½ oz. castor sugar. Draw the flour over and into the mixture, then knead dough lightly with the fingertips of one hand, until it is smoothly blended. Form into a ball. Allow pastry to relax in a cool place for at least one hour, then roll out into a round. Butter an 8-9 inch flan ring. Place it on a buttered baking sheet, and line ring smoothly with the pastry. Trim edges neatly. Prick base well with a fork. Bake in a moderate oven, 350 °F (Mark 3-4), for about 25 minutes, or bake at 400 F (Mark 5-6), for about 20 minutes.

Crème Patissière: Heat 1 pint milk nearly to boiling point. Beat 4 egg yolks and 6 oz. castor sugar until mixture turns pale yellow and thickens. Sift in 1 oz. cornflour. Stir until smoothly blended. Gradually stir in the hot milk, then pour the mixture into the milk saucepan, and bring again almost to boiling point, stirring constantly. Remove pan from stove. Beat 1 egg white till stiff. Whip 1 tablespoon thick cream lightly. Fold into egg white, then fold in 1 teaspoon vanilla

48

essence. Fold mixture gently into the custard. Cook over low heat for 1 or 2 minutes, gently stirring, then allow to cool.

YIELD: 6 servings.

MARIE-THÈRESE, BOLOGNA.

BRIOCHES (Fancy French Rolls)

1 yeast cake, ½ cup tepid milk, ½ teaspoon salt, 12 oz. flour, 8 oz. butter, 2 tablespoons castor sugar, 4 eggs.

Crumble the yeast cake into the milk. Stand for a minute or two, then stir till dissolved. Sift salt and about ½ cup of the flour into a basin. Add dissolved yeast. Cover with a cloth. Stand in a warm place until the sponge rises to double the quantity of milk and yeast. Cream butter in a mixing bowl. Gradually beat in sugar, then the eggs, one at a time, beating well for about 2 minutes after each addition. (The French housewife uses her hands for this operation.) When the yeast mixture is ready, add to batter, then stir in remaining flour. Knead for about 5 minutes to a smooth dough, then cover with a cloth. Leave in a warm place for 3 hours till double its bulk, then turn on to a lightly floured board. Knead well. Return to bowl. Cover and stand in a cool place for 30 minutes, then knead dough again on a floured board. Weigh dough and remove 3 oz. Cut remainder into 12 equal-sized pieces. With lightly floured hands, shape each into a small ball, and place a little apart in a greased baking tin. Divide remaining dough into 12 equal portions. Roll each into the shape of an apple or a pear. If liked, make a cavity in each with a small pointed spoon and insert small stems of dough, one in each. Leave brioches in a warm place for 15 minutes to rise, then brush with beaten egg. Bake in a hot oven, 450 °F (Mark 7-8), for 12-14 minutes. Serve with butter and coffee.

CROISSANTS * (Crescent Rolls)

8½ oz. butter, 1 teaspoon salt, 1¼ tablespoons castor sugar, 1 cup scalded milk, 1 oz. baker's yeast, ¼ cup warm water, 10-12 oz. sifted flour, 1 egg yolk, 2 tablespoons milk.

Place ½ oz. butter, salt and sugar in a basin. Pour in the milk. Cool till tepid. Add yeast, dissolved in the water. Stir

* In France croissants are served for breakfast with coffee.

for a moment or two. Add flour. Mix to a dough, then knead thoroughly until elastic and smooth. Cover basin. Stand in a warm place until dough doubles its size. Knead for a moment or two. Chill in refrigerator for 2 or 3 hours. Hold remaining butter under cold running water, and squeeze it well between the hands for about 2 minutes. Roll out dough into a strip thrice as long as wide. (For example, if strip is 8 inches wide, it should be 24 inches long.) Spread butter over the dough. Fold the ends in towards the centre, so that you have a square in 3 layers. Turn square halfway round and roll it out into a strip again. Fold in three as before, and chill in refrigerator for 30 minutes. Repeat this process twice more, but leave chilling, after last folding, for 1 hour, then roll out to $\frac{1}{4}$ inch thickness. Cut into 4 inch squares. Divide each square into 2 triangles, placing one with the wide base in front of you. Roll it towards its point, then shape into a crescent. Prepare all in the same way. Brush with beaten egg yolk. Place on a dry baking sheet, a little apart. Bake in a moderately hot oven, 375 °F (Mark 4-5) for 15-20 minutes. Serve hot with butter.

MILLE FEUILLES (A Thousand Leaves)

8 oz. puff pastry, crème pattisière, raspberry jam as required, whipped sweetened cream as required.

Roll pastry out into a strip $\frac{1}{8}$-$\frac{1}{4}$ inch thick. Cut into strips about 3 by 1$\frac{1}{2}$ inches. Brush a baking sheet with cold water. Place the strips a little apart on sheet. Bake in a hot oven, 450 °F (Mark 7-8), until well risen and delicately browned, in about 5 minutes, then place in the coolest part of the oven and leave for 5 minutes longer. Cool on a wire rack. Split each strip in two crosswise. Spread one with crème patisserière. Cover with another strip. Spread with raspberry jam. Cover with another strip. Spread with whipped cream, sweetened and flavoured with vanilla essence. Cover with another strip. Press down lightly. Dredge with sifted icing sugar, or cover thinly with water icing, flavoured if liked with rum, and sprinkle with a little chopped blanched pistachio nuts.

Note: In some parts of France, only 2 fillings are used, crème patissière, or whipped cream, and jam.

SORBET AU RHUM (Rum Water Ice)

8 oz. castor sugar, 2 cups water, 3 tablespoons lemon juice, 3 tablespoons rum, 1 egg white.

Place sugar in a saucepan. Add the water. Stir over moderate heat until dissolved, then bring to boil. Boil for 5 minutes. Remove from stove. Stir in lemon juice and rum. Pour into a chilled ice tray. Freeze until into a mush. Turn into a chilled bowl. Beat egg white till stiff, then fold into the rum mixture. Return to ice tray and freeze to a firmish mush. Serve in small wide-mouthed wine glasses, with friandises.

Friandises chez Barrier:
1. Maraschino cherries stuffed with almond paste.
2. Miniature cream puffs, filled with almond cream, made in this way. Drop choux pastry, in marble-sized balls, on to a buttered baking sheet, a little apart. Bake in a moderately hot oven, 375 °F (Mark 4-5), till delicately browned and dry in the insides. Cool on a wire rack. Make a small slit in the side of each puff and fill with whipped creams, sweetened and flavoured with vanilla essence, or with crème patissière.

YIELD: 6-8 servings.

FROM LE NÈGRE, TOURS.

VERMOUTH CASSIS (Vermouth Apéritif)

Place 2 ice cubes in a tall glass or tumbler. Add 1 liquid oz. of dry French vermouth, 4 dashes of Crème de Cassis, and a twist of lemon peel. Fill glass nearly to the top with soda water, or vichy.

YIELD: 1 serving.

FROM TOURS.

GERMANY

Prosit! —— Here's How!

GERMANY

Keeping house in Germany is a fascinating pastime. In a country where they boast they can produce a different soup for each day of the year, preparing meals is never a bore.

The German hausfrau, like the French, has much to teach the rest of the world on housewifery. She is careful in her choice of food, and never wastes a scrap. To give you an example, when cooking asparagus, she either uses only two-thirds of each asparagus stalk and boils the ends for soup, or she peels the stalks from the tips downwards so that the whole remaining stalk is tender when boiled and dressed. She also makes the most delicious soup from sieved boiled pea pods, as I used to do in Scotland. Again, you seldom find her, except in a case of emergency, running to the telephone to do her ordering. She shops by herself, or with her cook, if she has one, and insists on getting what she wants, not what the shopkeeper wants her to have, and when home with her purchases she is most painstaking in the preparation of her meals.

When entertaining, the German hostess takes great pride in her cheese platter, and one custom I liked when I lived in Germany was that of asking friends in after supper when lightly chilled wine was served with fresh fruit, followed by delicious Mokka coffee and friandises.

You have to go to Germany to enjoy to the full her wonderful wines and all the specialities this country has dreamed up for your delight.

ERBSENSUPPE MIT SAURER SAHNE (Cream of Green Peas)

1 pint shelled green peas, 1 quart white stock, 1 egg yolk, 1 oz. butter, 1 oz. flour, ¼ pint soured cream, 1 tablespoon minced parsley, salt and pepper, pinch of castor sugar.

Place peas in a saucepan. Add stock, brought to the boil. Boil, uncovered, until tender. Cool slightly. Beat the egg yolk with the butter and flour until blended. Stir into the soup. Rub through a sieve. Reheat nearly to boiling point. Mix the cream with the parsley. Add to the soup. Season with salt and freshly ground black pepper. Add sugar. Stir till nearly boiling. Serve with fried croûtons of bread, or garnished with " matches " of smoked tongue.

YIELD: 5 or 6 servings.

FLEISCHBRUEHE MIT KLOESSCHEN (Clear Soup with Dumplings)

1 lb. lean stewing beef, ½ lb. beef bones, 1 trimmed leek, 2 medium-sized carrots, 1 small peeled turnip, 2 peeled tomatoes, 2 tablespoons chopped onion, 1 sprig parsley, 1 small bay leaf.

Place meat, bones and all the vegetables, prepared and sliced, into a saucepan. Cover with cold water and bring to boil. Skim if necessary. Add herbs. Cover closely. Simmer very gently for 2½ hours. Strain through a fine wire sieve, then through a jelly bag, kept for the purpose. Reheat and season. Flavour if liked with sherry to taste. Garnish with marrow dumplings.

Markkloesschen (Marrow Dumplings): Mix 1½ tablespoons finely minced beef or veal marrow with ¼ cup stale white breadcrumbs, 1½ tablespoons minced parsley, salt and pepper to taste, ¼ teaspoon grated nutmeg, and ½ teaspoon grated lemon rind. With a wooden spoon, beat in just enough beaten egg to bind ingredients together. Shape into small balls, the size of large marbles, ¾-1 inch across. Bring a pint of beef stock to boil. Drop in the dumplings. Cover and boil for about 3

53

minutes. When they float they are ready, but it is best to test one out before turning them all into the soup.

Note: When making these dumplings for a family soup, simply boil them in the soup, just before serving.

YIELD: 5 or 6 servings.

BLAUER LACHS RHEINISCHE ART (Blue Salmon)

2 lb. middle cut of salmon, boiling tarragon vinegar as required, ½ bottle dry white Rhine wine, 6 black peppercorns, 3 bay leaves, salt as required, 1 sprig chervil, 1 sprig parsley, 1 sprig thyme, 4 oz. butter.

Wipe fish with a damp cloth. Place on a rack in a fish kettle. Cover with the vinegar. Remove pan to a table in a draught. Stand for 10 minutes. Add wine, peppercorns, bay leaves, salt to taste, herbs and butter. Bring quickly to boil. Reduce heat. Simmer very gently until flesh shows signs of coming away from the bone. Lift out rack with fish. Let any liquid run back into pan. Slide fish on to a heated platter. Garnish with ornaments of lemon and sprigs of parsley. Serve with Rémoulade or shrimp sauce.

YIELD: 4 or 5 servings.

KABELJAU MIT KUEMMELKRAUT (Cod with Caraway Cabbage)

2 oz. butter, 1 shredded white cabbage, 1 lb. potatoes, salt to taste, 1 dessertspoon caraway seeds, ½ cup boiling water.

Melt butter in a shallow saucepan. Add cabbage. Peel and slice potatoes, and add with the salt, caraway seeds and boiling water. Bring slowly to boil. Cover. Simmer gently for 30 minutes. Divide fish in 3 equal portions, using fillets for preference. Lay on top of cabbage. Cover. Simmer gently for 10-15 minutes, then lower temperature as far as possible and continue to cook for 10 minutes. Carefully dish up. Garnish with slices of lemon.

YIELD: 3 servings.

54

EISBEIN MIT SAUERKRAUT (Knuckles of Pork with Sauerkraut)

2 lb. knuckles of pork, cold water as required, 2 medium-sized carrots, 1 leek, 1 celery stick, 1 small parsnip, salt and pepper, 2 lb. sauerkraut, 1 chopped medium-sized onion, 1 chopped cooking apple.

Place knuckles in a large saucepan. Cover with cold water. Bring quickly to boil. Drain off water. Cover knuckles with boiling water. Slice in carrots, leek, celery stick and parsnip. Season with salt and pepper. Bring to boil. Cover and simmer gently for 3 hours. Pass stock and vegetables through a sieve. Bring purée to a boil, stirring frequently. Meanwhile, have the sauerkraut cooking with the onion and apple in a covered saucepan for about 2 hours, stirring frequently. When knuckles and sauerkraut are ready, dish up knuckles on a heated platter. Spoon the sauerkraut round. Serve vegetable purée in a heated vegetable dish, and arrange potatoes, baked in their skins, in another heated dish.

YIELD: 6 servings.

RINDFLEISCH IN BIER GESCHMORT (Beef Stewed in Beer)

3-4 lb. rump steak, slices of fat bacon, 1 or 2 onions, brown beer and water, ½ cup vinegar, 1 tablespoon golden syrup, 6 black peppercorns, 2 or 3 whole cloves, 1 bay leaf, salt.

Flatten beef steak lightly with a meat bat, then roll it up and tie round the side with string. Remove rinds from enough rashers of bacon to cover the bottom of a large shallow saucepan. Cover bacon with slices of onion. Lay meat on top. Mix enough beer with equal quantity of water to cover meat. Add with vinegar, syrup, peppercorns, cloves and bay leaf. Cover closely. Simmer gently over very low heat for 2 hours. Add salt to taste and continue to cook for about 1 hour, until meat is tender when tested. Dish up. Serve with boiled or mashed potatoes, boiled carrots and broad beans.

Note: This steak is enough for 5 or 6 persons for 2 meals.

GEBRATENE GANS (Roast Goose)

1 dressed goose (about 10 lb. in weight), apple stuffing, boiling water as required.

Season bird inside and out with salt and pepper. Stuff the inside, and sew up openings. Place on a rack, in a large roasting tin, breast downwards. Sprinkle with about ½ pint boiling water. Add a chopped onion to the tin. Bake in a moderate oven, 350 °F (Mark 3-4), for 35-40 minutes. Remove from tin, then take out the rack, and place the goose in the tin, breast upwards. Continue to roast, basting frequently with the liquid in tin, and pricking the skin from time to time over the wings and round the throat to extract the fat. When the bird begins to brown, start basting with goose dripping instead of water. At the end of 2 hours, skim off a little of the fat from the liquid in tin. 15 minutes before dishing up, baste with 3 or 4 tablespoons cold water to crisp the skin. When ready, dish up on a heated platter. Thicken gravy with cornflour or flour, and rub through a strainer into a small saucepan. Reheat, stirring constantly. Serve in a heated sauceboat.

Apfelfuellungen (Apple Stuffing): Peel and core 2 lb. cooking apples. Place in a strong shallow saucepan with just enough water to prevent burning, 5 oz. castor sugar, and 1 lb. of prunes, soaked in cold water to cover for 12 hours, then stoned. Add 1 oz. butter. Stir occasionally till boiling, then cover and simmer very gently until nearly as thick as jam and slightly browned in about 3 hours.

To Serve Goose: In some parts of Germany, the bird is carved neatly, and the joints and breasts arranged back in place, then the vegetables, potato croquettes and stewed red cabbage, are grouped alternately round. In other parts, the bird is garnished with watercress and the vegetables are served in heated vegetable dishes.

YIELD: 6-8 servings.

56

HASENRUECKEN MIT MEERRETTICH (Braised Saddle of Hare)

>*1 saddle of hare, salt, water as required, ½ gill port wine, grated nutmeg to taste, ground cinnamon to taste, 3 tablespoons redcurrant jelly, 1 dessertspoon grated horseradish.*

The saddle should be taken from a young hare and well larded. Rub all over with salt. Pour enough cold water into a large shallow saucepan to prevent burning. Place saddle in pan. Cover and cook gently for about 30 minutes. Add the wine, and a very little grated nutmeg and cinnamon. Cover and simmer gently until the sauce is reduced to half the original quantity, when meat should be tender. Add the jelly and horseradish, and a dust of pepper if liked. Stir till piping hot. Dish up hare on a heated platter. Pour the sauce round. Serve with boiled potatoes, garnished minced parsley, and with a green salad.

Note: In some parts of Germany, the spices are omitted, and soured cream is stirred into the liquid after it is reduced, then stirred till boiling. The hare is accompanied by redcurrant jelly, and horseradish is only added to the sauce if liked. If not, it is seasoned with pepper.

YIELD: 4 servings.

ROTKOHL (Stewed Red Cabbage)

>*1 large red cabbage, 1 oz. butter or beef dripping, 4 finely shredded cooking apples, 1 tablespoon chopped onion, 1 teaspoon castor sugar, 2 or 3 whole cloves, vinegar as required, ½ gill red wine.*

Trim cabbage. Wash thoroughly, then drain and shred finely. Melt fat in a shallow strong saucepan. Add cabbage, apple, onion, sugar, cloves and enough vinegar to cover base of pan, and so prevent burning. If liked, substitute water for vinegar. Cover closely. Simmer gently for 2 hours, stirring frequently, then stir in the wine. Cover and simmer very gently until the wine has been absorbed by the cabbage. (In some parts of Germany, a teaspoon or two of redcurrant jelly is stirred in just before serving, when the sugar is omitted.) Serve with roast duck, goose or pork.

YIELD: 4 servings.

SAUERKRAUT MIT AEPFELN * (Sauerkraut with Apples)

1 oz. fat, 1 lb. sauerkraut, 3 tart apples, 1 sliced onion, 1 teaspoon sugar, grated raw potato, salt and pepper, ¼ teaspoon caraway seeds, ½ oz. flour.

Melt the fat, preferably butter, in a large shallow saucepan. Add the sauerkraut. Fry for 2 minutes, stirring occasionally, then add boiling water to cover. Meanwhile, peel, core and slice the apples. Add to sauerkraut with the onion slices and sugar. Simmer very gently until tender, stirring occasionally. Add potato, salt, freshly ground black pepper, caraway seeds and the flour, mixed to a cream with water. Stir till boiling. Simmer for 10 minutes, stirring occasionally.

YIELD: 4 or 5 servings.

ADLON GEKUEHLTER WEINSCHAUM (Sherry Soufflés)

1½ lb. castor sugar, 6 egg yolks, 2 whole eggs, 1 bottle hock, 4 glasses sherry, 1½ pints stiffly whipped cream, orange or pineapple essence to taste, glacé cherries or pineapple.

Place sugar, egg yolks, whole eggs, hock and sherry in the top of a double boiler. Heat over *almost* boiling water, stirring constantly, then remove pan from over water, and allow contents to cool. Beat well. Heat again as before, then leave till cool, and chill. When ice-cold, add cream, flavoured to taste with orange or pineapple essence, and pour into soufflé cases, or into fruit glasses. Chill. Dust very lightly with sifted icing sugar, flavoured very delicately with cocoa. Garnish each with ornaments of glacé cherries or pineapple. Serve with friandises.

YIELD: 20 servings.

CHEF,
HOTEL ADLON,
BERLIN (1927)

---

* Sauerkraut, simmered slowly in boiling water to cover, for 1-2 hours, then seasoned with salt and pepper, and flavoured with caraway seeds, is usually served with Frankfurter sausages, simmered gently for about 10 minutes.

GOETTERSPEISE * (Food of the Gods)

1 cup pumpernickel crumbs, 4 oz. sifted castor sugar, 2-3 oz. grated sweet chocolate, 1 pint cream, arrack rum cherry jam.

To make this sweet perfectly, pumpernickel, sold in packets, must be made into fine crumbs. Mix crumbs in a basin with the sugar and chocolate until thoroughly blended. Place a thin layer in the base of a glass trifle dish. Whip the cream till fluffy. Sweeten and flavour delicately with arrack rum. Spread a thin layer over the crumbs. Repeat layers, making each one smaller until the sweet ends in a rounded peak. Place a teaspoon of cherry jam here and there on the cream. Chill and serve.

YIELD: 6 servings.

BERLINER KRAENZCHEN (Garland Cake)

1 lb. flour, 6 oz. butter, 8 egg yolks, 1½ oz. baker's yeast, warm milk as required, 4 tablespoons castor sugar, melted butter as required, almonds, currants and sugar, 1 beaten egg yolk, rose water, glacé icing.

Sift flour into a heated basin. Knead in butter. Add egg yolks, and yeast, dissolved in ¼ pint tepid milk, then stir in sugar and enough tepid milk to make a stiff dough. Knead thoroughly. Turn on to a lightly floured board. Roll evenly into a long square sheet. Brush with melted butter. Halve lengthwise. Cover one half fairly thickly with equal quantity of chopped almonds, currants and castor sugar, mixed well. Place remaining half on top. Press down lightly. Twist the two together to form a wreath and pinch edges together. Brush top with beaten egg yolk. Sprinkle to taste with finely chopped almonds. Bake in a moderate oven, 350 °F (Mark 3-4), until light gold in about 30 minutes. Cool on a wire rack. Coat with glacé icing, made with rose water instead of water.

* This is the way my Silesian cook, Ottilia, used to make this traditional sweet. In some parts of Germany, the chocolate mixture is folded into most of the cream, and the remainder of cream is lightly fluffed over the top, before decorating with the jam.

KAESEKUCHEN (Cheese Cake)

Murbeteig, 5 egg yolks, 5 oz. castor sugar, 1 lb. curd, 1 tablespoon cornflour, 5 egg whites, 1 oz. cleaned currants, grated rind 1 lemon, ½ teaspoon vanilla essence.

Line a 9 inch flan ring with Murbeteig. Ornament the edges and prick the base well with a fork. Beat egg yolks with the sugar for 5 minutes, then beat in the curd and cornflour. Beat egg whites till stiff. Stir currants, lemon rind and vanilla essence into cheese mixture, then fold in egg whites. Pile into pastry case, drawing filling up to the edge. Bake in a moderate oven, 350 °F (Mark 3-4), for about 45 minutes. Serve cold, cut in wedges.

Muerbeteig: Sift 8 oz. flour into a basin. Stir in 2 tablespoons castor sugar. Rub in 4 oz. butter. Make a hollow in centre of flour. Drop in 1 egg and a tablespoon of rum. Add a tiny pinch of salt. Gradually work the flour mixture into the egg and rum until you have a dough. Knead until quite smooth. Cover with a bowl. Stand in a cold place for 2 hours. Use this pastry not only for flan cases but for pie shells, tartlet cases, or when shortcrust is required for any kind of small cakes or pastries. Brush tins or pie dishes thinly with melted butter before lining with Murbeteig.

KUEMMELSTANGEN (Caraway Sticks)

4 oz. butter, 4 tablespoons cream, 8 oz. flour, 1 beaten egg yolk, salt and caraway seeds.

Beat butter to a cream in a basin. Add cream, and flour rubbed through a sieve. Mix to a firm dough. Knead well. Roll out thinly. Cut into narrow strips about 4½ inches long and ½ inch thick. Brush with beaten egg yolk. Sprinkle with salt and caraway seeds to taste. Place in a buttered baking tin, a little apart. Bake in a moderate oven, 350 °F (Mark 3-4), for about 15 minutes until golden brown.

KALTE ENTE * (" Cold Duck ")

1 bottle still hock, 4 lumps sugar, 1 lemon, 1 bottle chilled sparkling hock.

Place a jug or a small punch bowl in an ice bucket, with cracked ice below. Add the still hock and the sugar. Stand for 15 minutes, stirring occasionally. Wash and carefully peel lemon spirally until only a little remains round the stem end. If using a jug, balance lemon above the handle. If using a bowl, place lemon in a little plastic rack, covered with a vine leaf or nasturtium leaves, and suspend over the edge. Let the peel in either case just touch the hock. Add half a dozen ice blocks. Stand for 5 minutes. Remove lemon. Pour in sparkling hock. Serve in hot weather in squat tumblers or beakers.

YIELD: 12 servings.

* This is a famous Prussian summer drink.

GREECE

Is Ygian —— Good Health !

GREECE

Those of you who have been to Greece must remember with pleasure the delicious fruit and vegetables that are served at every meal. The Greeks are famous for their salads, for their ingenuity in presenting savoury meat mixtures stuffed in vine leaves, and for turning aubergines, green peppers and squashes into the most delicious entrées.

As olives are one of the chief products of this lovely country, everyone eats olives. Not only are they served with apéritifs, but they also appear as a relish at family and party meals.

In Greece, sweets and cakes made with nuts and flavoured with cinnamon are very popular. Some meat dishes are also flavoured with cinnamon. Almonds, chestnuts, pine nuts and pistachio nuts, grown in Greece, also play a large part in the Greek cuisine, as well as at the table. Pine nuts, in particular, appear in many baked stuffed fish dishes, such as mussels and squids.

All kinds of fresh herbs are used in Greek cookery and many of the dishes are prepared with yoghurt. Grated goat-milk cheese, Banir or Panir, is used like grated Parmesan in other parts of Europe.

It would be pleasant to be a vegetarian in this enchanting country, where nature yields the harvest that those who prefer a meatless diet dream of. Some day I hope to have a vegetarian adventure in Greece.

DOLMADES LAHANO * (Stuffed Cabbage Leaves)

1 tablespoon olive oil, 1 tablespoon minced onion, 4 oz. boiled rice, 4 oz. minced cooked lamb, salt and pepper, 2 peeled tomatoes, 2 oz. raisins, 18 cabbage leaves, ¾ pint lamb stock, 4 tablespoons tomato purée.

Heat the oil in a shallow saucepan. Add onion. Fry slowly for 2 or 3 minutes, stirring frequently, then stir in rice and lamb. Fry for 2 or 3 minutes, stirring frequently. Add salt and freshly ground black pepper to taste, tomatoes, and raisins, soaked overnight in cold water to cover, then thoroughly drained. Stir till blended. Remove pan from stove. Blanch the cabbage leaves. Drain and place on a pastry board. Place a spoonful of the mixture on the centre of each. Fold the leaves over the mixture to form small parcels. Secure with toothpicks. Arrange side by side in a shallow saucepan. Mix the stock with the tomato purée and pour over the parcels. Cover and simmer gently for 30 minutes. Cool. Serve as an hors d'oeuvre.

YIELD: 4 or 5 servings.

PSARI A LA SPETSIOTA (Baked Fish à la Spetsai)

3 lb. fish slices, salt as required, lemon juice as required, 1 cup tomato sauce, ½ cup white wine, 1 cup olive oil, 2 minced cloves of garlic, 2 tablespoons chopped parsley, salt and pepper, dry breadcrumbs as required.

Wash fish. Drain and sprinkle with salt and lemon juice to taste. Place in a buttered or oiled fireproof dish. Mix the tomato sauce with the wine, oil, garlic, parsley and salt and pepper to taste. Sprinkle over the fish, then scatter breadcrumbs evenly over the top. Bake, uncovered, in a moderately hot oven, 400 °F (Mark 5-6), until golden, in about 45 minutes.

YIELD: 6 servings.

NICOS TZEREFOS,
CHEF, CORDON BLEU,
S. S. ROMANTICA.

* In Greece, large vine leaves are frequently substituted for cabbage leaves.

SOUVLAKIA DE POISSON (Fish Kababs)

3 lb. 3 oz. fillets of fish, 1 tablespoon olive oil, 1 bay leaf, 1 sprig parsley, 1 sprig oregano, salt and pepper, tomato slices to taste.

Cut fish into small pieces. Mix the oil with the herbs and salt and pepper to taste. Add fish. Baste with the oil. Soak for 30 minutes, basting occasionally, then run on 8 or 9 metal or wooden skewers, alternately with a slice of tomato. Cook under a moderate grill, turning frequently, for about 15 minutes. Serve very hot with a potato or green salad.

YIELD: 8 or 9 servings.

P. TH. PETRACOPOULOS,
HOTEL GRANDE-BRETAGNE,
ATHENS.

ARNI ME CHICORY AVGOLEMONO (Lamb with Chicory and Egg-Lemon Sauce)

3 lb. 3 oz. shoulder of lamb, 2 or 3 medium-sized onions, ¼ pint water, 1 tablespoon flour, salt and pepper, 3 lb. 3 oz. chicory, egg-lemon sauce.

Ask the butcher to divide the lamb into 8 or 9 egg-shaped pieces. Peel and mince onions. Place meat in a metal-based casserole. Sprinkle with the onion and the water. Cook over moderate heat, turning frequently, until the meat is evenly browned and the water has evaporated. Add flour. Stir till brown, then pour in additional water to the level of the meat. Season with salt and pepper to taste. Meanwhile, clean chicory thoroughly in plenty of cold water, removing and discarding any discoloured or hard leaves. Chop chicory coarsely. Place in a saucepan of boiling water. Cook for a moment or two, then drain lightly and lay over the meat. Cover. When meat is tender, and only a little juice is left in casserole, make the egg-lemon sauce. Serve in a heated sauceboat.

Egg-Lemon Sauce: Stir the strained juice of 2 lemons gradually into 2 beaten egg yolks. Turn into a saucepan. Stir in enough hot juice from the casserole to give you a creamy

64

sauce, but do not allow to boil. Season with salt and pepper to taste.

YIELD: 8 or 9 servings.

P. TH. PETRACOPOULOS,
HOTEL GRANDE-BRETAGNE,
ATHENS.

MOUSSAKA A LA BOS (Meat and Potato Cake)

8 oz. minced meat, 8 oz. sliced onion, 1 teaspoon chopped parsley, ½ cup water, 2½ oz. butter, 8 oz. tomatoes, salt and pepper, 1½-2 lb. potatoes, ½ oz. flour, ¼ pint milk, 1 egg.

Place meat, onion, and parsley in a frying pan. Add water. Simmer until water is absorbed. Add 2 oz. of the butter. When melted, peel and slice tomatoes, and add the salt and freshly ground black pepper to taste. Fry slowly for about 20 minutes. Grease a cake tin, 8 or 9 inches across. Place a layer of potatoes, peeled, thinly sliced, and slightly fried, over the base. Cover with a layer of the meat mixture. Repeat, finishing with potatoes. Cover with greaseproof paper. Bake in a moderate oven, 350 °F (Mark 3-4), until potatoes are cooked, in about 1 hour. Remove paper. Cover with Béchamel sauce. Continue baking for 10-15 minutes. Turn on to a heated platter. Serve with any green vegetable.

Béchamel Sauce: Melt remainder of butter. Add flour. When frothy, stir in milk. Stir till boiling. Season to taste. Draw pan to one side, then beat egg and add. Stir till hot but do not allow to boil.

YIELD: 6 servings.

MOUSSAKA (Aubergine and Tomato Pie)

2 sliced aubergines, 4 tablespoons cooking oil, 4 tablespoons chopped onion, 1 lb. minced stewing steak, 4 sliced peeled tomatoes, ¼ pint stock, ¼ pint sieved canned tomatoes, 2 beaten eggs, ¼ pint cream, salt and pepper.

Choose young aubergines of medium size. Pour oil into a medium-sized frying pan. Place over moderate heat. When hot, add aubergine slices. Fry for a minute or two on each side, then arrange in a large shallow buttered fireproof dish. Place the onion and the steak in remaining oil in frying pan. Cook slowly until the oil is absorbed, stirring constantly. Place tomato slices on top. Blend the stock with the tomato purée and add. Continue cooking until meat is tender. Season with salt and pepper and a very little ground cinnamon if liked. When all the liquid is absorbed, spread over the aubergines. Cover with the egg, smoothly blended with the cream and seasoned to taste. Bake in a moderate oven, 350 °F (Mark 3-4), for 15-20 minutes, till sauce sets and turns golden brown.

YIELD: 4 servings.

PAPOUTSAKIA (Stuffed Courgettes)

6-8 parboiled courgettes, 1 medium-sized onion, 1 tablespoon olive oil, 4 oz. minced cooked meat, 2 oz. boiled rice, salt and pepper, ½ pint Béchamel sauce, grated cheese as required.

Halve the courgettes and scoop out the centres. Place shells, side by side, in a large shallow greased fireproof dish. Chop the onion. Fry in the oil till soft, then chop the courgette centres and add. Stir in the meat and rice. Season with salt and freshly ground black pepper. Stuff the courgettes. Pour the sauce over the tops. Sprinkle with the cheese. Brown under the grill or bake for 10 minutes in a fairly hot oven, 425 °F (Mark 6-7).

Note: Parboiled aubergines may be cooked in the same way.

YIELD: 3 or 4 servings.

HALVA * (Almond Dessert)

2 cups semolina, 6 oz. unsalted butter, 8 oz. castor sugar, 4 eggs, 1 cup chopped peeled almonds, 1 teaspoon ground cinnamon, syrup as required, 1 teaspoon lemon juice.

Place semolina in a basin. Beat butter till softened. Gradually beat in sugar. Add eggs, one at a time. Beat till thoroughly blended, then add almonds. Stir cinnamon into

* This is a traditional Easter pudding.

semolina, then add the almond mixture. Take a deep baking tin and brush well with melted butter. Add batter, which should fill it half full. Bake in a moderate oven, 350 °F (Mark 3-4), for 35-40 minutes. Meanwhile, make the syrup. Place 1 lb. castor sugar and 4 cups water in a saucepan. Stir over heat till sugar is dissolved, then bring to boil. Boil for a few minutes until syrupy. Stir in lemon juice. When Halva is ready, cover with the syrup. Leave until cold. Serve, cut in squares.

YIELD: 6 servings.

SVINGI (Lemon Pudding)

2 cups cold water, 4 oz. butter, 1 tablespoon castor sugar, 1 teaspoon salt, 8 oz. self-raising flour, 1 teaspoon grated lemon rind, 6 or 7 eggs.

Pour water into a saucepan. Add butter, sugar and salt. Boil till runny or syrupy, then remove from stove and stir in flour and lemon rind. When blended, cook for a few minutes over moderate heat, stirring constantly, until mixture is stiff, then remove pan from stove and add eggs, one by one. Beat each in before adding the next. Have a shallow saucepan ready, half full of hot oil or fat. Lower mixture in tablespoons into the oil or fat and fry till they float, when they should be the size of a medium-sized apple. Serve with honey, thinned with boiling water, then heated. Flavour, if liked, with ground cinnamon.

YIELD: 6 servings.

AMIGDALOPITA (Almond Cake)

4 separated eggs, 4 tablespoons castor sugar, 2 tablespoons brandy, 4 tablespoons dried breadcrumbs, 4 oz. ground almonds, 1 teaspoon baking powder.

Beat egg whites till stiff, but not dry. Stir in half the sugar. Beat well. Beat egg yolks with remaining sugar, adding brandy very slowly as you beat. Fold lightly into the egg whites. Mix the crumbs with the almonds and baking powder. Fold into the egg mixture. Bake in an oiled cake tin, in a moderate oven, 350 °F (Mark 3-4). Cool on a wire rack. When quite cold, cover with the syrup, then with the chocolate icing.

Syrup: Place 1 cup castor sugar and 1 cup water in a saucepan. Stir till sugar is dissolved, then boil until syrupy, without stirring. Add lemon juice.

Chocolate Icing: Melt 6 oz. plain chocolate in the top of a double boiler over boiling water. Add 1-2 oz. butter. Mix well. Remove pan from stove. Stir in a beaten egg white.

Mrs. A. Z. Alatzas,
London.

MELOPITTA * (Honey Cheese Cake)

1 lb. cottage cheese, 5 oz. castor sugar, 8 oz. extracted honey, 4 eggs, 6 oz. flour, 2½ oz. butter, a tiny pinch of salt, 1 dessertspoon ground cinnamon.

Place cheese in a large basin. Stir in sugar. Add honey. Mix with a wooden spoon until blended. Beat eggs thoroughly. Add to cheese mixture. Stir till blended. Sift flour into a basin. Rub in butter. Stir in salt. Make into a dough with ice-cold water. Line a small greased baking tin thinly with the shortcrust. Cover evenly with the filling. Bake in a moderate oven, 350 °F (Mark 3-4), until golden brown in about 30 minutes. Sprinkle evenly with the cinnamon. Leave until cold. Cut into diamonds or squares.

NISTISIMO (Cake with Olive Oil)

1 cup self-raising flour, 1 cup fine semolina, ½ cup sultanas, ½ cup chopped walnuts, if liked, ½ teaspoon ground cinnamon, ½ teaspoon ground cloves, 1 cup olive oil, 1 cup warm water, ½ teaspoon bicarbonate of soda, rind of 1 lemon and orange, juice of 1 lemon and orange.

Sift flour into a basin. Stir in semolina, sultanas, walnuts, if used, cinnamon and cloves. Stir in olive oil, then the water. Mix the soda with grated rind and strained juice of lemon and

* This is a traditional Easter dessert, made on one of the islands in the Greek archipelago.

68

orange and stir into mixture. Bake in an oiled cake tin in a moderate oven, 350 °F (Mark 3-4), until dry in the centre.

MRS. A. Z. ALATZAS,
LONDON.

ROMANTICA COCKTAIL

1 oz. Vodka, 1 oz. Cointreau, 1 oz. Grand Marnier, 2 oz. lemon, 1 oz. fresh orange juice, 3 drops Angostura bitters.

Measure all the ingredients into a cocktail shaker. Add cracked ice. Shake well. Serve in champagne glasses. Add a maraschino cherry and a slice of lemon and orange to each glass.

YIELD: 9 servings.

NICOS TZEREFOS.
CHEF, CORDON BLEU,
S. S. ROMANTICA.

SKORDALLA * (Garlic Sauce)

5 peeled cloves of garlic, 1 cup peeled blanched almonds, 1 teaspoon salt, 1 medium-sized boiled potato, 3 cups olive oil, ½ cup vinegar.

Crush the garlic with a pestle in a mortar, or use a heavy bowl and spoon. Slice almonds and add. Pound with the garlic into a smooth paste. Stir in salt. Mash potato and beat into the almond mixture. When blended, gradually stir in a few drops of the oil and of the vinegar alternately, until the mixture begins to thicken, then stir in a little more at a time, until all the oil and vinegar are incorporated, and the sauce is stiff enough to hold its shape.

* This traditional sauce is served with boiled, fried and grilled fish, fried aubergine, and with courgettes.

HOLLAND

Gezondheid! —— Good Health!

HOLLAND

Dutch fare somewhat resembles British, but it is richer, and more highly spiced and more substantial. Nutmeg is freely used for flavouring food, especially vegetables. Try diced boiled swedes, coated with melted butter, flavoured with grated nutmeg, and garnished with hard-boiled egg.

The Dutch are famous for their home-grown vegetables, of which large portions are served at dinner. Very often, especially in winter, potatoes and other vegetables are boiled together and mashed afterwards. These combinations have to be tasted to realise how delicious they can be.

There is not so much fish eaten in Holland as in Britain, but no hors d'oeuvre is complete without the celebrated Dutch herring salad, for which raw, salted or pickled herring is used.

Feast days are celebrated with great gusto in Holland. One of their special feasts takes place on Saint Nicholas Day, 5th December. On that day everyone gives and receives gifts, amusingly wrapped up. For this occasion the Dutch housewife makes all kinds of sweets, including chocolate letters, and Saint Nicholas dolls of spicy pastry.

One of the most popular beverages served both on Christmas and New Year's Eve, is Bishopswijn, a potent hot punch made of claret, flavoured with cinnamon and cloves. It does not only make you merry, but glow with contentment.

HARINGSLA (Herring Salad)

2 large raw salt herrings, 2 cooking apples, 1 small beetroot,
2 lettuces, 8 boiled medium-sized potatoes, 2 tablespoons
olive oil, 3 tablespoons vinegar, salt and pepper, 2 hard-boiled
eggs, 2 sweet pickled gherkins, 3 pickled onions.

Skin and carefully bone the fish. Cut the fillets into
small pieces. Peel, core and chop apples, and peel and dice
beetroot. Trim, wash, dry and shred lettuce. Dice potatoes.
Mix all these ingredients together in a basin. Beat oil with
the vinegar until thoroughly blended. Season with salt and
freshly ground black pepper to taste. Add to salad. Toss with
salad spoons till evenly coated. Turn into a salad bowl. Shell
and slice eggs. Slice gherkins. Garnish salad with the eggs,
gherkins and onions.

Note: Serve with toast and butter. May also be served
as a luncheon dish, but with bread and butter.

GROENTENSOEP MET BALLETJES (Vermicelli Soup)

4 cups white stock, 2 blades mace, $\frac{2}{3}$ cup vermicelli, $\frac{1}{2}$ cup
minced meat, salt and pepper, grated nutmeg, 1 beaten egg.

Pour stock into a saucepan. Add mace. Bring slowly
to boil. Simmer gently for 5 or 10 minutes, then strain.
Return to pan. Break up vermicelli and add. Mix the meat,
half pork and half veal, with salt and pepper, nutmeg and egg
as required. Shape into tiny balls. Roll in seasoned flour.
Bring soup to a full boil. Add balls. Cover closely. Simmer
steadily for at least 15 minutes. Season with salt and pepper.

YIELD: 3 or 4 servings.

HOLLANDSE HARING (Dutch Herring)

The exported Dutch herring, used in so many ways, is
more salt than the herring available in Holland, where it is
prepared and eaten almost as soon as it is brought ashore.

To Prepare Dutch Herring: Clean and skin. Soak in milk
or water for 24 hours, renewing the liquid at intervals. Serve
raw on small toasted canapés as an appetiser, or arrange on
ice cubes in a dish and serve with boiled potatoes and green
salad.

71

JACHTSCHOTEL (The Hunter's Dish)

2 large peeled onions, 1½ oz. butter, 1 lb. cooked meat, 2-3 lb. boiled potatoes, salt and pepper, pinch of grated nutmeg, ½ pint stock.

Slice onions. Melt the butter in a frying pan. Add onion. Fry over low heat until light brown. Cut meat and potatoes in slices. Grease a shallow fireproof dish. Fill with alternate layers of potato, meat and onion, seasoning each layer lightly with salt, pepper and nutmeg. Sprinkle with the stock. Cover with 2 or 3 tablespoons of breadcrumbs. Dab with bits of butter. Bake in a fairly hot oven, 425 °F (Mark 6-7), until lightly browned.

YIELD: 6 servings.

STAMPPOT VAN BOERENKOOL MET WORST * (Curly Kale and Sausages)

2-3 lb. curly kale, boiling salted water as required, 3 lb. potatoes, about 1 lb. Frankfurters, or smoked sausages, 4 tablespoons butter or margarine, pepper to taste.

Strip, wash and cut up the kale very finely. Boil in a little salted boiling water for about 40 minutes in a tightly closed saucepan. Peel and slice potatoes. Add to kale with sausages and just enough water to prevent burning. Cover and cook gently for 30 minutes. Remove sausages to a plate. Keep hot. Mash remainder. Stir in butter and enough boiling milk to make a smooth " mash ". Season with pepper to taste. Dish up. Garnish with the sausages.

YIELD: 4-6 servings.

BIETEN MET APFELN (Stewed Beetroot)

2 lb. boiled beetroot, 2½ oz. butter, 2 tablespoons chopped onion, 2 minced cooking apples, salt and pepper, a little sugar.

Peel and slice beetroot. Melt butter in a shallow saucepan. Add beetroot, onion, apple, salt, and freshly ground black

---

* " Stamppot " means that the vegetables are mixed to a smooth consistency. Typical winter dish in Holland. The Dutch have a saying, " Never eat curly kale before the frost has got at it ".

72

pepper to taste, and about a teaspoon of sugar. (If liked, add a grating of nutmeg.) Cover. Simmer very gently until into a pulp, in about 15 minutes, stirring occasionally. Serve with hot boiled gammon, meat balls or fried fish.

YIELD: 6 servings.

BRUSSELS LOF MET KAASSAUS, HAM, AARD-APPELCROQUETJES (Chicory with Cheese Sauce, Ham, and Potato Croquettes)

2 lb. chicory, cheese sauce, 2 lb. potatoes, 1 oz. butter, milk as required, grated nutmeg to taste, ¼ lb. hot sliced ham.

Cut a very thin slice off the base of the chicory heads. Place heads in a shallow saucepan. Cover with boiling salted water. Cover and boil for 20 minutes, then drain carefully. Place on a heated platter. Cover with cheese sauce. Serve with potato croquettes, arranged round the chicory alternately with slices of ham and halved hard-boiled eggs to taste.

Cheese Sauce: Melt 1 oz. butter in a saucepan. Add 1 oz. flour. When frothy, gradually stir in ½ pint hot water. When smooth and boiling, remove from stove, and stir in 4 oz. grated Gauda cheese. Season with salt and pepper to taste.

Potato Croquettes: Peel and boil potatoes in salted water, then drain thoroughly and mash till smooth. Add remaining butter and hot milk as required. Beat well with a wooden spoon. Season to taste with salt and pepper and a little grated nutmeg. Leave until cool. Divide mixture into 12-15 equal portions. Shape each into a croquette. Roll in lightly beaten egg white, and coat evenly with crumbs. Fry in deep hot fat until golden brown. Drain on absorbent paper.

YIELD: 6 servings.

DRIE IN DE PAN (Three in one Pan)

1 oz. baker's yeast, 3 cups tepid milk, pinch of salt, 8 oz. flour, 2 oz. currants, 2 oz. raisins, butter or oil as required, castor sugar.

Mix the yeast with 2 cups of the milk. Add salt and flour. Mix to a firm dough, gradually adding the remainder of the milk. Stir in currants and raisins. Cover and leave in a warm

73

place, until well risen in about an hour. Heat butter or oil in a shallow saucepan. Take one tablespoon of dough at a time, and shape it into a round or oblong cake. Fry slowly, three at a time, in the hot fat or oil, turning gently as required, until nicely browned. Drain on absorbent paper. Dredge with castor sugar and serve at once, as a dessert.

YIELD: 5 or 6 servings.

FLENSJES (Dutch Pancakes)

5 oz. flour, pinch of salt, 1 pint milk, 2 eggs, butter as required.

Sift flour and salt into a basin. Make a hollow in centre. Add half the milk and the eggs. Gradually beat in flour from the sides. When incorporated, beat batter till smooth. Gradually add remainder of milk and beat until bubbles form on the surface. Stand for at least one hour. Heat a frying pan with enough butter to cover the surface. When the butter stops sizzling, pour in just enough of the batter to cover the surface of the pan. When it starts to blister, turn pancake over with a palette knife. Fry till brown below. Turn and fry very lightly on the other side. Either sprinkle with sugar or spread with heated jam and roll up. Place on a warm platter and cover with a warm lid until all the pancakes are ready. Serve, garnished with lemon.

YIELD: 4 or 5 servings.

FROM AMSTERDAM.

BOTERKOEK (Dutch Butter Cake)

8 oz. flour, 8 oz. butter, 8 oz. Demarara sugar, pinch of salt, grated rind 1 lemon, 1 egg.

Sift flour into a basin. Rub in butter. Stir in sugar, salt and lemon rind. Mix to a dough with the egg. Pat dough into a shallow 8 inch round or square greased baking tin. Bake in a moderately hot oven, 375 °F (Mark 4-5), for about 30 minutes. Cool slightly on a wire rack. Cut into fingers. Serve with tea or coffee.

Note: In some parts of Holland, this cake is brushed with lightly beaten egg white, and sprinkled with chopped blanched almonds before baking. When baked, the centre should be a little moist.

74

ONTBIJTKOEK * (Spiced Loaf)

1 lb. flour, 3 oz. brown sugar, 1 teaspoon ground cinnamon, ½ teaspoon grated nutmeg, 1 teaspoon ground ginger, 1 dessert-spoon aniseeds, 3 teaspoons baking powder, 8 oz. golden syrup, ½ pint milk.

Mix all the dry ingredients in a basin. Stir the syrup into the milk. Make a hollow in centre of dry ingredients. Pour in liquid. Stir to a firm dough. Place in a well-greased loaf tin. Bake in a moderate oven, 350 °F (Mark 3-4), for 1-1½ hours. Stand till quite cold. Serve, sliced and buttered.

TULBAND MET ROZIJNEN † (Sultana Cake)

1 lb. flour, pinch of salt, 1 oz. baker's yeast, 3 oz. castor sugar, about ¼ pint tepid milk, 3 oz. butter, 2 eggs, 6 oz. sultanas, 2 oz. chopped candied peel, 2 tablespoons icing sugar.

Sift flour and salt into a warm basin. Make a hollow in the centre. Cream yeast with a teaspoon of the sugar, and pour into well. Add milk. Heap flour over from the side. Cover with a damp cloth. Set in a warm place to rise for about 30 minutes. Cream butter with remaining sugar. Beat eggs slightly. Gradually stir into the butter mixture, then add sultanas and peel. When the dough is well risen, stir in the fruit mixture. Beat well, and knock it down alternately, until it leaves the sides of the basin. (If eggs are small you will need a little more milk.) Cover bowl again with a damp cloth. Leave in a warm place to rise for 45 minutes. Place in a tubular tin, brushed with melted butter, and sprinkled with crumbs. Leave in a warm place until dough has risen to twice its original size. Bake in a moderately hot oven, 375 °F (Mark 4-5), for about 1 hour. Remove from oven. Stand for a minute or two. Sift the icing sugar over. Serve cold with tea or coffee. Sometimes this is served hot with golden syrup as a sweet.

* This is one of the famous national Dutch sweet loaves met with all over Holland. Sometimes it is made with wholemeal flour, sometimes with half wholemeal and half white flour, occasionally with half white flour mixed with quarter wholemeal and quarter rye flour. A thick slice is sometimes served with morning coffee.

† If you have a savarin tin which resembles an Arab's fez, use this for baking cake in, as Tulband means an Arab's fez.

75

SNEEUWBALLEN * (Snowballs)

4 oz. butter, 1 saltspoon salt, 1¼ cup cold water, 8 oz. sifted flour, 5 eggs, 3 oz. currants or sultanas, 2 tablespoons minced citron peel, 1 tablespoon rose water or rum, fat or oil for frying.

Place butter in a saucepan. Add salt and water. Bring quickly to the boil. Remove from stove. Stir in flour with a wooden spoon. Keep stirring until into a smooth paste, then add 1 egg at a time, beating well after each addition. Add the fruit, citron peel and rose water or rum. Heat fat or oil to between 365 and 379 °F. Dip a metal spoon in the hot fat or oil. Remove a spoonful of the batter. Drop into the hot fat or oil. Fry until golden brown, turning occasionally. (They should be very light and puffy.) Repeat until all the batter is cooked. Drain each on absorbent paper, and sprinkle with sifted icing sugar.

YIELD: 2 dozen.

NASSI GORENG † (Fried Rice)

Butter, margarine or oil as required, 3 tablespoons minced onion, garlic to taste, spice to taste, including ½ teaspoon coriander, ½ teaspoon caraway seeds, and ½ teaspoon minced chilli pepper, 1 cup chopped ham or cooked pork, salt and pepper, 3½ cups cold boiled rice, an omelet made of 3 eggs, and 1 cup cut-up shrimps if desired.

Melt butter or margarine or heat oil in a shallow saucepan. Add onion. Fry slowly till lightly brown. Add chopped garlic to taste, the spices and meat. Season with salt and pepper. Fry meat for a few minutes. Add fluffy dry boiled rice. Keep stirring until the rice browns lightly. If too dry, add a little meat stock. Lastly break up the omelet into thin slices. Place rice mixture in a shallow dish. Garnish with the slices of omelet, and shrimps if used. Serve if liked, with cucumber salad and a glass of beer.

YIELD: 5 or 6 servings.

* These " snowballs " are usually served at Christmas parties and on New Year's Eve.

† This dish comes from the Dutch East Indies, now Indonesia, and is very popular with Dutch families. It is served in soup plates and eaten with a large spoon. If liked " hotter " add a little chilli powder. Sometimes it is served with " kroepoek ", wafers made of dried shrimps which you fry in oil till crisp. You can buy them wherever Indian or Indonesian products are sold.

76

HUNGARY

Egészségére!——To your Health!
Jó Étvágyát Kivánok!——Good Appetite!

HUNGARY

The Hungarians have a natural gift for cooking as you will see for yourself if you go to Hungary. Unlike some of their neighbours, while marching with the times they take the greatest pride in preparing dishes from recipes handed down by their nomadic ancestors. Some, particularly in country places, are still cooked in copper cauldrons, suspended by a handle over an open fire.

Modern Hungarian cooking is characterized by the generous use of lard, onion, paprika, and sour cream. In the finer branches of cookery, fresh is used instead of sour. It was the Turks who introduced paprika to Hungary with the result that it has been a national spice for the past century.

No matter where you lunch or dine in Hungary you will be struck with the variety of noodles offered you. This is most pronounced on Fridays, sometimes called " Noodle Days ". Then you find tiny noodles in your soup, fried noodles with your meat in place of potatoes, and noodles with your cheese. Sometimes they are served, sugared and spiced, for dessert.

One of the most festive days in Hungary is St. Stephen's Day, held in memory of the patron saint. Then, the natives, dressed in traditional costume, celebrate heartily with beer and Tokay. Where money is no object, champagne is served instead of Tokay.

UJHÁZY TYÚKLEVES (Fowl Soup)

1 chicken, about 4 lb., 2 heads of celery, 1 carrot, 1 parsnip, 2 oz. mushrooms, salt, 6 black peppercorns, 2 sprigs parsley, small piece of root ginger.

Joint bird. Place in a saucepan. Cover with cold water. Bring quickly to boil, then drain off water. Rinse joints in cold water. Place in saucepan. Cover with boiling water, and bring to simmering point. Skim carefully as the scum rises. Cover and simmer gently till the bird is half cooked, time depending on whether the bird is a boiling or roasting chicken. Trim celery, scrape carrot, peel parsnips and remove stalks from mushrooms. Cut all into thin strips. Arrange in pan with chicken. Add salt to taste. Place remaining ingredients in a small muslin bag. Add to soup. Cover pan. Simmer gently till the joints are quite tender. Remove joints and bag. Dish up soup. Garnish with boiled pasta to taste.

YIELD: 6 or 7 servings.

RÁCPONTY (Baked Fresh Haddock)

1 large fresh haddock, salt as required, butter as required, fat bacon as required, 1 lb. potatoes, 1 dessertspoon flour, 1 dessertspoon paprika, soured cream as required.

Clean a fish, large enough for 3 or 4 persons. Slit open lengthwise. Rub the inside well with salt. Make incisions with a sharp knife, about 1½ inches apart, on top of fish. Stuff a knob of butter and a small piece of bacon in each. Brush a shallow baking tin lavishly with melted butter. Peel and slice potatoes into tin, and spread slices evenly over the base. Sprinkle with melted butter. Lay the fish on a rack and stand in the tin. Bake in a moderate oven, 350 °F (Mark 3-4), for 5 minutes. Mix the flour with the paprika. Sprinkle over fish. Continue baking, basting frequently, with sour cream, until the fish is cooked.

YIELD: 3 or 4 servings.

TEJFELES HAL * (Fish Steaks with Cream Sauce)

4 fish steaks, salt to taste, ½ cup minced parsley, slices of onion as required, ¼ cup minced green pepper, 4 slices of tomato, 2 thin slices of lemon, 2½ oz. butter, water as required, ¼ pint soured or fresh cream.

Wipe fish steaks with a damp cloth. Rub lightly with salt. Brush a large shallow baking dish with melted butter. Sprinkle with the parsley. Cover parsley with wafer-thin slices of onion. Sprinkle with the minced green pepper. Place the fish steaks, side by side, on top. Arrange a tomato slice on top of each steak, topped with half a slice of lemon. Melt butter only till runny and sprinkle evenly over the steaks. Add ¼-⅓ cup cold water. Bake in a moderate oven, 375 °F (Mark 4-5), until fish is tender, in 25-30 minutes, basting steaks every 10 minutes with the liquid in dish. Carefully remove fish to a serving platter. Cover and keep hot. Rub the vegetables and stock through a sieve into a small saucepan. Stir in cream gradually. Flavour if liked with a saltspoon of paprika, otherwise with pepper.

Note: When serving this as a main dish at any meal, pass boiled potatoes round as well.

YIELD: 4 servings.

ESTERHÁZY ROSTÉLYOS (Stewed Steak with Cream Gravy)

6 small sirloin steaks, 4 oz. lard, flour as required, stock as required, salt to taste, 2 medium-sized peeled onions, 3 trimmed carrots, 1 peeled medium-sized turnip, 1 peeled parsnip, paprika and pepper to taste, ¼ pint soured cream.

Trim steaks. Melt lard in a large frying pan. Dip steaks in flour. Shake lightly. Place, side by side, in pan. Fry quickly on both sides to seal in juices. Transfer to a shallow casserole. Cover with stock. Season with salt to taste. Cover. Simmer gently for 1 hour. Slice and cut onions, carrots, turnip and parsnip into small strips. Add to fat remaining in pan. Fry slowly until all the fat is absorbed, then sprinkle with a

* In Hungary perch or pike is usually used for this dish. If not available, substitute cod, halibut or turbot.

79

dessertspoon of flour. When blended, add to steak with paprika and pepper to taste. Cover. Simmer gently till tender, then gradually stir in cream, using fresh if sour is not available. In Hungary, a small wine glass of Madeira is sometimes stirred into the gravy 5 minutes before adding the cream. Drink " Bull's Blood ", claret or Burgundy with this steak.

YIELD: 6 servings.

HUNGARIAN CSARDA.

GULYÁS * (Meat Goulash)

1 lb. stewing steak, 2 oz. lean veal, 2 oz. ox kidney, 2 oz. ox heart, 2 oz. ox liver, 1 large peeled onion, 2 oz. dripping, 1 teaspoon salt, 1 teaspoon Hungarian paprika, 1 lb. tomatoes, ¾ lb. small potatoes.

Remove any skin and fat from the meat. Cut meat into neat cubes. Chop onion. Melt dripping in a shallow saucepan. Add onion. Fry till light brown, stirring occasionally. Remove to a plate. Add the steak, veal, kidney, heart and liver to pan. Fry over moderate heat, turning frequently, until all the contents are evenly browned. Return onion to pan. Add salt and paprika. Scald and peel tomatoes. Slice and add to pan. Cover and simmer gently for 1 hour, then add potatoes, scraped if new, otherwise peeled. Cover and simmer until tender in about 20 minutes. Serve meat on a heated platter. Cover with the sauce. Arrange potatoes round.

YIELD: 6 servings.

CSIRKEMÁJ GŐDŐLLŐ MÓDRA (Chicken Liver à la Gődőllő)

1½ lb. chicken livers, 5 oz. lard, 5 oz. chopped onion, 2½ seeded green peppers, 2 small tomatoes, ½ teaspoon salt, black pepper to taste, ¼ teaspoon dried marjoram, ½ teaspoon minced parsley, ½ teaspoon paprika.

Clean and trim livers carefully. Cut each in half. Melt half the lard in a shallow saucepan. Add onion. Fry slowly

* In some parts of Hungary no potatoes are added, but mashed potatoes are piped round it then the goulash is topped with fried onion rings, garnished chopped parsley. In other parts, it is made without kidney, heart and liver, when ½ lb. veal is used instead of 2 oz.

until golden brown, then add liver. Fry quickly till cooked to taste, turning occasionally. Melt remainder of lard in a frying pan. Coarsely chop peppers and add, with tomatoes, peeled and cut in cubes. Fry for 5 minutes. Mix with the liver. Add salt, freshly ground black pepper to taste, and marjoram, parsley and paprika. Stir over the stove till piping hot. Turn on to a heated platter. Garnish with galuska.

Galuska (milk noodles)

Mix a small nut of butter, beaten till creamy, in a basin with a teaspoon of beaten egg, 1 teaspoon sour milk, 2 teaspoons flour, a pinch of salt, a dash of pepper, and a pinch of chopped parsley. With a teaspoon, remove a tiny piece of the paste at a time, and drop into boiling stock or water, or soup if required for garnishing soup. Cover and cook over low heat for 2 minutes. Serve at once. They should be the size of a thimble.

YIELD: 5 servings.

PAPRIKÁS CSIRKE (Chicken with Paprika Sauce)

1 roasting chicken, 1 small bay leaf, 1 sprig parsley, 5 black peppercorns, salt to taste, cold water as required, 2 oz. butter 2 oz. seasoned flour, 1 peeled medium-sized onion, 4 oz. mushrooms, squeeze of lemon juice, 1 small can tomato purée, 1 dessertspoon paprika, 1 dessertspoon castor sugar, ¼ pint cream.

Choose a chicken about 4-4½ lb. and have it neatly jointed. Skin joints. Place skin in a shallow saucepan with the carcass bones, and the giblets, soaked in salt water for 30 minutes, then drained, Add the bay leaf, parsley, peppercorns and salt. Cover with cold water. Cover and simmer gently till stock is reduced to half its quantity. Melt butter in a shallow saucepan till it gives off a blue smoke. Dip joints in seasoned flour. Shake lightly. Place in pan. Fry till evenly browned all over, turning frequently. Remove from pan. Slice in onion, and add mushrooms. Fry slowly till onion just begins to colour, then stir in enough of the remaining seasoned flour to absorb the fat. When frothy, gradually stir in ½ pint of the strained chicken stock. Simmer for 5 minutes, stirring constantly, then season with salt and add lemon juice. Mix the

C.C.—F 81

tomato purée with the paprika, sugar and cream in a small basin. Stir in 2 tablespoons of the chicken sauce, then stir this mixture into remaining sauce in saucepan. When boiling, add chicken. There should be enough sauce to cover it. If not, add more stock as required. Cover closely. Simmer very gently until tender in about 30 minutes. Take care the sauce does not boil or it will curdle. Arrange a ring of fluffy boiled rice on a hot platter. Garnish lightly with paprika and chopped parsley. Place the chicken joints in the centre and cover with the sauce. Garnish, if liked, with fried mushrooms.

YIELD: 6 servings.

TŐLTŐTT PAPRIKA (Stuffed Peppers)

2 oz. lard, 1 tablespoon chopped onion, 6 oz. minced beef or pork, 3 oz. rice, boiled salt and black pepper, 1 minced clove of garlic, 6 large green peppers, 2 oz. butter, 3 oz. flour, 1 small can concentrated tomato purée, pinch of sugar, water as required.

Melt lard in a shallow saucepan. Add onion. Fry over slow heat until clear. Stir into meat. Add rice, salt, freshly ground black pepper to taste, and garlic. Mix well. If peppers are long instead of squat, pull out stems with the seeds, then pinch off tips. If squat, split, but do not remove tips. Fill with stuffing. Melt butter. Stir in flour. When frothy, stir in tomato purée, salt to taste, and enough water to make a very thin purée. Place peppers side by side in a shallow buttered fireproof dish. Cover with the purée. Cover. Cook very slowly at 300 °F (Mark 1-2) in the centre of oven for $\frac{3}{4}$-1 hour. Serve with boiled potatoes or rice.

YIELD: 6 servings.

HUNGARIAN CSARDA.

ALMÁSPITÉ (Apple Pie with Almond Crust)

1 lb. dessert apples, 6 oz. flour, 4 oz. butter, 1 egg yolk, about 2 tablespoons soured cream, 2 oz. ground almonds, 2 oz. castor sugar, strawberry jam as required, 1 egg white.

Stew the apples with only enough water to prevent burning, and sweeten to taste. Sift flour into a basin. Rub in butter.

82

Mix the egg yolk with the sour cream. Stir into flour mixture. Knead till smooth, then chill for 30 minutes. Brush a 7 inch sandwich tin lightly with melted butter. Divide pastry in 2 equal portions. Roll half into a round to fit tin. Line tin, then trim edge and ornament to taste. Prick base well with a fork. Bake in a moderately hot oven, 400 °F (Mark 5-6), for about 10 minutes. Meanwhile, mix the almonds with the castor sugar. At the end of 10 minutes, spread the inside of the pastry case with strawberry jam. Cover with half the almonds and sugar. Beat egg white to a stiff froth. Fold into apples. Spread evenly in the case. Sprinkle with remaining almond and sugar mixture, then cover with remaining pastry. Brush the top with egg white. Sprinkle with castor sugar to glaze. Bake in a moderately hot oven, 400 °F (Mark 5-6), for about 30 minutes. Leave until cold. Decorate round the rim with whipped cream, then top cream with glacé cherries to taste.

YIELD: 4 or 5 servings.

SOUFFLÉ MAGYAR (Magyar Soufflé)

2½ oz. rice, 1 pint milk, 5 oz. castor sugar, 2 separated eggs, apricot or strawberry jam, ½ pint sieved apples, brandy to taste.

Rinse and drain rice. Place in the top of a double boiler. Add milk. Stir frequently over boiling water, until the mixture comes to the boil, then cover and cook, stirring occasionally, until creamy, then cool slightly. Mix 1 oz. of the sugar with the egg yolks. Beat well. Stir into rice. Brush a shallow fireproof dish with melted butter. Spread a third of the rice in the base. Top with a thin layer of jam. Add alternate layers of rice and jam until rice is all in dish, then spread the apple purée over the top. Beat egg whites till frothy, then gradually beat in remaining sugar. Beat until the mixture forms peaks. Spread rockily over the purée, bringing in close to the edge of the dish. Bake in a moderate oven, 350 °F (Mark 3-4), for about 20 minutes. Sprinkle to taste with brandy. Set alight. Serve at once.

YIELD: 4 servings.

GESZTENYÉS KIFLI (Chestnut Crescents)

5 oz. flour, 4 oz. butter, 1 egg yolk, rum to flavour, chestnut filling.

Sift flour into a basin. Rub in butter. Beat egg yolk with a few drops of rum. Add to flour mixture. Stir until into a dough. Chill for 30 minutes. Roll out into a square, about the thickness of a penny. Cut into 1½ inch squares. Place a little chestnut filling on the centre of each square, and fold over the pastry to make crescents. Press edges together with a fork. Place a little apart on a shallow greased baking tin, dredged lightly with flour. Bake in a hot oven, 450 °F (Mark 7-8), until golden brown. Dredge with castor sugar. Serve with chocolate, tea, or ice cream.

Chestnut Filling

Slit 1 lb. chestnuts on the thick side with a sharp knife, then place in a saucepan. Cover with boiling water. Boil steadily for about 20 minutes until it is easy to remove the inner and outer skin. When peeled, place on a board. Chop until finely minced. Pour 2 tablespoons milk into a small saucepan. Add 3 oz. castor sugar. Stir over low heat till dissolved, then bring to boil. Add at once to the nuts. Stir till blended, then beat in 1 walnut of unsalted butter and a few drops of rum. Leave until cold before using.

MANDULÁS RÚD (Almond Sticks)

4 oz. ground almonds, 8 oz. sifted icing sugar, 1 egg yolk, 1 or 2 drops of rum, 1 egg white.

Mix the almonds with half the sugar, egg yolk and rum. Turn on to a pastry board, dredged with sifted castor sugar. Mould the paste into small strips, 3 inches long and ¾ inch wide. Place a little apart on a greased baking sheet. Beat egg whites till very stiff. Beat in remainder of sugar. Beat until quite thick. Pipe on top of each almond stick till evenly covered. Bake near the bottom of the oven at 250 °F (Mark ¼-½), for about 30 minutes, until dry but still white. They must not be allowed to change colour.

84

MINESTRA ALLA ROMANA (Roman Vegetable Soup)

2 tablespoons olive oil, 1 rasher of bacon, 1 tablespoon chopped onion, 1 sliced carrot, 1 clove of garlic, 2 teaspoons chopped parsley, ½ lb. peeled tomatoes, beef stock as required, salt and pepper to taste, 8 oz. green peas, 3 oz. vermicelli.

Heat olive oil in a saucepan. Remove rind from bacon. Chop bacon. Add to oil with onion and carrot. Peel and slice garlic. Add with the parsley. Fry for 2 or 3 minutes, stirring occasionally, then chop and add tomatoes and enough stock to cover the vegetables. Cover and simmer gently for 1 hour. Season with salt and pepper to taste. Rub through a sieve into another saucepan. Add peas and vermicelli. Cover and simmer gently, stirring occasionally, until the peas and vermicelli are soft. Serve with grated Parmesan cheese.

YIELD: 4 or 5 servings.

MINESTRONE

8 oz. ditali, 2 tablespoons olive oil, 1½ oz. butter, 1 tablespoon chopped onion, 3 sliced celery stocks, 2 diced large potatoes, 6 pints boiling water, 2 cups sliced string beans, 1 cup green peas, salt and pepper, 1 teaspoon minced parsley, 2 oz. grated Parmesan cheese.

Ditali is a tubular pasta, about ½ inch long and ¼ inch wide. Heat the oil and butter, then add the onion. Fry slowly till slightly browned in 3 or 4 minutes. Add celery and potatoes. Cover and simmer for 10 minutes. Add boiling water. Simmer for 15 minutes. Add beans, peas, ditali, salt and freshly ground black pepper, then cover. Bring quickly to boil. Simmer slowly for about 20 minutes. Serve at once in heated soupcups or plates. Sprinkle each portion with a little parsley and cheese.

YIELD: 6-8 servings.

ZUPPA DI PESCE (Italian Fish Soup)

¼ lb. sliced carrot, ¼ lb. sliced leeks, ½ lb. sliced tomatoes, 2 peeled cloves of garlic, 4 tablespoons olive oil, ½ lb. mackerel, 1 lb. whiting, pinch of saffron, 5 pints cold water, salt and pepper, 3 oz. vermicelli.

Prepare vegetables, then mince garlic and add. Heat oil. Add vegetables and garlic. Fry slowly for 10 minutes, stirring occasionally. Wash and behead mackerel and whiting, and add. When hot, add saffron, water, and salt and pepper to taste. Cover closely. Simmer gently for 45 minutes, then remove fish bones. Rub fish, vegetables and stock through a sieve into a fresh saucepan. Add vermicelli. Stir over heat till boiling. Simmer gently for 10 minutes, stirring frequently. Reseason if necessary. If wanted more highly flavoured, add to the water 1 sprig of parsley, 1 sprig of fennel if available, or two pinches of curry powder, and a blade of mace.

YIELD: 6-8 servings.

SCAMPI FRITTI (Fried Scampi)

2 dozen Dublin Bay prawns, 2 oz. flour, pinch of salt, 3 tablespoons tepid water, 1 dessertspoon salad oil, 1 egg white.

Shell prawns carefully. Sift flour and salt into a basin. Make a well in the centre. Pour in the water and oil. Mix to a smooth batter. Beat until bubbles form on top. Half fill a deep frying pan with cooking oil. Heat till smoking hot. Meanwhile, whisk the egg white to a stiff froth. Fold into the batter. Dip the prawns in the batter. Fry until crisp and golden. Pile on a heated platter. Garnish with sprigs of parsley and wedges of lemon.

Note: This is also a favourite first course at luncheon.

YIELD: 4 servings.

FRITTATA CON SPINACI (Egg and Spinach au Gratin)

2 lb. prepared spinach, 1 oz. butter, 5 eggs, 2 or 3 tablespoons grated Parmesan cheese, pinch of salt, black pepper.

Steam spinach for 20 minutes, then drain thoroughly. Return to pan with the butter. Stir over moderate heat till blended. Beat eggs with cheese, salt and freshly ground black pepper to taste. Place spinach with any butter remaining in pan in a shallow buttered fireproof dish. Pour the egg mixture over. Bake in a moderately hot oven, 400 °F

(Mark 5-6), until golden brown in about 15 minutes. Serve at once.

YIELD: 3 or 4 servings.

GIOSETTA ALLA ROMANA * (Parmesan cheese cakes)

2 oz. butter, 2 oz. flour, ½ pint white stock, 2 oz. grated Parmesan cheese.

Melt butter in a saucepan. Stir in flour. When frothy, stir in stock. Cook, stirring constantly, over low heat for 30 minutes. Remove from stove. Stir in cheese. Leave until cool. Shape into small flat cakes, about the size of a florin and ½ inch thick. Cover with finely crushed dried breadcrumbs. Fry in hot deep fat for 10-15 minutes. Drain on absorbent paper. Pile on a heated platter. Garnish with sprigs of parsley.

YIELD: 2 servings.

PIZZA ALLA SICILIANA † (Sicilian Pizza)

Line a shallow round or oblong baking tin thinly with shortcrust. Prick the centre well with a fork. Ornament the edges. Bake in a moderately hot oven, 450 °F (Mark 7-8), until nearly ready, then fill quickly with the following mixture. Sprinkle the base with grated Italian or Gruyère cheese, applying it evenly and fairly thickly. Cover with finely chopped onion, mixed with equal quantity of shredded green pepper. Place a layer of thinly sliced tomato, lightly fried in melted butter, on top. Lastly, garnish the top either with anchovy fillets to taste, or first with grated Parmesan cheese, then with minced parsley. Return to oven. Bake for about 5 minutes, just long enough to melt the cheese and brown off the pastry. Serve piping hot.

* Serve as a main course at lunch or a first course at dinner.

† There are many varieties of pizza served around Naples and further south made with bread dough instead of pastry. The most popular in Italy is made by covering the dough with fillets of anchovy, sliced peeled tomatoes, a few sliced black olives, and slices of Mozzarella cheese. The filling is then sprinkled with chopped marjoram and brushed with olive oil, and the pizza is baked in a moderate oven, 350 °F (Mark 3-4), for 30 minutes.

POLENTA PASTICIATTA

1½ pints water, seasoning to taste, 1 oz. butter, 3½ oz. maize flour, 1 oz. grated Parmesan cheese.

Bring water, seasoning and butter to a boil. Whisk in maize flour. Keep on whisking until paste begins to thicken, then draw pan to side of stove and allow mixture to cook slowly for about 30 minutes, stirring with a wooden spatula every 4 or 4 minutes. When Polenta is cooked, stir in cheese and remove pan from stove. Turn into a lightly greased casserole and leave overnight. When required, unmould, and slice as you would a sponge cake, but make slices big enough to fit the base of a buttered casserole. Place one slice in casserole. Cover with a layer of sauce and then with a layer of grated Parmesan cheese. Repeat layers, finishing with a liberal sprinkling of the cheese. (You will need 4 oz. altogether.) Place in the centre of a moderate oven, 350 °F (Mark 3-4). Bake for about 35 minutes, then serve at once.

Sauce for Polenta: Heat a frying pan. Add 1 oz. butter. When melted, stir in 4 oz. finely chopped onion and a minced peeled clove of garlic. Cook slowly for 2 or 3 minutes, stirring constantly, then add ½ lb. finely sliced button mushrooms. Cook slowly for 5 minutes, stirring frequently, then add 1½ lb. tomatoes, peeled, seeded and chopped. Add ½ glass white wine. Stir over moderate heat till reduced to a thick " saucey " consistency. Stir in 1 pint thick cream. Season and cook until the sauce is reduced by ½ pint.

YIELD: 4 servings.

MARIO GALLATI,
DIRECTOR,
CAPRICE,
LONDON.

RAVIOLI

12 oz. plain flour, ¼ teaspoon salt, 2 eggs, 2 tablespoons creamed butter, 1 cup tepid water, chicken and spinach filling.

Sift flour with salt on to a board. Make a hollow in centre. Drop in eggs, then add butter. Mix carefully till roughly blended, then gradually add enough cold water to make a rather stiff dough. Knead until smooth. Cover and stand about 10 minutes. Divide in two. Roll each half out very thinly on a lightly floured board. Drop teaspoonfuls of the filling, about 2 inches apart, on one piece of dough. Cover with remaining sheet. Gently press round each mound of filling to form little raised squares. Cut the squares apart with a pastry cutter. Place ravioli in a large deep saucepan, containing 8 quarts of fast boiling salted water. Cover. Cook for about 10 minutes. Remove carefully with a fish slice. Pile on heated individual plates. Top with a little tomato sauce. Dredge with grated Parmesan cheese. Serve at once.

Chicken and Spinach Filling: Beat 2 eggs lightly. Gradually stir in 1 cup minced boiled chicken, 1 cup minced boiled spinach, ½ cup breadcrumbs, 2 tablespoons grated Parmesan cheese, ½ clove garlic, finely minced, 2 teaspoons minced parsley, and salt and freshly ground black pepper to taste. Add enough beaten egg to hold the ingredients firmly together.

YIELD: 3 or 4 servings.

RIGATONI CON SALSICCIA (Shell Macaroni with a Piquant Sauce)

1 lb. rigatoni, 1 lb. pork sausages, 1 tablespoon chopped onion, 1 lb. mushrooms, 1 peeled clove garlic, salt and pepper, 1 large can tomato purée, 1 bay leaf, ½ cup grated Pecorino cheese.

Heat 4 quarts water till boiling. Add salt to taste, then the rigatoni. Cook until tender in about 20 minutes, then drain. Rinse, drain and place in a buttered fireproof dish. (In Italy, an Italian version of pork sausage is used. When not available, use a local brand.) Cut sausages into 1 inch lengths. Heat 3 tablespoons olive oil in a shallow saucepan. Add sausage. Fry till a slight brown in about 10 minutes. Add onion, mushrooms, cut in slices, garlic, and salt and pepper to taste. Cover. Simmer for 15 minutes. Add tomato purée and bay leaf. Cover pan. Simmer gently for 1 hour, then remove bay leaf and garlic. Spoon the sauce over the rigatoni. Mix well.

Sprinkle with cheese. (If not available, use any goat milk cheese.) Bake in a moderate oven, 350 °F (Mark 3-4), for about 10 minutes.

YIELD: 6-8 servings.

FROM AMALFI, BAY OF SALERNO.

RISOTTO ALLA MILANESE

8 oz. chicken giblets, 4 oz. butter, 1 tablespoon sliced onion, 2 cups Patna rice, 4 cups chicken stock, ½ teaspoon saffron, 4 oz. grated Parmesan cheese, salt and pepper.

Clean and cook the giblets in boiling salted water to cover until tender. Remove from pan. Mince finely. Melt butter in a large shallow saucepan. Add onion. Fry over low heat until brown in about 5 minutes, then remove onion. Rinse and drain rice thoroughly. Add to butter. Stir for 5 minutes over moderate heat, then add 1 cup chicken stock, and stir well. Place the saffron in ½ cup stock. Stand for 5 minutes, then strain the stock into rice. Stir well. Gradually add remainder of stock, stirring it in until all the stock is added and the rice is cooked in about 30 minutes. Add half the cheese. Stir well, then add the minced giblets, still stirring. (If the rice has become too dry, add a little more stock.) When ready, the risotto should be creamy and moist. Dish up. Sprinkle with remaining cheese.

YIELD: 6 or 7 servings.

TAGLIERINI (Taglierini with Chicken Liver Sauce)

12 oz. chicken livers, 1½ oz. butter, 1 minced clove of garlic, 1 can tomatoes, 1 cup boiled peas, salt and pepper. 12 oz. tagliarini, 3 quarts boiling salted water.

Chicken Liver Sauce: Wash, trim and quarter the livers. Melt butter in a saucepan. (If you prefer, use 3 tablespoons olive oil.) Add garlic and tomatoes. Cover. Simmer very gently for 30 minutes. Stir in peas. Simmer very gently for about 15 minutes. Season with salt and pepper before serving.

Throw the noodles into the boiling salted water. Boil till tender, in about 10 minutes. Drain, rinse under cold water

92

tap, and drain again. Reheat. Pile on heated plates. Coat with the sauce. Sprinkle to taste with any grated Italian cheese, except gorgonzola.

YIELD: 4 servings.

OSSOBUCO * (Stewed Knuckle of Veal)

Knuckle of veal as required, 2 tablespoons flour, salt and pepper, ¼ pint dry white wine, 1 cup water, 1 teaspoon minced parsley, ½ clove garlic, 4 snippets of lemon peel, 1 chopped anchovy fillet, 1 tablespoon veal stock, ½ oz. butter.

Grease a deep large saucepan lavishly with butter. Dip 4 pieces of knuckle of veal, 4 inches long, with meat attached, in flour. Season with salt and pepper to taste. Place side by side in pan. Fry until evenly browned all over, turning bones occasionally. Add wine. Cook until all the wine evaporates. Add water and cover pan. Cook over low heat for 1 hour, adding a little more water at a time if and when necessary. Five minutes before dishing up add parsley. Chop garlic and add with the lemon strips, an inch long, and the anchovy. Cook for 2 minutes longer, turning the bones at half time. Arrange bones on serving dish. Add stock to liquid in pan, then butter. Stir till boiling. Pour over bones. Serve with rice.

* Sometimes this traditional dish, occasionally spelt Ossi Bucchi, is cooked in this way:

Heat 1½ oz. butter in a large shallow saucepan. Add 2 knuckles of veal, cut into 3 inch lengths. Fry for about 10 minutes, turning frequently until evenly browned. Add 1 heaped tablespoon chopped carrot, ¼ cup chopped celery, 2 level tablespoons chopped onion and salt and pepper to taste. Cover. Simmer gently until carrots are soft, in 10-20 minutes. Blend 1½ tablespoons tomato paste with 1 cup sherry. Stir into vegetables, then cover closely. Simmer slowly till veal is tender, in 30-45 minutes. (If gravy is wanted, add water to taste at half time.) Add 1 teaspoon minced parsley. Serve with rice boiled in veal stock, or with mashed potatoes and spinach.

YIELD: 4 servings.

93

VITELLO TONNATO * (Veal with Tunny Sauce)

2 lb. filleted veal, 1 chopped carrot, 1 chopped celery stick, 2 medium-sized onions, sprig of rosemary, 1 bay leaf, 3 whole cloves, ½ pint water, 2 tablespoons white wine, ¼ lb. anchovies, ½ lb. tunny fish, 2 egg yolks, olive oil as required, juice of 1 lemon, salt and black pepper, 1 or 2 capers.

Rinse and dry veal. Place in a shallow saucepan. Add carrot and celery. Peel and chop onions. Add with rosemary, bay leaf, cloves and water. Bring to boil. Turn into a heated casserole. Cover with buttered paper. Place in a slow oven, 275-300 °F (Mark ½-1). Bring to a slow simmer, then adjust heat, to keep at slow simmering. Cook till tender, but not discoloured. Remove meat and leave till cool. Measure liquid in pan, then return to pan and cook until reduced to half its quantity. Strain and chill. Pound anchovies and tunny fish in a mortar or strong basin, then rub through a very fine sieve. Beat egg yolks with a wooden spoon. Add olive oil, drop by drop, until the mixture is into a thick mayonnaise. Gradually beat in lemon juice, then enough veal gravy to make a creamy dressing. Lastly, stir in the fish purée. Whisk till smooth, then rub through a sieve. (This sauce should be fairly liquid. If liked, beat in a little more of the gravy.) Season with salt and freshly ground black pepper to taste. When veal is quite cold, carve it into neat slices. Cover with the sauce. Chill. Garnish with capers and slices of stuffed olive. Sometimes, fans of gherkin and chopped parsley are substituted for the capers and olives.

YIELD: 6 or 7 servings.

PETTO DI POLLO DARIO (Suprême Dario)

1 tender chicken, seasoned flour as required, butter as required, Sauce Leoni.

Cut the white meat from the breast of chicken to include the wing bones and beat out flat. Pass through the flour and fry in hot melted butter until golden brown, turning occasionally. While breasts are cooking, prepare the sauce. Dish up

* This recipe was given to me by Signor Barberi when he reigned over Isola Bella in Soho.

94

breasts. Pour sauce over. Garnish each portion with a few drops of tomato sauce.

Sauce Leoni: Place 1 tablespoon chopped shallot, 2 oz. chopped tarragon stalks, 3 oz. chervil, some mignonette pepper, pinch of salt, and 4 tablespoons of vinegar into a small enamel saucepan. Bring to boil. Simmer until the vinegar is reduced by two-thirds, then remove pan from stove. Leave until mixture is slightly cooled, then stir in yolks of 5 eggs, one at a time. Return pan to stove. Gradually add ¾ cup melted butter. Whisk over low heat till smoothly blended, then rub through a tammy cloth into another saucepan. Stir in a teaspoon each of chopped chervil and tarragon leaves. Season delicately with cayenne pepper.

Note: This sauce should not be served very hot as it is really a mayonnaise made with butter. If over-heated it might curdle.

YIELD: 2 servings.

PEPPINO LEONI,
QUO VADIS RESTAURANT,
SOHO, LONDON.

SUPREME YOLANDA (Chicken Breasts Yolanda)

2 breasts of chicken, seasoned flour as required, beaten egg as required, grated Parmesan cheese as required, 6 or 8 boiled asparagus tips, melted butter.

Remove the white meat from the breasts of a chicken to include the wing bones. Beat meat out flat with a meat bat or a rolling pin. Dip in seasoned flour, then in beaten egg, and lastly, in grated Parmesan cheese. Fry in 2 tablespoons heated olive oil till golden brown below, then turn and brown on the other sides. Cover and cook for about 2½ minutes on each side till tender, then dish up on a heated fireproof plate. Arrange 3 or 4 asparagus tips lengthwise on top of each. Sprinkle with grated Parmesan cheese and melted butter. Grill for a minute or two, then transfer to 2 individual heated plates.

YIELD: 2 servings.

PEPPINO LEONI,
QUO VADIS RESTAURANT,
SOHO, LONDON.

TACCHINO RIPIENO ALLA SALERNO (Roast Turkey Salerno)

1 medium-sized turkey, 1 pint chestnuts, 1 dozen prunes, 4 apples, 1 turkey liver, 2 oz. butter, ½ gill white wine, salt and pepper.

Prepare turkey for roasting. Slit, boil and peel chestnuts. Soak, scald, halve and stone prunes. Peel, core and quarter apples. Bring liver to a boil in water to cover, then drain and mince finely. Melt butter in a shallow saucepan. Add nuts, prunes, apples and liver. Fry gently for 5 minutes, stirring occasionally, then drain off butter. Stir wine into the fruit mixture. Season with salt and freshly ground black pepper. Cool. Stuff breast of turkey only. Skewer the skin on to the back over the stuffing. Place 4 or 5 rashers of fat bacon in a cold frying pan. Fry for 2-3 minutes, then place over breast. (There must be enough bacon to cover breast completely.) Tie in place with string. Place bird on rack. Allowing 25 minutes per pound, bake till tender, in a slow oven, 300 °F (Mark 1-2). Remove bacon about 20 minutes before dishing up. When ready, untruss. Dish up. Garnish with fried sausage meat balls. Serve with Panna potatoes and celery al fritto or Tuscan peas.

Panna Potatoes: Peel 12 large potatoes. Rinse and dice. Place in boiling salted water. Stand for 5 minutes. Drain thoroughly. Melt 4 oz. butter in a large shallow saucepan. Add potato dice. Shake gently over moderate heat until they have absorbed all the butter. Season with grated nutmeg and butter to taste. Shake gently again. Dish up. Sprinkle with finely minced parsley.

Celery al Fritto: Scrape stalks of tender celery. Rinse and cut in short lengths. Dip in seasoned flour. " Egg and Crumb ". Fry in deep hot fat till golden. Drain on absorbent paper.

Tuscan Peas: Place 1½ lb. shelled peas in a shallow saucepan. Remove rinds from 1½ rashers of bacon. Cut bacon into small pieces and add to peas. Peel 1½ cloves of garlic and add. Sprinkle with 3 tablespoons olive oil, salt and pepper to taste

96

and ½ pint boiling water. Bring quickly to boil. Simmer gently till peas are tender. Remove garlic. Drain peas and serve.

YIELD: 8-10 servings.

CASTAGNE (Chestnut Purée)

1 lb. chestnuts, water as required, ¼ teaspoon salt, 4 tablespoons sifted icing sugar, ¾ cup cream, ¼ teaspoon grated nutmeg or 1 teaspoon vanilla essence.

Place chestnuts in a saucepan. Cover with boiling water. Cover and boil for 15-20 minutes. Drain thoroughly. Remove peel and skin. Place nuts in a saucepan with 1½ cups boiling water. Add salt. Cover closely. Stew gently until soft enough to mash. Mash until smooth or rub through a sieve. Beat in sugar. Whip cream to a stiff froth. Stir two-thirds into the mixture. Flavour with nutmeg or vanilla essence. Pour into a shallow glass dish. Chill in refrigerator for at least 6 hours. Garnish with remaining whipped cream.

YIELD: 4 servings.

PIZZA NAPOLETANA * (Sweet Pizza)

Puff pastry or shortcrust, ¼ pint milk, 2 oz. castor sugar, barely 1 oz. flour, 1 egg, 1 egg yolk, 6 oz. milk curd, 2½ oz. sweet almonds, 3 bitter almonds, lemon or vanilla essence to taste.

Make a thin flan case with either puff pastry or shortcrust, and ornament edges to taste. Prick the base well with a fork. Pour milk into a saucepan. Stir in the sugar mixed with the flour and then the egg. Stir till smooth and the mixture begins to thicken. Remove pan from stove. Stand for 2 or 3 minutes. Stir in the egg yolk, then the milk curd, almonds, blanched, peeled and finely pounded, and lemon or vanilla essence to taste. Spread over the pastry, bringing it right up to the edge of the case. Brush edges of pastry with cold water, then cover with a thin round of pastry and notch the edges together. Decorate with the trimmings, cut into fancy shapes. Brush

* Pizza is the Italian name for an open pie or flan. This one comes from Southern Italy.

with beaten egg yolk. Bake in a moderate oven, 350 °F (Mark 3-4), until golden, in 25-30 minutes. Leave until cold. Dredge with sifted icing sugar.

    YIELD: 6 servings.

TORTA ALLA CREMA (Custard Layer Cake)

4 level tablespoons cornflour, 4 cups milk, 4 fresh eggs, 4 tablespoons castor sugar, 1 lemon rind, grated, ½ teaspoon almond essence, 2 lb. Victoria sandwich or Genoese sponge, whipped cream to taste, vanilla essence and rum as required.

Mix cornflour to a cream with a little of the milk. Stir in remainder of milk. Beat and stir in eggs, then sugar. When blended, pour into the top of a double boiler. Add lemon rind. Stir over hot water, nearly at boiling point, until custard comes to the boil, then remove at once or it will curdle. Stir in almond essence, then leave until cool. Cut the cake into rounds, ¾ inch thick. Place a round in a large round serving dish, about 10 inches in diameter. Cover with a ½ inch layer of custard, then with another layer of cake. Repeat layers until all the cake and filling are used up, then top with whipped sweetened cream, half of it flavoured to taste with vanilla essence and the other half with rum. Decorate with chocolate flakes, citron peel and glacé cherries. Sometimes this torta is covered with cream on the sides as well as on the top. Chill lightly before serving.

ZABAGLIONE (Wine Custard)

6 egg yolks, 6 level teaspoons castor sugar, 6 half egg shells of Marsala.

Place egg yolks in the top of a large double boiler. Add sugar. Beat with a rotary egg beater until thoroughly blended and a light lemon colour. Gradually beat in Marsala. Fill lower part of the double boiler with boiling water coming almost up to the base of the top pan. Insert top pan. Beat the mixture frequently over the water until it begins to thicken, in about 5 minutes. Remove top pan as soon as the first sign of bubbles appear. Do not allow to boil or the mixture will curdle. Leave until cool, beating occasionally, then chill in refrigerator. Divide equally between 6 fruit glasses. Serve with sponge fingers or Italian almond macaroons.

YIELD: 6 servings.

ITALIAN SALAD DRESSINGS
For Green Salads

Mix 4 tablespoons wine vinegar with ½ cup olive oil, salt and freshly ground black pepper to taste and a clove of garlic. Add 3 tablespoons chopped sweet basil. Stand for 3 or 4 hours, then remove garlic. Use for dressing all green salads, including chicory, endive, lettuce and cos lettuce.

For Tomatoes

Mix 1 tablespoon oregano with 4 tablespoons olive oil and salt and freshly ground black pepper to taste. Use for dressing 6 large firm tomatoes. Chill before serving.

ITALIAN SPICE

½ oz. sweet basil, ½ oz. ground cloves, ½ oz. white pepper, 2 oz. grated nutmeg, 2 oz. ground cinnamon, ½ oz. crushed dried thyme, ¼ oz. crushed dried bay leaves.

Pound all the ingredients in a mortar with a pestle. Rub through a hair sieve with the back of a wooden spoon. Bottle and seal.

SALSA DI POMIDORI (Tomato Sauce)

4 tablespoons olive oil, 2 tablespoons chopped onion, 1 sprig sweet basil, 1 chopped peeled clove garlic, 1 large can tomatoes, ½ teaspoon castor sugar, salt and pepper, pinch of oregano if liked.

Heat the oil in a shallow saucepan. Add onion, basil and garlic. Fry for about 5 minutes, stirring occasionally. Rub tomatoes with juice through a sieve. Pour into saucepan. Stir till boiling. Cover and simmer very gently until thick, in about 45 minutes, stirring frequently. Add sugar, salt and pepper to taste and oregano. Stir till blended. Simmer gently for 15 minutes, stirring occasionally.

Note: This sauce can be used for pouring over any boiled pastas. Allow this quantity to 1 lb. uncooked pasta, such as macaroni, spaghetti, etc.

POLAND

Na Zdrowie —— Good Health!

POLAND

Eating in Poland is a gastronomic adventure. After a portion of caviar and a glass of vodka, the fruits of Poland are yours for the choosing.

Nowhere else in all Europe do you have a better choice of fresh and pickled fish and pickled, salted and smoked meats than in Poland. Freshwater fish are always available all the year round. Carp, which to the Poles is a symbol of strength, always appears on the tables on festive days. It is to the Poles what salmon is to the Scots.

Many of the soups and savoury dishes have a mysterious flavour, due to the addition of " kwas ", slightly fermented beetroot juice, which contributes a pleasant acid tang.

Christmas Eve is a meatless day in Poland. The midday meal usually takes the form of gruel or a simple soup followed by baked potatoes served with butter and salt, and sometimes pickled herring.

Before the hostess lays the table for Christmas dinner, she spreads a thin layer of fragrant hay over it to commemorate the manger at Bethlehem, then she carefully lays her immaculate white damask tablecloth over the top. The real celebrations start when the first star appears in the East and the Christmas tree is lit. This ceremony takes place before dinner. All the members of the party gather round the table and break the unleavened wafer called " Oplatek ", and if any member of the family is absent, a piece of the " Blessed Wafer " is sent by post with Christmas greetings.

Tradition lives on in Poland.

SLEDZ MARYNOWANY ZE ŚMIETANA (Herrings with Sour Cream)

4 herrings with soft roes, milk as required, ¼ pint white wine, 2 or 3 tablespoons vinegar, 1 sliced medium-sized onion, 1 chopped clove of garlic, 6 black peppercorns, 2 tablespoons soured cream, yolks of 2 hard-boiled eggs, 1 teaspoon French mustard, salt and paprika to taste.

Soak herrings in milk to cover for 1 hour. Pour wine and vinegar into a saucepan. Add 2 tablespoons of water, onion, garlic, peppercorns, and a sprig of parsley, and of chervil and fennel if available. Drain herrings and add. Bring to boil. Simmer gently until herrings are tender in a few minutes. Remove carefully to a platter or shallow dish. Leave until cold. Beat the soured cream into the egg yolks. Stir in mustard, salt and paprika to taste, and enough of the strained herring stock to make a creamy sauce. Coat the herrings with the sauce. Sprinkle with minced chives if liked.

YIELD: 4 servings.

BARSZCZ (Beetroot Soup)

2½ pints rich stock, 1 lb. baked beetroot, 1½ tablespoons wine vinegar, ¼ pint thick cream.

Bring stock to boil. Mince beetroot and add with the vinegar. Simmer for 2 minutes. Strain off beetroot stock. Gradually stir in the cream. Season if necessary. Serve in heated soup cups.

YIELD: 4 servings.

STAROPOLSKA ZUPA CEBULOWA * (Onion Soup)

8 oz. peeled onions, 2 oz. butter, 3 oz. bread croûtons, 1 quart boiling water, 4 egg yolks, ¼ pint cream, salt and pepper.

Slice onions. Melt half the butter in a small saucepan. Add onion slices. Cook slowly, stirring occasionally, till they turn a pale gold. Meanwhile, place the croûtons, made of rye bread for preference, otherwise wholemeal, in a baking

---

* This old-fashioned Polish soup is sometimes garnished with thin 2-inch long strips or ½ inch squares, cut from a plain pancake.

tin. Sprinkle with remaining butter, melted only till runny. Place tin in a slow oven, 325 °F (Mark 2-3). Bake the croûtons, turning them occasionally, until golden brown. Place the croûtons with the onions. Add water. Cover and simmer for 40 minutes. Strain liquid into another saucepan. Rub the onions and croûtons through a sieve. Add purée to the liquid. Reheat, stirring constantly, then thicken with the egg yolks, beaten and blended with the cream, but do not allow to boil. Season with salt and freshly ground black pepper.

YIELD: 5 servings.

PIEROGI Z KAPUSTA (Sauerkraut Pasties)

Shred white cabbage leaves and fry slowly in butter till tender. Roll out puff or rough puff pastry thinly and cut it into small oblongs as you would for sausage rolls. Place a little of the cold fried cabbage on each oblong. Cover with a layer of chopped hard-boiled egg, then with a thin layer of cooked sauerkraut. Top with egg, then with fried cabbage. Brush edges with cold water and roll up. Place, join downwards, on lightly greased baking sheets. Bake in a hot oven, 450 °F (Mark 7-8), till pastry is risen and set, then lower to moderate, 350 °F (Mark 3-4), and bake till golden brown in a few minutes.

FLADRA S SMAŻONA (Sole Polonaise)

4 skinned soles, 1 oz. seasoned flour, beaten egg as required, 1 lemon, dill butter, shredded horseradish.

Rinse soles in cold water. Dry. Coat with seasoned flour, then dip in beaten egg. Coat with sieved breadcrumbs. Melt enough butter or hot vegetable oil in 2 large frying pans to cover the base of each. Place 2 soles in each pan. Fry until light golden brown below, then turn and fry on the other sides. Arrange lengthwise on a heated oblong platter. Garnish with lemon slices, sprinkled minced chives or parsley, and place a small ball of dill butter, flattened with the prongs of a fork, on top of each. Sprinkle horseradish round.

Dill Butter: Wash a bunch of dill leaves in cold water. Toss in a cloth till dry, then mince finely. Beat 4 oz. butter to a cream. Gradually beat in the strained juice of $\frac{1}{2}$ lemon, salt and pepper to taste and the dill. Chill. Cut in small thin slices, or shape into small balls with buttered hands. Sometimes these balls are served on fluted rounds of lemon on top of fish or steaks.

Yield: 4 servings.

BIGOS * (Traditional Meat and Cabbage Dish)

8 oz. cooked pork, 1 large white cabbage heart, 3 cooking apples, 4 oz. lard, salt, 1 teaspoon caraway seeds, 2 tablespoons vinegar, tomato ketchup to taste, 8 oz. garlic sausage.

Cut meat up into small pieces. Wash and shred cabbage. Peel, core and shred apples. Heat the lard in a deep frying pan. Add the meat, cabbage and apples, salt to taste and the caraway seeds. Cover. Cook very gently over low heat for about 2 hours, shaking the pan occasionally, and adding a little water if required. Stir frequently. Add the vinegar and sauce, and any scraps of left-over meat, such as sliced pork sausage or small pieces of cooked game or poultry, and an ounce of lean gammon, cut into small pieces, if liked. Cover and simmer gently for another hour. At the end of 30 minutes, peel and dice the garlic sausage, and stir into the mixture. Cover and cook for remaining half hour.

To Vary: Substitute sauerkraut for the cabbage and reduce apples to 1 or 2. Add, if liked, $\frac{1}{2}$ gill of red or white wine and $\frac{1}{2}$ gill of vodka, in small quantities, in place of water.

Yield: 6 servings.

PIECZEN HUSARSKA (Stuffed Roast Round of Beef)

2$\frac{1}{2}$ lb. round of beef, $\frac{1}{2}$ cup malt vinegar, 2 oz. butter, $\frac{1}{2}$ cup beef stock, 1 large peeled onion, onion stuffing.

Pound the meat well, in one piece, with a meat bat. Heat vinegar to boiling point in an enamel saucepan and pour over the meat. Turn in the vinegar then drain thoroughly. Melt

* This traditional dish is popular at shooting luncheons, heated up on the spot. In Poland, it is heated over a wooden fire. If sauerkraut is used, it must be thoroughly washed, blanched in boiling water and drained before substituting for cabbage. Serve with Vodka.

butter in a large shallow saucepan. Add beef. Fry till brown, turning frequently, until seared all over. Heat stock and add. Quarter onion and lay alongside. Cover and simmer gently for 1½-2 hours. Thirty minutes before dishing up, remove meat to a board. With a sharp knife, cut meat crosswise in thin slices nearly to the base. Divide the stuffing equally between the slices. Press into shape and secure the openings with toothpicks. Lift carefully into pan. Sprinkle evenly with a tablespoon of flour. Cover and cook for another 30 minutes, adding a little stock if necessary to prevent meat scorching. Serve with mashed potatoes and stewed cabbage.

Onion Stuffing: Mix 1 cup stale breadcrumbs with melted butter to moisten, 2 minced medium-sized onions and salt and freshly ground black pepper to taste.

YIELD: 5 or 6 servings.

OGORKI ZAPIEKANE (Baked Cucumbers)

12 small cucumbers, 1 oz. butter, 2 tablespoons plain flour, 1 cup milk, salt and pepper, 2 tablespoons stale breadcrumbs, 3 tablespoons grated cheese, paprika to taste.

Peel cucumbers thinly. Steam till tender. Place in a greased casserole. Melt butter in a saucepan. Stir in flour. When frothy, stir in milk. Cook until boiling, stirring constantly, then season with salt and freshly ground black pepper to taste. Pour over cucumbers. Mix the crumbs with the cheese and paprika to taste. Sprinkle over the sauce. Bake in a moderate oven, 350 °F (Mark 3-4), till browned.

In Poland, baked cucumbers are served as a hot hors d'oeuvre.

YIELD: 3 or 4 servings.

PLACKI KARTOFLANE (Potato Pancakes)

2 cups grated raw potato, 2 teaspoons salt, pepper to taste, 4 oz. flour, milk as required.

Drain potato well before measuring. Place in a basin. Add salt, pepper, flour and enough milk to make a fairly stiff dough. Roll out on a lightly floured board into a round about ½ inch thick. Cut into small rounds, about 2½ inches across.

Melt enough lard to cover the bottom of a large frying pan. Add the cakes. Fry till brown below, then turn and brown on the other sides.

The Poles usually eat these pancakes with sour cream, but sometimes they are served with apricot jam, or rolled up and sprinkled with lemon juice and sugar when the pepper is omitted.

YIELD: 2 or 3 servings.

UFORMOWANA-KAPUSTA (Cabbage and Bacon Timbale)

1 large cabbage, 2 medium-sized onions, 1 oz. butter, salt and pepper, 8 oz. minced gammon, 1 cup stale breadcrumbs, 2 beaten eggs, 6-8 rashers of bacon, lemon sauce.

Choose a good-hearted cabbage, 1½-2 lb. in weight. Strip off the outer leaves. Discard any that are blemished. Separate outer leaves and soak them in hot salted water for 10 minutes, to make them pliable. Drain and put aside. Peel and mince onions. Melt the butter in a large frying pan. (If preferred, heat 2 or 3 tablespoons olive oil instead.) Add the onion. When beginning to brown, add the cabbage heart, finely shredded, and the salt and pepper to taste. Fry over low heat, stirring frequently, for about 8 minutes. Turn on to a platter. When nearly cold, mix the minced gammon with the breadcrumbs and eggs. Remove rinds from the bacon rashers which should be very thin. Line a large round mould with the rashers, and then with the soaked cabbage leaves. Fill mould alternately with the cabbage mixture and the gammon mixture. Cover with remaining bacon rashers, placed close together. Bake in a moderate oven 350 °F (Mark 3-4), for 1½ hours, with cover on top for 1 hour, then uncover, and finish cooking. Remove bacon from top. Unmould on to a heated platter. Garnish with sprigs of parsley. Serve with lemon sauce.

Lemon Sauce: Make ½ pint white sauce, after frying 1 dessertspoon minced shallot in the butter. Season with cayenne pepper and salt to taste. Gradually stir in the strained juice of half a lemon. Serve in a heated sauceboat.

YIELD: 4 or 5 servings.

JABLA PIECZONE (Baked Stuffed Apples)

2 lb. cooking apples, ½ pint wine, 7 oz. castor sugar, 2 table-spoons apricot jam.

Choose fairly large apples of equal size. Peel and core. Pour the wine into an enamel saucepan. Add the sugar. Stir over moderate heat till dissolved. Stuff the apples with jam. Pour the wine syrup into a fireproof dish with a lid. Add the apples. Cover. Bake in a slow oven, 275-300 °F (Mark ½-1), for about 1 hour, basting twice during cooking. Transfer carefully to a heated serving dish. Pour the syrup over. Place a dab of apricot jam on the top of each apple. Serve with whipped cream and small fancy biscuits.

YIELD: 6 servings.

MALDRZYKI (Vanilla Puffs)

1 lb. cream cheese, 6 eggs, 2 oz. butter, 2 tablespoons cream, 2 oz. castor sugar, pinch of salt, 4 oz. flour.

Rub the cheese with the back of a wooden spoon through a sieve into a basin. Gradually beat in the eggs, one at a time. Beat butter till softened, then gradually beat into the mixture. Beat in the cream, sugar and salt, then the flour. Rub through a sieve. Shape with floured hands into little balls. Flatten them slightly with a palette knife. Melt 3 oz. butter. When hot, fry the puffs. If preferred, bake them in greased tins, in a moderately hot oven, 400 °F (Mark 5-6), until golden brown. If fried, drain on absorbent paper. Arrange on a heated platter, lined with a paper doiley. Dredge with vanilla sugar. Serve at once.

MAZUREK ROZANY (Wild Rose Sandwich)

8 oz. flour, 4 oz. butter, 2 oz. castor sugar, 2 oz. ground almonds, 2 hard-boiled egg yolks, ½ lemon, wild rose icing.

Sift flour into a basin. Rub in butter. Stir in sugar and almonds. (If preferred, add finely chopped blanched almonds in place of ground.) Sieve egg yolks and add to mixture. Grate in the lemon rind, and strain in lemon juice. Add, if liked, a few grains of salt. Mix to a dough and knead until smooth. (If necessary, increase butter to 6 oz., or mix an egg yolk with the lemon juice before adding.) Stand for 1 hour. Divide in two equal portions. Pat and roll out into two even equal-sized rounds to fit two 9 inch sandwich tins. Place a round of pastry in each. Bake in a moderate oven, 350 °F (Mark 3-4), until pale gold, then cool on a wire rack. Put layers together with strained rose jam. Cover with rose icing, then sprinkle with finely chopped blanched pistachio nuts before the icing sets.

Rose Jam: Remove enough petals from richly scented red roses to give you 8 oz. when the light tips at the base of the petals are cut off. Sprinkle with 1 oz. citric acid. Squeeze petals with your fingers until they are moistened, then press into a glass jar and leave for 24 hours. Place 2 lb. castor sugar in a saucepan. Add ¾ pint cold water. Bring to boil. Boil until into a thin syrup, then add the rose petals and simmer until the syrup is thick and the petals are clear. Use as a filling, when cold, for sponges or for coating small sponge cakes to be covered with chopped nuts.

Wild Rose Icing: Sift ½ lb. icing sugar into a basin. Mix with boiling water to a spreading consistency. Add a few drops of lemon juice, 2 drops of rose essence and rose-pink colouring to taste.

SERNIK (Polish Cheese Cake)

1 pastry case, 8 by 8 inches, 8 oz. cream cheese, 6 egg yolks, 2 oz. butter, 8 oz. castor sugar, vanilla essence to taste.

To make case, rub 4 oz. butter into 8 oz. flour. Stir in 2 oz. castor sugar, then 1 egg yolk. Knead lightly, then roll out into a square to fit a greased baking tin, 8 by 8 inches. Place pastry in tin. Chill slightly. Tie the cheese in a piece of muslin and squeeze out any moisture. Crumble it into a basin. Stir in egg yolks. Melt butter. Stir into mixture, then add sugar and vanilla essence. Beat thoroughly till smooth, no matter how long it takes. Spread evenly in pastry case. Bake in a moderate oven, 350 °F (Mark 3-4), for about 1 hour. When cold, cut into 12 squares. Spread smoothly with a little glacé icing, flavoured with rum or vanilla essence.

TORT MOKKA (Mocha Layer Cake)

6 egg whites, 8 oz. sifted icing sugar, juice of ½ lemon, 8 oz. ground almonds, mokka filling.

Whisk egg whites to a stiff froth, then beat in the sugar, a little at a time. When all is added, beat in the lemon juice, then fold in the ground almonds. Divide mixture equally between 3 sandwich tins (7 inches across) smoothly lined with greased paper. Smooth the mixture evenly in tins. Bake in a cool oven, 275-300 °F (Mark ½-1), for about 40 minutes. When cold, put layers together with mokka cream. Stand for 24 hours in a cool place, then coat smoothly with coffee fondant or glacé icing. Decorate to taste with chopped roasted almonds or with whole almonds, blanched and peeled.

Mokka Filling: Beat 6 oz. unsalted butter till softened, then gradually beat in 1 oz. sifted icing sugar. Beat till creamy. Add 1 egg yolk and beat again. Add 1 teaspoon powdered coffee, a pinch at a time, and beat between each addition. If preferred, substitute ¼ gill very strong black coffee. When thoroughly creamed, stand in a refrigerator until stiffened before using.

Mokka Fondant: Dissolve 1 lb. castor sugar in ½ pint boiling coffee. Simmer very gently for 45 minutes. Stir with a wooden spoon, then dilute slightly with thick cream.

PORTUGAL

Saude! —— Here's How!

PORTUGAL

The Portuguese cuisine is slightly akin to the French, Italian and Spanish. I feel this every time I visit Portugal.

In this delightful country people live largely on soup, beans, fish, rice and bread. Sometimes several varieties of cooked beans are served at one meal.

The Portuguese, like the Spanish, are expert at bean and fish cookery. You have to taste freshly caught cod, which is the mainstay on the marine coast, cooked with aubergines and tomatoes, as it is on the Estoril, to realise how delicious cod can be.

One of the most appetising meats that appear on the menus is smoked pig's back, usually served with green peas or spinach, and smoked ham. Beef is apt to be a little tasteless, perhaps due to the fact that oxen are made to work in Portugal, but the Portuguese housewives are wizards at making meat palatable. Sometimes they lard it with fat bacon. Again, they rub it with garlic and soak it in a marinade before cooking.

Wine is freely used in the Portuguese kitchen, and many of the savoury dishes are flavoured with onion and tomato. No luncheon or dinner table is complete without a pepper mill, and freshly ground black pepper is also used in the kitchen for seasoning. The Portuguese are masters at seasoning and garnishing food. Like the French and Spanish, they believe in appealing to the eye as well as to the palate.

ACEPIPES DE ATUM (Tunny Fish Hors d'Oeuvre)

Tunny fish makes a delicious hors d'oeuvre as it comes from the tin, or flaked and mixed with mayonnaise.

1. Drain and turn on to a round platter lined with crisp heart of lettuce leaves. Serve with crisp toast and butter as a single hors d'oeuvre.

2. Place on the centre of a large platter. Encircle with small sprigs of watercress. Arrange alternately round the platter one Portuguese sardine, a row of overlapping slices of hard-boiled egg, overlapping slices of firm tomato, sprinkled with chopped chives, and slices of truffled liver sausage. Dust the egg slices with paprika. Place a curled anchovy fillet on the centre of the tunny fish. Serve with potato salad and mayonnaise, and crisp toast and butter.

Note: If preferred, flake tunny fish, mix to taste with mayonnaise, and season with salt and freshly ground black pepper. Pile on the centre of a platter. Garnish here and there with capers.

CALDO VERDE (Green Broth)

½ *saucepan boiling water, olive oil as required, salt and pepper,*
1 or 2 sliced peeled potatoes, kale leaves as required.

When water is at full boil, hold a bottle of olive oil over the saucepan, and allow the oil to run in a very fine stream, as slowly as when making mayonnaise, into the water, until about 2 tablespoons have been added. Season with salt and pepper to taste. Add potatoes. Cover and simmer until potatoes are soft, then mash roughly with a fork. While potatoes are boiling, roll some washed kale leaves into as tight a roll a possible, and with a very sharp knife, shred them into fine threads. Plunge in the boiling soup, and finish cooking in two or three minutes. Serve at once.

YIELD: 4 servings.

SOPA DE TOMATE E OVOS (Tomato and Egg Soup)

3 lb. ripe tomatoes, 2 peeled medium-sized onions, 1½ oz. butter, 4 pints boiling water, 1 heaped tablespoon chopped parsley, salt and pepper, 3 or 4 hard-boiled eggs.

Wash and quarter tomatoes. Slice onions. Place them in a large saucepan. Add ½ oz. butter. Fry for about 15 minutes, crushing tomatoes occasionally with the back of a wooden spoon. Add the water and parsley. Bring quickly to boil. Cover and simmer gently for 1½-2 hours. Remove pan from stove. Rub soup through a sieve into a basin. Reheat. Season with salt and pepper. Add remaining butter, bit by bit, stirring constantly. Shell and slice the eggs into a heated soup tureen. Pour the soup over.

YIELD: 6 servings.

BACALHAU FRESCO Á PORTUGUESA (Cod à la Portugaise)

4 oz. Patna rice, ½ oz. butter, 2 sliced medium-sized onions, 2 lb. cod fillet, ¼ pint olive oil. 1 lb. peeled tomatoes, 1 peeled clove of garlic, ¼ pint Portuguese white wine, salt and pepper.

Throw the rice into boiling salted water to cover. Boil for 10 minutes, then drain thoroughly. Meanwhile, melt the butter in a frying pan. Add onion. Fry slowly till lightly browned on both sides. Cut fillet into 4 portions. Heat the oil in a shallow saucepan. Add fillet and onion. Slice in the tomatoes. Mince garlic finely and add with rice, wine, and salt and freshly ground black pepper to taste. Cover. Simmer gently for about 15 minutes till fish is cooked through. Dish up fillet. Add chopped parsley to taste to the sauce. Stir well and pour over the fish.

YIELD: 4 servings.

ESCALOPINHOS DE VITELA AO MADEIRA (Scallops of Veal Madeira)

4 scallops of veal, salt and pepper, butter as required, Madeira as required, ½ cup cream, ½ cup fried mushrooms.

Beat scallops out flat. Season with salt and pepper. Melt enough butter to cover the base of a large frying pan, or

112

use two pans if necessary. Add scallops. Fry over moderate heat till brown below, then turn and brown on the other sides. Dish up. Add Madeira to taste to pan, then the cream and mushrooms. Stir till piping hot. Spoon over the scallops.

YIELD: 4 servings.

FIGADO DE VITELA Á TRANSMONTANA (Calf's Liver á Transmontana)

1 lb. 1 oz. sliced calf's liver, 3 sliced boiled eggs, 4 oz. lean smoked ham, 1 crushed clove of garlic, 1 teaspoon minced parsley, salt and pepper, 2 oz. butter, 1 chopped medium-sized onion, 3 tablespoons boiling water.

Place liver slices on a board covered with greaseproof paper. Lay a slice of egg, a little ham, garlic and parsley on each slice, until all is used up. Season with salt and pepper to taste. Roll each up and tie in place or secure with cocktail sticks. Melt the butter in a large frying pan. When hot. add the onion. Fry slowly till tender. Stir in the water. Place rolls side by side in a large shallow fireproof dish, Sprinkle with the onion sauce. Cover. Bake in a slow oven, 300 °F (Mark 1-2), until tender and cooked through, in about 1 hour. Untie or remove sticks. Serve with buttered new potatoes or mashed potatoes and buttered green peas.

YIELD: 4 servings.

ALENTEJO (Stewed Partridges)

2 partridges, 2 cups olive oil, barely 1 cup vinegar, 1½ gills white wine, 2 small peeled onions, 2 crushed cloves of garlic, 1 bouquet garni, 1 bay leaf, salt and pepper, 1 teaspoon chopped parsley.

Clean and truss birds. Place, side by side, in a large saucepan. Add the oil, vinegar and wine. Cover. Simmer gently for 2 hours, shaking the pan now and again to prevent the birds sticking to the base. Uncover and add onions, roughly chopped, garlic, bouquet garni, bay leaf, salt and pepper to taste, and parsley. Cover and simmer gently for 1 hour longer. Serve each bird on a slice of fried bread.

YIELD: 2 servings.

LEBRE Á CAÇADORA (Braised Hare)

1 young hare, red wine as required, olive oil as required, 8 oz. bacon rashers, 1 heaped tablespoon chopped onion, 1 sprig parsley, 1 bruised clove of garlic, pepper, grated nutmeg, ½ bay leaf, 3 tablespoons white stock, salt to taste, ½ gill port wine, squeeze of lemon juice.

Place hare in a saucepan. Cover with boiling water. Stand for a minute or two, then drain thoroughly. Place in a shallow dish. Add enough wine to come half up the hare, then stir 2 or 3 tablespoons olive oil into the wine. Soak for 6 hours, then turn and soak on the other side for another 6 hours. Remove hare and cut into neat joints. Remove rind from bacon rashers. Line a shallow saucepan with the bacon. Sprinkle with the chopped onion. Add parsley, garlic, freshly ground black pepper to taste, and grated nutmeg to taste. Cook over stove for five minutes, then add ½ gill red wine, or white if preferred, bay leaf and white stock and salt to taste. Arrange joints of hare on top. Cover pan. Simmer very gently for 1 hour. Add port wine. Cover and simmer gently for about 2 hours until tender. Dish up hare. Add a squeeze of lemon juice to the gravy. Strain gravy over.

Note: If liked, substitute tomato purée for the stock.

YIELD: 4 or 5 servings.

FEIJAO VERDE GUIZADO (Stewed Green Beans)

2 lb. green beans, 1 oz. butter 2 tablespoons minced parsley, juice ½ lemon, pepper to taste.

Wash beans and string if necessary, using French or runner. Place in a saucepan. Cover with boiling salted water. Bring quickly to boil. Boil until tender. Drain thoroughly. Melt butter in a shallow saucepan. Add parsley and lemon juice. Season with pepper. Simmer for a minute. Dish up beans. Pour the sauce over.

YIELD: 6 servings.

COGUMELOS COM ARROZ (Mushroom Risotto)

*½ cup olive oil, 1 pint sliced mushrooms, ½ pint minced onion,
½ clove garlic, ¼ cup Patna rice, ¼ teaspoon salt, 1½ tablespoons
tomato purée, 1 teaspoon minced parsley.*

Heat the oil in a frying pan. Add mushrooms. Cook until
slightly softened, then drain the oil into a strong shallow
saucepan. Reheat oil. Add onion. Mince garlic and add.
Fry until lightly coloured, stirring occasionally. Meanwhile,
rinse, drain and dry rice. When onion is a light yellow, add
the rice. Cook for 3 or 4 minutes, then add from ½-¾ pint
boiling water, depending on how much water is required to
cover the rice from ½-¾ inch. Add salt, tomato purée, parsley
and mushrooms. When boiling, turn into a casserole. Cover.
Bake in a moderately hot oven, 375 °F (Mark 4-5), for about
45 minutes, when rice should be soft, yet fluffy.

YIELD: 4 servings.

ARROZ DOCE (Sweet Rice)

*1 cup rice, 2 cups milk, snippet of lemon peel, 2 or 3 egg
yolks, ground cinnamon to taste.*

Rinse and drain rice. Pour milk into a saucepan. Add
lemon peel, or a vanilla pod if preferred. Sprinkle in the rice.
Stir till boiling. Cover and simmer very gently till rice is
tender, then remove pan from stove, and peel or pod from
rice. Beat egg yolks. When rice is slightly cooled, stir in egg
yolks, and return pan to stove. Stir till thick, but do not allow
to boil. Pour into a large platter. Chill. Sprinkle with ground
cinnamon, in a criss-cross design if possible.

YIELD: 2 servings.

TORRIJAS DE NATA (Fried Cream)

*3 egg yolks, 1 cup thick cream, beaten egg as required, ¼ cup
sifted icing sugar, ½ teaspoon ground cinnamon.*

Beat egg yolks lightly. Whip cream till fluffy, then whip
in the yolks. Spread to the depth of ½ inch thickness
in a shallow buttered tin. Cook over low heat till thickened,
then cool. Cut into small pieces. Remove each with a spatula,

and brush lightly on both sides with beaten egg. Melt enough butter to cover the base of a large frying pan. Fry over moderate heat till golden below, then turn and cook on the other sides. Meanwhile, mix the icing sugar with the cinnamon. When the torrijas are fried, arrange on a hot platter, covered with a paper doiley, and sprinkle with the cinnamon sugar.

YIELD: 4 servings.

BOLO MADEIRA (Cake to serve with Madeira)

4 oz. butter, 8 oz. castor sugar, 9 egg yolks, 5 egg whites, 8 oz. flour, 1 saltspoon ground cinnamon, grated rind ½ orange.

Beat butter till softened. Gradually beat in sugar. Add the egg yolks. Beat until creamy. Whisk egg whites till stiff, then beat into batter, a little at a time. Sift the flour with the cinnamon 3 or 4 times. Stir in orange rind. Fold into batter. Line the base of a large greased shallow baking tin with a layer of oiled greaseproof paper. Place batter in tin. Bake in a moderate oven, 350 °F (Mark 3-4), until firm and pale gold, in about 30 minutes. Cool on a wire rack. Cut in slices like bread and toast on both sides. Serve when cold.

ALPERCES OU PESSEGOS EM BRANDE (Brandied Apricots or Peaches)

Brandy as required, castor sugar as required, ripe apricots or peaches.

Fill a large glass jar with a tightly fitting lid three-quarters full of brandy, sweetened with a quarter its weight of castor sugar. Stir frequently till sugar is dissolved. Wash apricots or peaches, then cut halfway through. Do not stone. Fill jar right up with the fruit. Add enough additional brandy to cover the fruit to the depth of ½ inch. Cover and stand for about 9-12 months, then strain off the brandy into another bottle, and cork and serve as a liqueur. Serve the apricots or peaches with ice cream or any cold milk mould.

Gingas em Aguadente (Brandied Morella Cherries)

Substitute cherries for apricots or peaches, but do not cut them.

116

SPAIN

"Brindo Por!" —— Here's How!

SPAIN

The Spanish cuisine is a symphony in colour, but it varies from province to province. Some say that the finest food comes from the Basque country. Catalonia claims to make the best paella. All over Spain the food is full of flavour, highly seasoned and exciting from the Entremesas to dessert. In most parts, olive oil is used for frying. They say in Andalucia where fish is superbly cooked, that every boy is an expert fish fryer in olive oil by the time he is eleven.

If you wish to cook some of the Spanish dishes you fancied while on holiday, you must have garlic, herbs, olive oil, and plenty of nuts on hand, as they are all freely used in Spanish kitchens.

In country districts the traditional cocida, a three-in-one meal, made with chicken or ham, or beef and sausage, and potatoes and other vegetables in season, is often the highlight of Almuerzo (lunch), enjoyed with local red wine. Sometimes the vegetables are eaten as a first course, then the meat and sausage follows with bread and wine. In the towns, paella is more frequently served than cocida.

The Spaniards are small meat eaters but they make a great to-do about their fish, and if you are a lover of fish, you will enjoy the way in which it is presented to you when on holiday on any part of the Spanish coast.

If visiting the Costa del Sol, be sure to try some churros with your morning coffee, and bring back some saffron from Spain if you wish to make paella.

PIMIENTOS MORRONES (Pimiento Hors d'Oeuvre)

4 green or red peppers, 2 tablespoons olive oil, 1 tablespoon vinegar, 1 teaspoon salt, 1 teaspoon chopped parsley, 1 cup olives.

Slit peppers. Remove the seeds. Boil peppers in salted water to cover in a covered saucepan until tender. Drain and leave until cold. Cut each into 4 petals, lengthwise. Arrange them in an hors d'ouevre dish. Coat with oil, smoothly blended with vinegar and salt. Sprinkle with the parsley. Garnish with the olives.

YIELD: 4 servings.

GAZPACHO (Traditional Cold Soup)

½ lb. firm ripe tomatoes, 2 oz. white breadcrumbs, ¼ cup olive oil, 1 pint water, 1 peeled clove of garlic, ¼ cup vinegar, salt.

Wipe and slice tomatoes into a basin. Add breadcrumbs and olive oil. Stir in fully half the water. Beat, with an electric mixer if possible, until smoothly blended. Rub serving bowl with garlic. Stir remainder of water, vinegar and salt to taste into the tomato mixture. Chill slightly.

To Garnish Gazpacho: Add 2 oz. diced green pepper, 2 oz. diced firm tomatoes. 2 oz. diced cucumber, and 2 oz. fried croûtons. If preferred, these garnishes can all be served in separate small dishes so that guests can help themselves.

YIELD: 4 or 5 servings.

SOPA DE ALMENDRAS (Almond Soup)

2 tablespoons olive oil, 4 oz. minced peeled almonds, 1 table-spoon minced onion, ½ teaspoon minced garlic, 1 teaspoon minced parsley, 1 oz. stale breadcrumbs, 1 quart chicken stock, salt and pepper.

Heat olive oil in a shallow saucepan. Add the almonds, onion, garlic and parsley. Stir over low heat for 5 or 6 minutes, but do not allow to brown. Add crumbs. Cook slowly, stirring constantly, for 3 minutes. Add stock and salt and freshly ground black pepper to taste. Stir frequently till boiling. Cover and simmer gently for 15 minutes.

YIELD: 4 or 5 servings.

MERLUZA MARBELLA (Baked Hake Steaks)

6 hake steaks, salt and pepper, dash of cayenne pepper, ¼ teaspoon grated nutmeg, 1 tablespoon olive oil, 1 large thinly sliced onion, 1½ tablespoons chopped pimiento, 6 fillets of anchovy, 2 large peeled tomatoes, 2 tablespoons minced chives, 4 oz. mushrooms, ¼ cup white wine, ¼ cup water, 1½ oz. butter, 3 tablespoons breadcrumbs.

Rinse and dry fish steaks. Mix salt and freshly ground black pepper to taste with the cayenne pepper and nutmeg. Season steaks on both sides with the mixture. Pour the oil into a shallow oval fireproof dish with a cover. Cover bottom of dish with the onion slices and sprinkle with the coarsely chopped pimiento. Lay the steaks side by side on top, and crown each with a fillet of anchovy, then with a thick slice of tomato. Sprinkle with the chives. Thinly slice the mushrooms over the top. Mix the wine with the water and sprinkle over mushrooms. Dab here and there with the butter. Cover. Bake in a hot oven, 450 °F (Mark 7-8) for 25-30 minutes. Sprinkle with the breadcrumbs, then with enough melted butter to moisten. Continue to bake until crumbs are well browned.

YIELD: 6 servings.

TRUCHA CON JAMÓN * (Trout with Ham)

6 fresh trout, 6 small thin rashers of bacon, 2 tablespoons olive oil, salt and pepper, ½ gill dry white wine.

Trim, clean and wash trout. Split carefully and remove the backbones. Rinse again, then dry. Remove rinds from bacon. Slip one on to each fish. Fold into shape. Pour oil into a large shallow fireproof dish. Lay the trout side by side in dish. Season with salt and freshly ground black pepper. Sprinkle with the wine. Bake in a moderate oven, 350 °F (Mark 3-4), for about 20 minutes, basting occasionally with oil in dish. Serve from dish.

YIELD: 6 servings.

* On the Costa del Sol, each trout is garnished on top with a crisply fried rasher of lean bacon. Sometimes fresh herrings are cooked in the same way.

119

RIÑONES AL JEREZ (Stewed Calf's Kidneys)

1 oz. butter, 1 tablespoon minced onion, 1 pair calf's kidneys, salt and black pepper, ¼ pint sherry.

Melt butter in a shallow saucepan. Add onion. Fry slowly till soft and light brown. Meanwhile, skin, core, wash, dry and slice kidneys. Place in pan. Season with salt and freshly ground black pepper to taste. Add sherry. Simmer gently till tender, in 5-10 minutes. Dish up. Garnish with sprigs of watercress.

YIELD: 4 servings.

RIÑONES AL TIO PEPE (Kidneys, Tio Pepe)

8 lamb kidneys, butter as required, ¼ pint Tio Pepe, dash of Worcester sauce, Spanish sauce to taste.

Skin, core and cut kidneys into slices about ⅛ inch thick. Melt 1 oz. butter in a frying pan. Add kidneys. Fry over strong heat for a moment or two on each side. Remove to a plate. Add ½ oz. butter and the Tio Pepe to butter in pan. Simmer gently, uncovered, for about 5 minutes, then add Worcester sauce and Spanish sauce to taste. Stir till at boiling point. Add ½ oz. butter, but into pats, and the sliced kidneys. Simmer for half minute. Serve with boiled rice.

YIELD: 4 servings.

PEPE SOLSONA, CASA PEPE.

PAELLA VALENCIANA (Traditional Rice Dish)

12 oz. diced raw chicken, 12 oz. diced raw pork, 2 tablespoons olive oil, 1½ cloves of garlic, 1 small peeled onion, 3 peeled tomatoes, about 1¾ pints water, 2½ oz. green peas, 8 oz. rice, 8 oz. lobster meat, 8 oz. shelled mussels, 3 sliced pimientos, salt to taste, good pinch of saffron.

Mix the chicken with the pork. Heat oil in a shallow saucepan. Peel and chop garlic. Slice and chop onion and tomatoes.

Add to oil. Stir well for a moment or two, then add barely ½ pint of the water, and green peas. Cover and simmer for about 30 minutes until the chicken and pork are tender and the liquid has evaporated. Add rice. Stir for a moment or two, then add remainder of water, brought to boil. Cut up lobster. Add to mixture in pan with the mussels, pimientos, salt to taste, and the saffron, soaked in a tablespoon of hot water for 10 minutes. (Add water as well.) Boil for 2 minutes. Turn into a round shallow casserole. Bake in a moderate oven, 350 °F (Mark 3-4), for about 15 minutes.

To Serve Paella: Garnish with pieces of pimiento, placed equal distance apart round the edge, then arrange 1 or 2 small shellfish, such as Dublin Bay prawns, or crawfish tails, boiled and heated in olive oil, round the top like a necklace. Plant a " lemon basket " in the centre containing sprigs of parsley pushed through the handle from each side.

> YIELD: 6 servings.
> FROM EL REMO, TORREMOLINOS, COSTA DEL SOL.

ALCACHOFAS CON SALSA (Stewed Artichokes)

1 medium-sized onion, 1 clove of garlic, 1 sprig parsley, 2 oz. chopped bacon, 3 tablespoons olive oil, 1 cup white wine, 1 tin artichokes (12), 3 tablespoons white stock or water, salt and pepper and paprika to taste.

Peel and chop onion and garlic. Mince parsley. Place in a shallow saucepan with the bacon and olive oil. (If preferred, melt 1½ oz. butter and use in place of oil.) Add wine and drained artichokes. Sprinkle with stock or water. Season with salt and freshly ground black pepper, and paprika, to taste. Cover. Simmer very gently for about 15 minutes.

> YIELD: 4 servings.

BIZCHOCHO BORRACHO DE GUADALAJARA *
(Drunken Sponge)

1 sponge ring (about 9 inches across), 4 tablespoons castor sugar, 4 tablespoons water, 1½ gills cream, ¼ pint brandy or rum, glacé cherries and angelica.

Place sponge ring in a trifle dish. Dissolve sugar in the water. Simmer for 6 or 7 minutes, then pour at once over the sponge. Chill. Whip cream till fluffy. Sweeten to taste. Pile into the centre. When required, sprinkle sponge with brandy or rum. Decorate with glacé cherries and spikes of angelica. When strawberries are ripe, they are frequently substituted for cherries and angelica.

YIELD: 6 servings.

CHURROS † (Spanish Fritters)

5 oz. flour, 2 oz. butter, ½ pint water, 1 saltspoon salt, 3 large eggs, orange flower water to taste.

Sift flour. Cut butter into small pieces, and place in a saucepan with the water and salt. Stir over low heat until butter melts. Bring to boil. Remove pan from stove. Add flour. Stir rapidly with a wooden spoon until into a smooth paste, then return to stove, and stir until the paste shrinks from side of pan. Beat eggs slightly, then beat a little at a time into the paste. Stir in a few drops of orange flower water, rum or vanilla essence if preferred. Pack paste into an icing syringe with a piping funnel, fully ¼ inch wide. Squeeze paste into a pan of hot frying oil in rings or in long strips. Fry till pale gold. (They should swell into about an inch in thickness, and if strips are prepared, they will curl as they cook.) Drain on absorbent paper. Keep warm until all are ready, then sprinkle with vanilla sugar. Serve piping hot.

* In Malaga, another version of this sweet is served. Bake sponge in an oblong, greased and floured, baking tin. When cold, cut into bars, about 1½ inches wide, 1½ inches deep and about 4 inches long. Soak in rum till evenly moistened. Pipe " diamonds " of meringue over the top of each and slip under a hot grill for a moment or two till crisp but not discoloured. Chill at room temperature. Serve with cream if liked.

† Fritters prepared in this way, are often served in the afternoon with hot chocolate or coffee.

CREMA DE VINO DE JEREZ (Sherry Cream)

1¼ oz. ground almonds, 1 cup milk, 3-4 drops essence bitter almonds, 5 egg yolks, ¼ cup cream, castor sugar to taste, ½ cup medium sherry.

Mix the almonds with the milk in a saucepan. Bring to boil, stirring constantly. Add essence. Remove pan from stove. Leave until mixture is cold. Beat egg yolks, then beat in the cream, castor sugar to taste, and then the sherry. Stir into the almond milk. Stir over moderate heat till thick and piping hot, but do not allow to boil. Cool slightly. Stir again, then pour into fruit glasses. Chill before serving.

YIELD: 4 servings.

BIZCOCHO DE NARANJA ESPAÑOL (Spanish Orange Sponge Cake)

4 separated eggs, 12 oz. castor sugar, 10 oz. flour, ½ teaspoon baking powder, ½ cup strained orange juice, 3 tablespoons melted butter, rind of ½ orange.

Beat egg whites until stiff. Gradually beat in half the sugar. Chill. Beat egg yolks. Gradually beat in remaining sugar. Sift flour with baking powder. Stir the orange juice, butter and orange rind, finely grated, into the egg yolks. Beat till blended, then stir in the flour very slowly. Fold in egg whites. Place in a buttered cake tin about 10 inches across. Bake in a moderate oven, 350 °F (Mark 3-4), until ready in about 1 hour.

Note: When mandarin oranges are available use mandarin juice instead of orange juice. Sometimes this cake is baked in a square or oblong tin, when it should be cut into squares or oblongs before serving.

HUEVOS A LA FLAMENCA (Flamenca Eggs)

Butter as required, 6 fresh eggs, 8 oz. diced boiled potatoes, 2 chopped peeled tomatoes, 4 oz. chopped bacon or ham, 2 chopped canned pimientos, 4 oz. cooked green peas, 12 slices chorizo.

Brush 6 individual shallow eared fireproof dishes lavishly with butter, or use olive oil. Mix the potato with the tomato, bacon or ham, pimiento, and peas. Divide in 6 equal portions. Shape each portion into a nest in each dish. Bake for about 5 minutes in a moderate oven, 350 °F (Mark 3-4). Drop an egg into each nest. Season. Place 1 slice of chorizo (garlic sausage) at the edge of the egg in each dish, and place another facing it. Bake until the eggs are set in about 6 minutes. Serve at once.

YIELD: 6 servings.

HUEVOS A LA SEVILLANA (Eggs Sevillana)

8 rashers of bacon, 1½ oz. butter, 5 tablespoons milk, 5 eggs, 1 tablespoon chopped canned pimiento, salt and pepper, 4 slices hot buttered toast.

Halve and remove rind from each rasher of bacon. Fry or grill bacon till crisp. Meanwhile, melt butter in a small saucepan. Add 3 tablespoons of the milk. Break eggs into a basin. Beat well. Stir in remaining milk, pimiento, parsley and salt and freshly ground black pepper to taste. Beat till blended. Pour into saucepan. Stir over low heat until mixture begins to set. Remove from stove. Stir till creamy. Divide equally between the toasts. Garnish each with 2 rashers of bacon.

YIELD: 4 servings.

SALSA ESPANOLA (Spanish Sauce)

1 dessertspoon pork fat, 2 rashers bacon, 2 tablespoons minced onion, 2 chopped carrots, 1 peeled clove of garlic, 2 bay leaves, ½ gill white wine, 4 black peppercorns, pinch of mixed spice, salt to taste.

Place the pork fat in a saucepan. Remove rinds from bacon. Cut up bacon and add to pan with the onion, carrot, garlic, and bay leaves. Heat slowly for a minute or two, then add the peppercorns, mixed spice and salt to taste. Simmer for a minute or two until the mixture becomes brown, then thicken with flour to a paste. Stir in wine. When blended, add 1 or 2 chopped firm peeled tomatoes, and stock or water to make a saucy consistency. Simmer for 5 minutes, then rub through a sieve, and cool. Skim off fat. Return sauce to saucepan.

Reseason if necessary. This sauce is a variation of a brown sauce used in many Spanish recipes, known as " dark sauce ".

PEPE SOLSONA, CASA PEPE.

TORTILLA ESPANOLA (Spanish Omelet)

5 tablespoons olive oil, 1 small peeled onion, 1 clove of garlic, 1 ripe peeled tomato, 1 small peeled potato, 2 fried peeled red peppers, 2 oz. boiled green peas, 6 eggs, salt and black pepper.

Place a large steel frying pan, not an aluminium one, on the stove, and add the oil. Chop onion, garlic, tomato and potato. When the oil reaches boiling point, add and fry till they begin to brown. Chop peppers. When vegetables are starting to brown, add peppers and the peas. Stir until evenly mixed, then beat the eggs and stir into mixture. When thoroughly blended, fry for about 20 seconds over moderate heat, to allow bottom of omelet to brown. Turn at once. Place a lid or plate over frying pan, large enough to overlap edge. Fry for another 20 seconds to brown the second side, then serve at once.

YIELD: 4 servings.

SENOR PEPE, CASA PEPE.

SWITZERLAND

Bon Appetit   —— French speaking

Buon Appetito —— Italian speaking

En Guete   —— Swiss German speaking

SWITZERLAND

To cook à la Swisse you require ingredients of the highest quality. Rich cream and milk from the golden Simmenthal cows, and butter and wine are freely used in the Swiss kitchen. Switzerland is the gourmet's paradise.

Over there, in the arms of the immortal Alps, you can enjoy not only traditional fare, such as raclette and the celebrated Cheese Fondue, but the most delectable confectionery and aromatic salads and savouries in a setting you will always remember. If you like fish you will find that the Swiss are masters of the art of cooking fish. In the Bernese Oberland they have brought this art to perfection. I shall always remember La Danseuse de la Rivière, mountain trout, served with parsley butter and new potatoes. It was a glorified Trout à la Meunière. If you adore mushrooms, visit Gossau near Zurich, famed for its champignons, and try the traditional Jalousie aux Champignons. If you are a cheese fan, you will enjoy the tempting hot Emmenthaler cheese savouries.

Swiss fare, unlike that of other Continental countries, includes a blending of three distinctive cuisines, the French, German and Italian. No matter where you happen to stop for a meal, you will discover this from the menus yourself.

To the lover of beautiful scenery, good food and wine, Switzerland draws you like a moth to the candle. It is a Mecca to which one always longs to return.

MUESLI * (Original Recipe)

1 medium-sized tablespoon rolled oats, juice of ½ lemon, 1 medium-sized hard crisp cooking apple, 1 dessertspoon sweetened condensed milk.

Place oats in a small basin. Cover with cold water. Cover and stand overnight. Strain in lemon juice. Remove a thin slice from the blossom and stem end of apple. Grate apple. (In Switzerland a special Birchner-Benner grater is used.) Stir until thoroughly mixed, then stir in sweetened condensed milk to taste. Beat well. Serve in a small bowl or glass dish for breakfast in place of a fruit and a cereal.

YIELD: 1 serving.

PAUPIETTES MARIE-ROSE (Smoked Trout Rolls)

1 smoked trout, smoked salmon as required, heart of lettuce leaves, 1 lemon, 2 maraschino cherries.

Fillet trout carefully. Wrap each fillet smoothly and neatly in thinly sliced smoked salmon. Place each on an individual plate. Garnish with heart of lettuce leaves, and half a lemon, prepared like grapefruit. Tuck a maraschino cherry into centre of each half lemon. Serve with slices of thinly buttered 24-hour-old brown bread.

YIELD: 2 servings.

FROM M. PAUL LEHRIAN,
CHARING CROSS HOTEL,
LONDON.

CHAESSUPPE (Cheese Soup)

½ lb. stale brown bread, ¾ lb. cheese, 1¼ pint boiling water, ¼ pint dry white Swiss wine, salt to taste.

Remove crusts from bread and cut bread and cheese into small thin slices. Place alternately in the bottom of a heated soup tureen. Pour in boiling water. Cover and stand for

---

* It is possible to use prepared Scotch oats in place of rolled oats. They only need soaking for 10 minutes. Honey or yoghurt may be substituted for condensed milk. Other fresh fruit, such as bananas, raspberries, strawberries, or sultanas, can be added in place of the apple.

about 2½ hours. Turn into a saucepan. Bring quickly to boil.
Cook, mashing the bread and cheese with a wooden spoon
until into a purée. Add wine and salt to taste. Serve piping
hot.

YIELD: 5 or 6 servings.

ESCALOPE DE VEAU, CORDON BLEU (Scallop of Veal, Cordon Bleu)

2 small thin scallops of veal, matching in size, lean boiled ham
as required, Gruyère cheese as required, salt to taste, freshly
ground black pepper to taste, beaten egg as required, seasoned
flour as required.

Cover one scallop with small pieces of lean boiled ham,
then with wafer-thin slices of Gruyère cheese. Top with a
remaining scallop. Press firmly together. Season on both
sides with salt and pepper. Brush with egg. Dip in flour.
Melt enough unsalted butter in a small frying pan to give you
¼ inch depth. Place scallop in pan. Fry till brown below, then
turn and fry till brown on the other side. The heat will melt
the cheese sufficiently to keep the slices of veal together. Serve
with pommes allumettes (Potato straws), or buttered new
potatoes, garnished minced chives, and with green peas or
French beans.

YIELD: 1 serving.

FONDUE BOURGUIGNONNE (Steaks on Sticks)

1½ lb. rump steak, 1 pint olive oil, assorted mayonnaise,
minced parsley, minced shallot, and French bread.

Have the steak cut ¾ inch thick, then with a sharp knife,
divide it into ¾ inch squares. Pile on two meat platters. Heat
the oil in a casserole on top of a table stove with a spirit lamp
below, placed on centre of table. Stand a plate of meat in
front of two guests facing each other across the table to the left
of the stove. Arrange the second plate of meat on the opposite
side of the stove facing the remaining two guests. (This
arrangement is necessary so that all the guests can cook their
steaks simultaneously.) Set on the right at each cover a long
handled fork or two baguettes, long pointed sticks, about 15

inches in length, and stand a plate of French bread, cut in slices, on the outer side of the steak plates, with a dish of butter balls beyond each. Before starting to cook the steak, arrange a plate the size of a small meat plate, at each cover, with a heaped teaspoon of 6 different kinds of flavoured mayonnaise, placed equal distance apart, around the centre. Drop a dessert-spoon of parsley and shallot, mixed in equal quantities, on centre of each plate. Now, let each one take a baguette or a fork and, with it, pierce a square of steak, and place it in the oil, heated till it stops sizzling. Prepare another steak in the same way. By the time it is ready to place in the oil, the first one is ready to remove. Still impaled on the stick or fork, dip in any one of the varieties of mayonnaise you prefer, then roll in the parsley and shallot, and eat, with French bread and butter as an accompaniment, and Dole wine for preference.

Mayonnaise for Fondue: Place 1½ tablespoons home-made mayonnaise in 6 cups. Flavour one with paprika to taste, another with curry powder to taste, the next with mustard to taste. Mince garlic finely, and add a teaspoon into the fourth portion. Add 1 heaped teaspoon minced shallot to the fifth, and the same quantity of chopped chives to the sixth.

YIELD: 4 servings.

AS SERVED BY MADAME LUCETTE,
CAFE L'INDUSTRIE,
LAUSANNE.

LAPIN A LA MOUTARDE (Rabbit with Mustard Sauce)

1 rabbit, 3 oz. butter, 5 large peeled onions, 4 oz. diced streaky bacon, 1½ oz. flour, 1 pint chicken stock, bouquet garni, salt and pepper, 1 heaped dessertspoon French mustard, fried croûtons.

Joint rabbit. Soak joints for 12 hours in equal quantity of vinegar and salt water to cover. Drain and dry thoroughly. Melt butter in a large heavy, shallow saucepan. Peel onions and cut up coarsely. Remove rind from bacon and cut bacon in dice. Add the onion and bacon to the butter. Cook over low heat for 5 minutes, then add the rabbit joints. Increase

* This fondue makes an ideal dish for a buffet party.

the heat and fry till the joints are golden brown, turning frequently. Shake in the flour so that all the joints are roughly coated. Fry slowly for 5 minutes, stirring occasionally, then add the stock, bouquet garni, salt and pepper to taste, and the mustard. Bring slowly to boiling point, then simmer till the rabbit is quite tender, in about 1 hour. If necessary, correct the consistency of sauce, and season again, towards the end of cooking.

To serve, transfer rabbit joints to a hot fireproof dish. Pour the mustard sauce over. Garnish with fried croûtons to taste.

YIELD: 4 servings.

CHAMPIGNONS AUX FINES HERBES (Fried mushrooms with fine herbs)

7 oz. mushrooms, 1 oz. butter, 1 dessertspoon minced onion or shallot, salt and pepper, pinch of crushed herbs, a few drops lemon juice, 1 heaped teaspoon minced parsley, 1 tablespoon stock.

Wash and dry mushrooms but do not peel. Cut in slices about ¼ inch thick. Melt the butter in an enamel or stainless steel frying pan. Add onion or shallot. Fry slowly till soft. Add mushrooms. Fry for about 5 minutes, stirring constantly. Season with salt and pepper to taste. Add herbs and lemon juice. Stir in parsley and stock. Serve with chops and steaks.

YIELD: 3 servings.

MADAME HAUSER,
GOSSAU-ZURICH,
SWITZERLAND.

COMICE AUX MARRONS GLACES (Stuffed Comice Pears)

2 Comice pears, 4 oz. castor sugar, 1 cup boiling water, 2 marrons glacés, 4 oz. plain chocolate, 2 sponge rings, Kirsch as required.

Peel pears carefully without removing stalks. Dissolve the sugar in the water. Bring to boiling point. Dip pears in lemon juice, then cook slowly in the syrup for about 10 minutes with lid on pan. Remove to a platter. Leave until quite cold.

Carefully scoop out the cores with a pointed spoon or a curved grapefruit knife from the blossom ends. Fill each hollow with a chopped marron glacé. Melt chocolate in just enough water to give a coating consistency. Cool slightly, then coat pears carefully. Cut 2 rings of sponge from a sponge layer, making each about 2½ inches across. Sprinkle with Kirsch, just enough to soak sponge. Place 1 pear on centre of each ring. Pipe whipped cream round the base. Decorate cream with crystallized rose petals, or split toasted almonds.

YIELD: 2 servings.

SAVARIN AU RHUM (Rum Savarin)

10 oz. flour, pinch of salt, ¼ pint tepid milk, ½ oz. baker's yeast, 1 teaspoon castor sugar, 3 eggs, 3 oz. creamed butter, 1 oz. sifted icing sugar, 6 oz. castor sugar, ¼ pint water, rum to taste, whipped cream as required.

Sift flour and salt into a slightly warmed basin. Heat in a warming cupboard for about 10 minutes. Stir the milk into the yeast, creamed with the sugar. Make a hollow in the centre of the flour. Add yeast. Beat and add eggs. Gradually beat the liquid with the flour, drawn from the sides of the hollow, until all the ingredients are blended. Cover with a damp cloth. Stand in a warm place for about 40 minutes. Beat in the butter, then the icing sugar. Brush a tubular round cake tin with melted butter. Dredge with flour then shake out any surplus flour. Pour in the mixture, which should be about one-third deep. Cover. Leave in a warm place until the dough nearly fills the tin. Bake in a hot oven, 450 °F (Mark 7-8) for 10 minutes. Lower to moderate, 350 °F (Mark 3-4), and bake for about 20 minutes. Unmould on to a serving platter or shallow dish. Place the castor sugar in a saucepan. Add the water. Stir till sugar is dissolved, then bring quickly to boil, and boil for 5 minutes. Remove from stove. Add rum to taste. Gently spoon this syrup over the savarin. Stand for 30 minutes to allow any of the drops that run into the platter or dish to be absorbed. Serve cold. When required, sprinkle with rum to taste. Cover with whipped cream. Decorate with cherries and angelica.

YIELD: 6 or 7 servings.

CHRÄBELI (Aniseed Biscuits)

2 eggs, 1 lb. castor sugar, 10 oz. flour, 2 tablespoons aniseeds, ½ teaspoon baking powder.

Beat eggs and sugar till frothy. Stir in flour mixed with the aniseeds and baking powder. When thoroughly blended, roll out thinly and cut into strips 1 inch thick. Cut strips into pieces 3 inches long. Make three small cuts on one side of each piece, then place them side by side, slightly curved, and a little apart, on a floured shallow baking tin. Leave in a warm room for 12 hours, then bake in a rather slow oven till lightly coloured, in about 25 minutes.

SWISSAIR,
LONDON.

FLORENTINES

3½ oz. butter, 4 oz. castor sugar, 2 oz. broken walnuts, 2 oz. almonds, 1 oz. sultanas, 1 oz. glacé cherries, 1 oz. chopped candied peel, ½ egg cup cream, 4 oz. block chocolate.

Melt butter in a shallow saucepan. Add the sugar. Stir over low heat till dissolved, then bring to boil. Boil for 1 minute. Stir in remaining ingredients in order given, folding in the cream, whipped till fluffy. Drop in small well-spaced heaps on shallow baking tins, brushed with melted butter then dredged with flour. Bake in a moderate oven, 350 °F (Mark 3-4), until golden brown, in about 10 minutes. Remove at once. Cool slightly, then press edges into a neat shape. Place on a wire tray. Melt the chocolate over boiling water. Spread over biscuits, then draw the prongs of a fork, or a comb kept for the purpose, over the chocolate.

ZIMTSTERNE (Cinnamon Stars)

3 egg whites, 3 cups sifted icing sugar, 3 cups ground almonds, 1 tablespoon lemon juice, 1 small tablespoon ground cinnamon, 8 oz. castor sugar.

Beat egg whites to a stiff froth. Gradually beat in the icing sugar. Stir for 20 minutes, or for 1 minute only in an electric mixer on medium speed. Reserving 1 cup of the mixture stir all remaining ingredients into the remainder of mixture. Stand for 30 minutes. Dredge a pastry board lightly with castor sugar. Roll out dough to about ½ inch thickness. Cut out with a star cutter. Place a little apart on a well-greased baking tin. Brush over with the reserved mixture. Bake in a very slow oven, 275 °F (Mark ½), for about 15 minutes. (If too hot the icing will turn yellow and spoil the effect.)

SWISSAIR,
LONDON.

FONDUE

" Fondue isch guet und git e gueti Luune ")

(" Fondue tastes good and promotes a happy and gay atmosphere ")

This is a traditional Swiss dish. To prepare it, you need a Caquelon, which is a round casserole with a metal base, a spirit stove, and long-handled forks or pointed sticks called " baguettes ".

Before preparing and serving Fondue, lay the table. Arrange at each cover a long-handled three pronged fork or baguette, a wine and a liquer glass, and a table napkin. (The wine glass should be the size of a port glass.) Pile cubes of crusty bread in a bread basket, and provide a pepper mill, and bring a bottle of lightly chilled dry white Swiss wine, such as Fendant, to the table.

> *1 clove of garlic, ½ pint white wine, 1½ lb. grated Swiss cheese, 1 teaspoon cornflour, 1 small glass Kirsch, pinch of bicarbonate of soda, pepper to taste, nutmeg or paprika to taste.*

Peel and halve clove of garlic. Rub the inside of the fondue pan with a cut side, then place the pan on the stove. Add the wine. When warm, gradually stir in the cheese. As soon as the mixture starts to bubble, stir in the cornflour, mixed to a paste with the Kirsch. Cook for 2-3 minutes, stirring constantly, then add the soda, pepper and nutmeg or paprika. Carry quickly to the table and place on a table stove or on top of a spirit cooker, where it can gently simmer.

To Serve Fondue

Let each one spear a piece of bread with fork or baguette and dip it in the fondue until well coated, then eat it. If not seasoned to your taste, grind a little pepper on it. Drink wine with this dish until it is half finished, then fill the liqueur glasses with Kirsch and drink this before finishing the meal, and the wine. If preferred, the wine used in making the fondue can be served with the meal in place of Fendant, and tea can also accompany it.

YIELD: 4 servings.

KURSALLE,
BERNE.

JALOUSIE AUX CHAMPIGNONS (Venetian Blind with Mushrooms)

Puff pastry as required, mushroom filling, 1 beaten egg.

Roll 2 strips of puff pastry to $\frac{1}{4}$ inch thickness, one strip $4\frac{1}{2}$ by 16 inches, and the other 5 by 17 inches. Place the smaller strip on a baking tin, brushed with melted butter. Spread with a layer of mushroom filling to about $\frac{1}{2}$ inch of the edge all the way round. Turn up the edges. Brush with egg and cover with the larger strip, prepared as follows:

Fold strip lengthwise. With a sharp pointed knife cut slits, in the fold, $\frac{1}{4}$ inch apart to within $\frac{1}{4}$ inch of the margin. Open out again very carefully to avoid breaking, then lay it directly over the filled strip. Press edges smoothly together. Brush pastry with a beaten egg. Bake in a hot oven, 450 °F (Mark 7-8), for about 25 minutes. Serve hot or cold, cut in slices.

Mushroom Filling: Wash and dry $1\frac{3}{4}$ lb. mushrooms. Cut into thin slices. Melt $1\frac{1}{2}$ oz. butter in a shallow saucepan. When hot, add 2 oz. finely chopped onion and sliced mushrooms. Fry quickly. Stir in salt and pepper to taste, and a pinch of mixed herbs.

YIELD: 12-14 servings.

MADAME HAUSER,
GOSSAU-ZURICH
SWITZERLAND.

RACLETTE * (Traditional Cheese Dish)

Cut one large 10 lb. semi-hard cheese in halves crosswise. Prepare a dish of boiled new potatoes in their jackets. Place over a table stove and keep hot, covered with a lid or a linen cloth. Provide small dishes of sweet pickled gherkins and pickled onions. Place one half of the cheese close to the bars of an electric fire for one minute, then with a long knife quickly draw off the bubbling cheese on to a heated individual plate, and serve at once.

* This alpine dish is made with Bangne cheese, a local cheese made in the south of Switzerland and not exported. Use any sharp-flavoured semi-hard cheese you like. You peel your own potatoes and eat them with the cheese, seasoned to taste with salt and freshly ground black pepper, if liked, and pickles. This I enjoyed at a place called Savièse, prepared by a buxom Swiss girl called Veronica. You can enjoy this with either Fendant or Dôle wine or any other Swiss wine you please. I preferred it with Dôle.

TURKEY

"Serefinize!" —— (Here's How!)
"Sihhatinize!"—— (Good Health!)

TURKEY

It is an exciting adventure keeping house in Turkey. In that hospitable country, housewives seldom economize on food and inexpensive substitutes are not popular. If nine eggs are required to make a sweet then nine eggs are used.

Turkey, encircled by the Black Sea and the Mediterranean, has a fine supply of fresh fish. There, the housewife can buy fresh anchovies, bass, gurnet, mackerel, grey and red mullet, sturgeon, swordfish, tuna fish, and many another. Buying fish along the shores of the Golden Horn is an event. Freshly caught, they are arranged on slabs, glistening in a frame of emerald green parsley sprigs, garnished with lemons. Olive oil, one of the most important products of Turkey, is generally used for frying fish.

Unlike in many other European countries, meat is brought to the markets freshly killed, so to prevent chops, joints and steaks being tough, the Turkish housewife beats them with a heavy mallet until they are twice their original size, and sometimes soaks them in onion juice to tenderize them. They are left in the juice for a day or two before cooking, but are turned and basted with the juice at least once or twice a day.

The Turks are very hospitable. When entertaining, the sky is the limit, but you will never find the Turkish host offering you larks' tongues, or exotic dishes made of song birds you are sometimes treated to in other countries. Even the pigeons are protected by the Moslems.

CACIK (Cucumber Yoghurt)

1 pint yoghurt, 3 tablespoons roughly chopped cucumber, 3 bruised cloves of garlic, about 3 teaspoons olive oil.

Place yoghurt in a basin. Beat well with a wooden spoon. Gradually stir in cucumber. Crush the garlic to a pulp. Stir into the yoghurt with salt to taste, and olive oil. Chill thoroughly. Serve in small bowls or soup cups, in place of soup.

To Vary: Gradually stir 1 tablespoon wine vinegar into the yoghurt in place of the oil. Add, if liked, 2 chopped olives, and finely chopped fresh mint to taste.

YIELD: 3 servings.

CIRCASSIAN CORBASI (Circassian Soup)

2 bay leaves, ½ cup diced carrot, ½ cup chick peas, ¼ cup shredded celery, 3 pints stock, ¼ pint tomato juice, 2 oz. barley, salt and pepper, ½ oz. butter, 2 tablespoons minced onion, 1 cup mashed potatoes, 2 chilli peppers, 1 bottle yoghurt.

Soak the bay leaves with the vegetables for 12 hours, then drain vegetables thoroughly. Bring stock and tomato juice to boil in a large saucepan. Add bay leaves and vegetables, then barley. Bring to simmering point. Skim if necessary. Cover and simmer gently until the vegetables are soft. Season with salt and pepper to taste. Melt the butter in a small saucepan. Add the onion. Fry slowly till clear, then stir into the soup. Add potatoes. Stir till blended, then add chilli peppers. Cover and simmer for 45 minutes. Remove peppers. Garnish each portion of soup with a tablespoon of yoghurt.

YIELD: 6 or 7 servings.

KAGITTA BARBUNYA (Baked Red Mullet)

6 medium-sized red mullet, 1 oz. butter, 1 tablespoon chopped parsley, juice of 1 lemon, ¼ cup olive oil, salt and pepper to taste.

Clean the fish without removing the heads or tails. Wash thoroughly and pat with a clean cloth till dry. Melt the butter. Take 12 pieces greaseproof paper, large enough to wrap up each fish. Pair the pieces and brush the top of each pair lavishly with creamed butter. Wrap up the fish. Tie securely with string. Place on a baking sheet. Bake in a moderately hot oven, 400 °F (Mark 5-6), for about 45 minutes. Mix the parsley with the lemon juice, olive oil and salt and pepper to taste. When fish is ready, unwrap carefully. Arrange on 6 individual heated plates. Sprinkle with the parsley mixture.

YIELD: 6 servings.

KABAK MUSAKKASI (Courgette and Meat Pie)

1 lb. minced shoulder of lamb, 1 cup chopped onion, 2 beaten eggs, ¾ cup chopped parsley, salt and pepper, 2 lb. courgettes, 2 sliced tomatoes, 1 cup water.

Brown the lamb in 2 tablespoons melted butter, stirring constantly, then add onion. Mix well. Cover and simmer gently for 10 minutes. Remove from stove. Stir in eggs, parsley and salt and pepper to taste. Slice the courgettes lengthwise in strips ¼ inch thick. Place a layer of the strips in the bottom of a greased fireproof dish. Cover with a layer of the meat mixture, then with another layer of courgette. Repeat layers. Top with tomato slices. Pour the water over. Bake in a moderate oven, 350 °F (Mark 3-4), for 1 hour. Serve with pilaff.

YIELD: 5 or 6 servings.

NEVVAR HICKMET,
GATWICK MANOR,
NEAR CRAWLEY,
SUSSEX.

KUZULU PILAV (Lamb Pilaff)

4 tablespoons dripping, 2 cups long-grained rice, 1 lb. cooked lean lamb, 8 oz. lamb's liver, 2 oz. butter, 2 spring onions, 1 chopped medium-sized onion, 1 tablespoon pine kernels, salt and pepper, 1 tablespoon currants, 1 teaspoon sugar, 1 rosemary leaf, 3 sprigs parsley, 1 tablespoon dill, 1 chopped peeled tomato, 1½ cups white stock, 1 teaspoon ground cinnamon, butter and yoghurt.

Melt the dripping in a shallow saucepan. When hot, add the rice, rinsed, drained and tossed in a cloth till dry.

Stir for a few minutes until the rice looks transparent, then add 2 quarts boiling water, and boil rapidly for 10-12 minutes, time depending on the kind of rice. (Do not overcook.) Cut the lamb into small pieces. Wash and dry liver. Cut into small pieces. Melt half the butter and add liver. Fry for 3 minutes, stirring occasionally, then remove, cover, and keep warm. Trim and slice spring onions. Fry in remaining butter in pan for 2 minutes. Place beside the liver. Add remaining butter to butter in pan, then the onion. Fry slowly until onion starts to brown. Add pine kernels. Fry until golden brown, stirring frequently so that the onion does not brown. Add salt and pepper, currants, sugar, rosemary leaf, parsley, dill, tomato and stock. Stir till thoroughly blended, then cover and cook rapidly for 5 minutes. Lower heat. Add rice and spring onions. Cover and cook until the rice has absorbed all remaining liquid in about 7 minutes. Add liver. Stir lightly, then cover with a linen towel and a lid. Stand in a warm place on stove, but not over heat, for 30-40 minutes. Dish up. Garnish with ground cinnamon, then reheat the lamb in a little butter and yoghurt, with lid on pan, and arrange round the rice. Sprinkle pilaff with minced parsley.

To Vary: Substitute mutton for lamb, but roast the mutton for 30 minutes in a baking tin, basting it frequently with the clarified dripping, then remove and keep warm. Add 1 oz. raisins with the currants.

YIELD: 5 or 6 servings.

SHASHLIK (Mixed Lamb Grill on Skewers)

¾ lb. leg of lamb, marinade, thick slices of firm tomato, thin slices blanched onion, boiled rice.

Cut meat into bite-size pieces. Place in a shallow dish. Sprinkle with enough olive oil to moisten, then with a dessert-spoon of vinegar, 1 tablespoon chopped onion, 2 or 3 whole cloves, 1 dessertspoon chopped parsley, and freshly ground black pepper to taste. Soak for 1 hour, stirring occasionally. Drain meat. Run alternately on 4 skewers, each piece separated by a slice of tomato and onion. Finish with a piece of meat. Grill slowly for about 10 minutes, turning frequently

139

until the meat is evenly cooked all over. (In some parts of Turkey, 1 mushroom, or 2 mushrooms, are run in centre of each skewer. If two, place them back to back.) Arrange an oval mound of rice on a heated oval platter. Prop the skewers on the rice, points upwards. Garnish rice with minced parsley.

Pilaff (boiled rice): Wash and drain 6 oz. Patna rice. Melt 2 oz. butter in a shallow saucepan. Add a chopped peeled tomato, and a pinch of salt. When the butter is hot, add rice. Fry for 5 or 6 minutes, stirring frequently, until rice is slightly coloured. Add ¾ pint boiling water. Cover. Simmer until rice has absorbed all the water in 15-20 minutes, adding more salt as required when nearly ready. Stir lightly with a wooden spoon. Dry over very low heat until the rice looks fluffy and the grains are separated.

YIELD: 4 servings.

YOGURTLU KEBAP (Kebap with Yoghurt)

1½ lb. lamb or mutton, 1 large onion, 4 slices wholemeal bread, 2 cups stock, 3 bottles yoghurt, paprika and pepper.

Rub the lamb or mutton with the onion. Cut into squares and marinate. Toast the bread. Arrange slices in a heated serving dish. Pour the stock over the toast. Place dish in a moderate oven until toast is hot. Grill meat on skewers. Arrange on the slices of toast. Pour the yoghurt into a saucepan. Stir with a wooden spoon over very low heat until just warm, then pour over the meat on toast. Sprinkle with the paprika and pepper. Serve at once.

YIELD: 4 servings.

NEVVAR HICKMET,
GATWICK MANOR,
NEAR CRAWLEY,
SUSSEX.

CERKES TAVUGU (Circassian Chicken)

1 whole chicken, 4½-5 lb., fresh walnuts, 2 slices bread, 1½ pints chicken stock, 1 tablespoon paprika, salt and black pepper.

Boil chicken until quite tender. When cool, remove meat from bones and cut into small pieces ready for serving. Blanch the walnuts, then put them twice through a mincing machine. Soak bread in water to cover for 5 minutes. Squeeze dry. Mix with the walnuts and put through a mincer. Season with salt and freshly ground pepper to taste. Put twice through mincer. (It is important to obtain as much as possible from the walnuts. After all this mincing there should be at least $\frac{1}{2}$ cup oil, after draining it from the paste. The paste now should be very smooth.) Stir stock gradually into the paste until the mixture is into a thick rich sauce. Cover the chicken completely with this sauce. Mix the paprika with the walnut oil and pour thinly over the sauce, in as an attractive design as possible.

YIELD: 6 servings.

NEVVAR HICKMET,
GATWICK MANOR,
NEAR CRAWLEY,
SUSSEX.

SALATA (Watercress Salad)

2 bunches watercress, 4 hard-boiled eggs, salad cream as required, nasturtium flowers or buttercups.

Pick over and thoroughly wash watercress. Place in a basin of ice-cold water and leave there until crisp. When required, remove and shake well, then tear into small sprigs. Chop eggs. Prepare a salad cream, very slightly sweetened. Place a layer of the watercress in a salad bowl. Add a few nasturtium flowers or buttercups. Sprinkle with half the egg, then coat with dressing. Repeat layers. Arrange a wreath of flowers round the edge, and cluster one or two on the centre.

YIELD: 4 servings.

IRMIK HELVASI (Semolina Castle Puddings)

6 oz. castor sugar, $\frac{1}{4}$ pint water, 4 oz. butter, 4 oz. semolina, 2 oz. seedless raisins, grated rind of 1 orange, 2 oz. ground almonds, 4 cardamon seeds, ground cinnamon to taste.

Place sugar in a saucepan. Add water. Bring to boil, after sugar is dissolved. Boil until syrup thickens, then remove from stove. Melt butter in a shallow saucepan. Add semolina. Fry till slightly browned, then add raisins, orange rind, almonds and seeds. When blended, stir in the syrup. Cook over low heat, stirring constantly, until thick. Pour into wet castle pudding moulds. Chill. Unmould on to a platter. Sprinkle lightly with ground cinnamon. Serve with cream.

YIELD: 4 servings.

KUŞ UZUMU TATLISI (Blackcurrant Whip)

1 tablespoon powdered gelatine, ¼ cup cold water, 1 cup hot blackcurrant juice, 2 tablespoons lemon juice, 6 oz. brown sugar, 2 egg whites, ½ pint whipped cream, ¼ cup ripe black currants.

Soak the gelatine in the water for 5 minutes. Add the fruit juices and sugar. Stir till the sugar is dissolved, then strain and cool, stirring occasionally. When beginning to set, beat with a rotary egg beater till frothy. Beat egg whites to a stiff froth. Fold into mixture, then beat again until stiff. Divide between 6 fruit glasses. Chill thoroughly. Top with swirls of whipped cream. Decorate with the currants.

YIELD: 3 or 4 servings.

ÇİLEKLİ PASTALAR (Strawberry Cream Puffs)

4 oz. butter, 1 cup water, 4 oz. sifted flour, 4 large eggs, 1 cup thick cream, ½ cup sifted icing sugar, 1 cup halved straw- berries.

Place butter in a small saucepan. Add water. Heat to boiling point. Add flour. Stir constantly until the mixture thickens and leaves the sides of the pan clean, and forms a ball. (This takes 1½-2 minutes.) Remove pan from stove. Let mixture cool slightly, then beat in the eggs, one at a time. When all are added, beat till mixture is smooth and glossy. Drop from a tablespoon on to an ungreased baking sheet, in rounds or ovals, keeping them about 3 inches apart. Bake in a moderately hot oven 400 °F (Mark 5-6), for about 45 minutes, until puffy and a pale gold. Remove to a table out of a draught and allow to cool slowly. When quite cold, remove tops with a sharp knife. Scoop out any soft inside dough very carefully. Whisk cream until very stiff, beating in the icing sugar as you whisk. Fold in the berries. Spoon into the cases. Replace the tops. Dredge lightly with sifted icing sugar.

GÜL REÇELI (Rose Petal Jam)

1½ lb. rose petals, 3½ lb. castor sugar, 1½ pints water, 1 lemon.

Take the rose petals and 1 lb. of the sugar. Place in layers alternately in a large saucepan. Cover with a cloth, then with a tightly fitting lid. Stand for 12 hours. Bring the water to a full boil. Pour over the petals and sugar. Cover again with the cloth and lid. Leave for 48 hours. Stir thoroughly. Replace lid and leave for 24 hours. Strain off the water into another saucepan. Add remaining sugar. Stir frequently till dissolved, then pour over the petals. Bring to a boil. Skim. Strain in the juice of the lemon. Pot, seal and label.

Nevvar Hickmet,
Gatwick Mabor,
Near Crawley,
Sussex.

KAHVE (Turkish Coffee)

6 coffee cups cold water, 12 rounded teaspoons, Turkish coffee, castor sugar to taste.

In Turkey, coffee is generally brewed in a copper-lined saucepan with a long-handle over charcoal. If not available, use a small saucepan kept exclusively for coffee making.

Pour the water into pan. Add coffee and sugar, allowing 1-2 heaped teaspoons for each cup, according to taste. Bring very slowly to boiling point, stirring until all the sugar is dissolved. As soon as coffee froths, remove from stove, and let the froth subside. Repeat, bringing to boiling point, and letting froth subside three times, then serve, pouring only a little into each cup to start with, so that the brown froth is equally shared.

In some parts of Turkey, a few drops of rose water is added to each cup before serving.

Yield: 6 servings.

RAHAT LOKOUM (Turkish Delight)

2 lb. castor sugar, 2 cups cold water, 4 tablespoons cornflour, ½ gill green grape juice, 1 tablespoon lemon juice, 1 teaspoon cream of tartar, 3 teaspoons rose water, a few drops of cochineal, 1 tablespoon minced pistachio nuts, 1 cup sifted icing sugar.

Place the sugar and water in a saucepan. Stir over low heat till sugar is dissolved, then bring to boil. Boil for 20 minutes. Cream cornflour with the grape and lemon juice. Gradually stir this into the syrup, then stir in the cream of tartar. Boil until the mixture thickens, and the smell of cornflour has disappeared, then remove pan from stove. Stir in rose water, cochineal and pistachio nuts. Pour into a long shallow baking tin, brushed with almond oil. Leave until cold. With a sharp knife, cut into squares. Roll each square in icing sugar.

To Vary: In some parts of Turkey, finely minced peeled blanched almonds are substituted for the pistachio nuts, or half almonds and half pistachio nuts are used. In other parts, the juice of raspberries and strawberries are used in place of the grape juice or half of it.

YUGOSLAVIA

Zivili!——Here's How!

YUGOSLAVIA

If you are a vegetable lover you can make an interesting meal of vegetables in Yugoslavia. The Yugoslavians, like the Greeks and Turks, are superb vegetable cooks. You have to taste dishes made with aubergines, courgettes, green peppers and okra in this lovely country to realise what I mean.

The favourite seasoning, as in Austria and Hungary, is paprika, and fennel and mint are often used for flavouring cold meat dishes and salads. Many of the casseroles of meat and vegetables, so popular in Yugoslavia, are seasoned not only with paprika, but flavoured with garlic and tomato.

Whole lambs and sucking pigs, cooked on a spit, are the pièce de résistance at festive meals, such as wedding banquets and anniversary dinners. In country homes, they are sometimes cooked for family meals over wood fires in the open. The Yugoslavians are particularly fond of lamb and pork. Like their neighbours, they specialize in kebabs.

There is one Serbian custom which always intrigues me, and that is serving Slatko to guests as they arrive. This is a delicious preserve usually made with raspberries, strawberries or watermelon rind. If you are privileged to be a guest in Yugoslavia, do not look confused if your hostess offers you a dish of one of these preserves with a spoon and a glass of water. This is an old custom which still prevails in many parts, so help yourself to a spoonful and then accept a drink.

The wines of Yugoslavia are as good as the food.

JAGNJEĆA ČORBA (Lamb Soup)

1 lb. lean tender lamb, cold salted water as required, 2 table-spoons chopped onion, 1 tablespoon lard, 1 tablespoon flour, pinch of paprika, 1 beaten egg, 1 dessertspoon vinegar, 2 teaspoons minced parsley.

Cut lamb into small squares. Place in a shallow saucepan. Cover with cold salted water. Bring quickly to boil. Skim carefully. Add onion. Cover and simmer gently until meat is tender. Melt the lard in a separate saucepan. Add flour and paprika. Stir till frothy, then mix to a saucy consistency with some of the soup. Stir till boiling. Add to soup. When boiling, stir in egg and vinegar. Serve in heated soup cups or plates. Garnish equally with the parsley.

YIELD: 4 servings.

BRODET OD MORSKIH RIBA * (Stewed Fish with Tomato Sauce)

2 lb. fillet of fish, 1 oz. seasoned flour, 6 tablespoons olive oil, 3 medium-sized onions, 1 clove garlic, 1 teaspoon chopped parsley, ¼ pint vinegar, 3 tablespoons tomato purée.

Wipe the fillets and cut into 2 inch lengths. Dip in seasoned flour. Heat the olive oil in a large shallow saucepan. Add fillets. Fry till browned below, then turn and brown on the other side. Remove to a platter. Slice and add the onions. Fry until the slices turn yellow, then chop garlic and add with the parsley and the fillets. Mix the vinegar with the tomato purée and pour over the fish. Add enough cold water to cover fillets. (If preferred, substitute 1 tin tomato juice for the tomato purée.) Bring quickly to boil. Cover and simmer very gently for 30 minutes, taking care not to break the fillets. Dish up. Serve, garnished round the edge with boiled noodles or macaroni.

YIELD: 4 servings.

* Sometimes this dish is made with mackerel, and again with red mullet. They can be filleted or left whole with only heads removed.

RIBA SA PAPRIKOM (Cod steaks with Paprika Sauce)

1 tablespoon olive oil, 1 pint chopped onion, ½ cup chopped tomato, 1 pint chopped green peppers, 2 cups chopped potato, 1 bay leaf, 6 black peppercorns, 12 oz. fillet of fish, 1 quart cold water, 3-4 lb. cod steaks, salt and pepper, 1½ teaspoons paprika, ½ oz. butter.

Heat the olive oil in a frying pan. Add onion. Fry until it begins to brown, then place in a large casserole. Add tomato, peppers, potato, bay leaf, peppercorns, and fish, then the water. Bring to simmering point. Cover and simmer gently until the contents are soft. Rub through a sieve into a large shallow saucepan, then measure. If the quantity is less than 1 pint, add enough water or stock to bring it up to that amount. Return to pan. Thoroughly rinse cod steaks. Place in pan. Add salt and pepper to taste, and paprika. Baste steaks with the purée. Melt butter. Sprinkle over the steaks. Cover closely. Simmer gently, basting once or twice, until cod is showing signs of coming away from the bone in about 30 minutes. Dish up steaks. Garnish round the edge with thick slices of boiled potato. Sprinkle potato with paprika. Garnish with sprigs of parsley.

YIELD: 6 servings.

DJUVEČ (Pilaff of Pork)

1 lb. onions, 1½ tablespoons lard, 6 or 7 green peppers, 1 chilli pepper if liked, 1 lb. pork, 2 or 3 potatoes, salt and pepper, 1 cup rice, ½ lb. tomatoes.

Slice onions. Melt the lard in a shallow saucepan. Add onion. Slit pepper and remove seeds. Cut peppers in slices and add to pan with chilli pepper if used. Fry slowly for 3 or 4 minutes, then add the pork, cut in small pieces. Peel and slice in potato. Season with salt and freshly ground black pepper. Cook for 2 or 3 minutes, then add the rice. Slice in the tomato. Stir till thoroughly blended, then transfer to a casserole. Bake in a moderate oven, 350 °F (Mark 3-4), for about 1½ hours. Serve, piled on a heated platter.

YIELD: 5 or 6 servings.

JAGNJEĆI ĆEVAP (Lamb Kebabs)

1 lb. lean boned lamb, olive oil as required, 1 tablespoon minced onion, 1 or 2 bay leaves, 1 large sliced onion, sliced firm tomatoes as required, salt and pepper.

Beat the meat with a meat bat, then cut into small squares. Pour the olive oil into a large shallow dish, just enough to cover base. Add chopped onion. Run pieces of lamb on skewers, alternately with a bay leaf, slice of onion and tomato. (If liked, add to each skewer a small piece of tender lamb's liver and kidney.) Season with salt and freshly ground black pepper. Grill under fierce heat, turning skewers frequently until meat is well cooked.

YIELD: 5 servings.

SRPSKA SVINSKA PEČENKA (A Serbian Way with Pork)

1 oz. butter or dripping, 2 tablespoons minced onion, 12 oz. minced pork, salt and pepper, 1 egg, 2 oz. breadcrumbs, 6 oz. rice, 4 seeded green peppers, 1 small tin tomato purée, ¼ pint cold water, ¼ pint sour milk.

Melt the fat in a shallow saucepan. Add onion. Fry slowly till soft. Stir in the meat, salt and freshly ground black pepper to taste, egg and breadcrumbs. Mix till thoroughly blended. Turn on to a board, covered with a sheet of greaseproof paper. Shape into an oblong loaf. Place on the centre of a large well-greased baking tin. Throw the rice into boiling salted water to cover. Boil for 10 minutes, then drain well. Place a layer of rice along either side of the loaf. Cut the peppers into thin slices. Cover rice with slices of pepper, then repeat layers of rice and pepper, making the last layer rice. Mix the tomato purée with the water and milk. Pour over the meat and rice. Cover with a sheet of greaseproof paper, then with a lid. Bake in a moderate oven, 350 °F (Mark 3-4), for about 45 minutes. When ready, cut loaf in slices, and arrange the slices, overlapping, on an oblong or oval heated platter. Surround with the rice and pepper slices. Dredge if liked with a little paprika.

YIELD: 3 or 4 servings.

PEČENI PUNJENI PLAVI PATLIDŽANI (Baked Stuffed Aubergine)

1 large sound aubergine, 3 or 4 ripe tomatoes, 1 teaspoon minced parsley, 1 tablespoon minced onion, salt and pepper, 2 tablespoons olive oil, 1 cup white stock.

Place aubergine in a saucepan. Cover with boiling water. Simmer for about 5 minutes, then drain and dry. Make 3 deep cuts lengthwise, equal distance apart, on one side. Peel and chop tomatoes. Mix the parsley with the onion, tomato, and salt and freshly ground black pepper to taste. Stuff this mixture into the cuts. Tie in place with strong cotton to prevent vegetable splitting while cooking. Place in a shallow fireproof dish. Mix the oil with the stock and pour over. Bake in a moderate oven, 350 °F (Mark 3-4), until tender in about 30 minutes, basting frequently with the oil and stock. Untie. Serve on a heated platter.

YIELD: 2 servings.

SOČIVO SALATA (Lentil Salad)

1 lb. lentils, water as required, 1 large clove garlic, ¼ teaspoon salt, ¼ teaspoon paprika, ¾ cup wine vinegar, ¾ cup olive oil, 1 crisp lettuce.

Rinse and soak the lentils in cold water to cover for 3 hours. Place in a saucepan. Add cold water to the depth of 2 inches above the lentils, then simmer for 3 hours until tender. Drain thoroughly and leave until quite cold. Peel, mince and bruise the garlic. Mix with salt and paprika, then stir into the vinegar. Add the oil. Stir vigorously until dressing is thoroughly blended. Toss the lentils in a cloth to dry and separate them, then place in the dressing. Stir well, then chill. Trim a large crisp lettuce and rinse thoroughly. Suspend from a hook until dry. Place in a salad bowl. Draw leaves apart to form a large cup. Pile lentils in the centre.

YIELD: 6 servings.

DROBLJENAC OD BRAŠMA (Lemon Batter Pudding)

4 separated eggs, 2 oz. castor sugar, ¾-1 pint milk, 8 oz. sifted flour, grated rind 1 lemon, pinch of salt, 3 oz. lard, sifted icing sugar as required.

Place egg yolks and sugar in a basin. Beat well, then stir in the milk, flour, lemon rind and salt. Beat well. Beat egg whites to a stiff froth. Fold into mixture. Heat the lard in a Yorkshire pudding tin. Pour in the batter. Bake in a moderately hot oven, 425 °F (Mark 6-7), for 20 minutes, then turn the pudding as you would a pancake. Continue to bake for 15 minutes until well browned on both sides. Remove from tin. Leave until cold. Break into small irregular pieces. Sprinkle with sifted icing sugar. Serve with fruit sauce.

YIELD: 6 servings.

OKRUGLJICE OD ŠLJIVA (Plum Dumplings)

1 lb. boiled potatoes, 3 oz. butter, 4 oz. flour, pinch of salt, 1 egg, 1 lb. plums, castor sugar to taste, 1-2 oz. breadcrumbs.

Sieve potatoes while still hot into a basin. Beat in 1 oz. of the butter, then the flour sifted with the salt. Stir in egg and enough ice-cold water to make a stiff dough. Knead till smooth. Turn on to a lightly floured board. Roll to ¼ inch thickness. Cut into 4 inch squares. Place a stoned plum on the centre of each square. Top with 1 teaspoon castor sugar. Brush edges of squares with cold water. Twist together to form a ball. Lower into rapidly boiling salted water. Cover and boil for 5 minutes. Melt remaining butter in a frying pan. Add to breadcrumbs. Fry till golden. Strain the dumplings. Place on a heated platter. Sprinkle with the fried crumbs.

YIELD: 6 servings.

PIRE OD VOĆA * (Fruit Purée)

2 lb. cooking apples, 2 tablespoons castor sugar, 1 pint cold water, 2-3 tablespoons potato flour.

Peel, core and slice apples into a rinsed saucepan. Cover and simmer gently, stirring frequently, until soft, then rub

* To make this sweet with cranberries or currants, follow the recipe as described, substituting the berries or currants for the apples.

through a sieve. Place purée in the saucepan with the sugar. Blend the potato flour with 1 cup of the water and stir very slowly into the apples and sugar. Stir over low heat until the sugar is dissolved, then stir to simmering point. Simmer for 2 or 3 minutes, stirring frequently, then turn into a bowl and leave until cool. Serve with cream.

YIELD: 4 or 5 servings.

JADRANSKE ŠTANGLE OD MEDA (Adriatic Honey Bars)

4 oz. flour, 3 oz. butter, 1 tablespoon water, 4 oz. cream cheese, 2 oz. extracted honey, 2 oz. castor sugar, ½ teaspoon ground cinnamon, 2 beaten eggs, castor sugar and ground cinnamon.

Sift flour into a basin. Rub in the butter. Mix to a paste with the water. Roll out and smoothly line a shallow greased oblong flat baking tin. Mix the cheese with the honey, sugar, cinnamon and eggs. Beat till blended. Spread over the pastry. Sprinkle the top with castor sugar, flavoured with ground cinnamon to taste. Bake in a moderate oven, 350 °F (Mark 3-4), for about 30 minutes. When nearly cold, cut into bars.

KOLAČ OD LEŠNIKA (Hazelnut Sponge Cake)

4 large eggs, 8 oz. castor sugar, 8 oz. ground hazelnuts, 8 oz. seedless raisins, 4 oz. flour, grated rind ½ lemon.

Place eggs and sugar in a basin. Lower into a saucepan of boiling water coming to within ½ inch of base. Beat mixture with a rotary beater until it thickens and turns a light yellow, then remove from over water. Fold in first the nuts, then the raisins. Sift and fold in the flour. Place in a greased cake tin, 7 inches in diameter, dredged with flour and lightly shaken to remove surplus. Bake in a moderate oven, 350 °F (Mark 3-4) until risen and lightly browned in 1¼-1½ hours. Stand for 10 minutes, then remove very carefully to a wire rack to cool.

KROFNE (Fried Yeast Buns)

½ oz. baker's yeast, ½ cup tepid milk, 2 oz. butter, 3 separated eggs, 12 oz. flour, ¼ teaspoon salt.

Mix the yeast in a heated basin with the milk. Stir till dissolved. Cover and stand in a warm place for 15 minutes. Beat butter till creamy. Beat in egg yolks, one at a time, then stir in the yeast. Beat egg whites to a stiff froth. Fold into mixture. Sift the flour with salt, then add to egg mixture, one cup at a time, stirring gently after addition until smoothly blended. Cover and stand in a warm place for 1 hour, then turn on to a lightly floured board. Roll into a round about ½ inch thick, then cut into rounds with a 2-2½ inch cutter. Stand in a warm place for 30 minutes to allow to rise again. Fry in deep hot fat until golden brown. Drain on absorbent paper. When cold, dredge with sifted icing sugar. These must be eaten on the day they are made.

YIELD: 3 dozen.

Logan's Gun

In the 1880s New Mexico was ruled by the law of the gun. Josh Logan and his pard, Randy, thought life was looking pretty rosy until John Dog Crandal and his gang of renegades attack their ranch, burn it to the ground and run off their herds of cattle and horses.

Logan straps on his Colt Lightning and swears revenge. When the down-and-out pair reach Peg Leg Fanny's whorehouse in Stinking Springs they bump into a boozy old pal, Paco Quinn, who offers them a lifeline running his stagecoach business.

But, apart from beating off murderous stage robbers, Logan has his hands full dealing with Quinn's crazy wife, Kate, who has the hots for him.

When John Dog Crandal and his thugs attack the Quinns' home the bullets fly fast and furious. Can Logan meet Crandal in single combat and, at the same time, deal with Kate's double-crossing treachery?

Logan's Gun

John Dyson

A Black Horse Western

ROBERT HALE · LONDON

© John Dyson 2008
First published in Great Britain 2008

ISBN 978-0-7090-8575-1

Robert Hale Limited
Clerkenwell House
Clerkenwell Green
London EC1R 0HT

www.halebooks.com

Typeset by
Derek Doyle & Associates, Shaw Heath
Printed and bound in Great Britain by
Antony Rowe Limited, Wiltshire

ONE

The air was sucked out of Logan's body as the stallion, Satan, kicked for the sky. One ... two ... three big bucks as the rancher hung on, one-handed, slapping his hat, whooping with excitement, daring the black beast to do his worst.

An older man by some thirty years, Randy Newbolt, chuckled as he watched, corral-side. 'I can still see too much daylight 'tween ya pants an' the saddle.'

Josh Logan gritted his teeth as the powerful brute went into a series of spins, frantic to get this thing off his back. When Satan's hoofs hit the deck it jarred every bone in Logan's body. The horse, however, seemed to sense that this time he wasn't going to win. Suddenly, he came to a halt and stood, eyes rolling, his sweat-flecked body shuddering.

'Steady,' Josh crooned, holding his bridle tight,

5

feeling the power of the stallion between his thighs. 'It ain' no use buckin'. You gotta learn who's boss.'

'Jeez!' Randy gave a whistle of awe. 'I think you finally got him tamed.'

'Yeah,' the rider murmured, easing Satan into a steady trot around the corral. 'He ain't gonna be no trouble no more.'

It was the triumphant conclusion to a long battle. They had trapped the stallion and his harem of wild mares and fillies in a box canyon out on the Staked Plains. A rope around his neck, they had dragged him back a hundred miles, the females following their leader, to this small ranch amid the bleak sage-blue scrapland on the eastern border of New Mexico.

The mares hadn't proved much trouble to tame, but Satan had struggled and kicked in a battle for supremacy that had gone on these past three days.

'I sure am tired of gittin' tossed back an' forth like a rag doll.' The tall, lean Texan eased himself down from the saddle and gentled the stallion's neck, soothing him. He took the harsh spade bit from Satan's mouth and set him free. 'You're gonna be OK now, boy.'

'Ain't he a proud beauty?' Randy opined, as the stallion skittered away. 'We'll git a hundred dollars fer him at Fort Stanton.'

Randy Newbolt had a face like hewn mahogany

beneath the wind-bent brim of his hat, which he rarely removed. When he did his bald cranium was as white as a hard-boiled egg. He appeared the archetypal frontiersman, with his walrus moustache, red bandanna, cross-over canvas shirt, and flapping batwing chaps. 'I was born in the saddle,' he would say to explain his bowed legs. 'That's where I like to be.'

He had teamed up with the young Texan on a cattle drive across parched lands and on up the Pecos. They had fought off Comanches, sided each other in troubles, and stuck together a long while. Tired of working for others, six months previously they had homesteaded this land along the rugged Alamosa Creek.

'I dunno about selling him,' Logan mused. 'He'd make me a fine saddle horse.'

Randy scratched at what hair he had straggling down from the back of his head and slapped his hat back on. 'That weren't the idee.'

'You ain't had to friggin' ride him. Three days battling has given me a bond with that critter. Don't gimme that look. All them mares and fillies'll be sure'n fetch twenty dollars each.'

Theirs was an easygoing partnership, but Newbolt generally deferred to the younger man. He was in awe of the fact that the young Texan could actually read and write and had a certain civilized charm. Whereas *his* only skills were of survival on the frontier.

'Suit yaself,' he said. 'You're the boss.'

'We're partners.' Logan grinned as he dusted down his faded denim shirt and jeans and ran fingers through his thick flaxen hair. 'But as I'm the one who does most of the work round here I get the bigger share of the vote.'

He ambled towards the ramshackle cabin they called home, jumped up on to the veranda, his boot spurs jingling, and waved towards a larger corral where they had 300 steers and calves rounded up and branded, all ready to move out. 'We'll get at least twelve dollars a head for them at the fort. Don't worry, pal, we ain't gonna starve.'

Randy took a notebook from his shirt pocket, licked a pencil stub and did some figuring. 'Hey, man,' he hooted. 'We could raise four thousand bucks. Can that be right?'

'I told ya there was money in ranching.' Josh eased himself down into an old cane chair and sought his cigarette makings. 'Maybe this time we'll recoup our losses.'

Since being paid off at the end of the cattle drive things hadn't gone too well. They had slogged at gold-mining up at White Oaks but were too late in the stampede to make much profit. They had tried driving stage for Quinn's new company. But a troublesome woman had put paid to that. Logan wanted to get right away, make a

8

success on his own, so he had suggested they try their own ranch. So, here they were, in the back of beyond.

'What wouldn't I give for a glass of cold beer,' he drawled. 'My throat's as dry as dust.'

'Ye'll have to wait 'til we git to Stinkin' Springs for that.' Randy had gone inside and poured them two tin mugs of hot coffee from the pot on the stove. 'This is all we gonna git 'til then.'

'Thanks.' Logan took the scalding mug of black brew. 'Ya know, pard, I got a feelin' this may be the start of something big. One of these days we're gonna be rich as Chisum. First light we'll get these longhorns moving. We'll get a good price from the colonel at the fort. Or at the Mescalero agency. In a week's time we'll be celebrating in Rosie's saloon at Lincoln with money to burn.'

How wrong, he thought afterwards, could a man be? For, as he put the coffee to his lips and squinted out into the flickering sunset, suddenly, about a mile away, on a ridge of sagebrush, a line of darkly silhouetted riders had appeared and were heading towards them, fast.

'What the hell does this bunch want?' he muttered, reaching to loosen the stud of his holster. He gripped the rosewood stock of his .38 calibre Colt Lightning. It was as if a black cloud had appeared to block his ambitions, for each of the riders had a rifle or carbine held in a threatening manner. A shiver of fear ran through him. 'I don't like the look of 'em.'

'Who *are* these dingbats?' Randy began to back into the cabin to grab his own long-barrelled Greener rifle.

'Who knows?' Logan said, as he got to his feet. 'They got the drop on us, that's fer sure.'

Their homestead, adjacent to the edge of the Staked Plains, gave them access to this vast table of grass that stretched for 300 miles down towards Mexico. On the north Texan side of the border lay some big ranches, the LX, the LIT, and others. Winter 'northers', checked by barely a single tree, drove remnants of their herds south-west across the plateau. At first Logan thought the men might be from one of these spreads. But his conscience was clear. The escaped longhorns bred and prolif-erated, and his stock consisted of previously unbranded young ones. Surely, such fellow-ranch-ers would have no grudge?

'These scum are bandits,' Randy gritted out, raising his rifle. 'Shall we let 'em have it?'

'Hold your fire.'

Closer and closer the dark horsemen came, charging towards them across the rocky terrain, until they swirled to a halt in a cloud of dust. There were about two dozen of them, hauled in about thirty paces from the cabin in a threatening line.

'OK, boys.' Logan tried to stay calm, for they

looked the kind who needed little excuse to shoot them down. 'What do you want?'

An evil-looking bunch, they were a mix of Mexicans in huge sombreros and range leathers, strung with *banderillos* of bullets, and shabby, hard-faced Americans, riff-raff of the frontier. They sat in grim silence.

'What do we want?' A muscularly built man, obviously their leader, nudged his mustang forward a few paces. A worn buckskin jacket hung from his big shoulders, open to reveal a once red, now faded woollen vest. A thick gold necklace hung around his neck. A battered hat was slung over his back, and black hair flowed to his shoulders around the coppery planes of a harsh face. This split into a sneering grin. 'What the hell you think we want?' He rubbed thumb and finger together. 'Dollars. Pesos. Cash.'

'You're outa luck, pal,' Randy hooted, aiming the Greener at him. 'Ye've picked the wrong chickens to pluck. We're broke. On our uppers. Penniless. You savvy? So you better git outa here fast.'

The stranger waved his carbine at the nearby corrals of horses and cows. 'You got stock. So you musta got cash.'

'Nope.' The tall Texan's pale-blue eyes glimmered beneath the shadow of his hat brim. 'We sunk all we had into buying this homestead. Those cattle and horses we've brought in outa the wild. This is the Leanin' Ladder ranch. They got our brand. So touch them at your peril, mister.'

'Touch them at our *peril?*' The big man gave a hoot of laughter. 'You don't seem to understand, my friend. I am here to offer you protection from the *bandidos* who roam these wilds. You pay us. We protect you. Your first payment will be all this stock. You go back to work and next time we might not be so hard.'

'Ye're joking,' Randy hooted. 'We've worked our butts off to raise this stock. You lazy good-fer-nothings can git lost.'

'So, you don't want to co-operate with my business proposition?' The *jefe* grinned at them. 'You want a fight? An unwise decision, my friends.' He raised an arm, indicating the line of rifles and carbines, their deadly mouths aimed at them, their owners waiting the order to fire. 'What's it to be?'

'You'll go first,' Randy threatened, cocking the Greener's hammer. 'Ye'll be knocking at the gates of hell.'

'Maybe. But I suggest it would be wiser if you just toss your weapons off the porch down into the dust here in front of me. In fact, we'll give ya to the count of ten.'

'It ain' no use,' Logan whispered. He carefully removed his Lightning from the holster and threw it forward. 'They got us hogtied, Randy.'

12

He tried to memorize the line of faces for future reference. That's if he was to have any future, which at that moment seemed highly unlikely. Then the leader's dark features struck a chord with him.

'Crandal,' he said. 'I remember you. John Dog Crandal. The murdering spawn of a Fort Worth whore. Raised in her own thievin' ways. The Rangers ran you outa Texas. So this is where you got to?'

'You shut your mouth,' one of the men growled. 'Shall I kill him, John Dog?'

'No, he's right.' Crandal's gold teeth flashed. 'I sure am one hundred per cent sonuvabitch. My mama was a pig. But, believe me mister, I'm a real swine.'

Suddenly a noose came spinning from one of his sidekicks dropping neatly over Logan's shoulders, whipcord tight, and he was hoisted from his porch to sprawl in the dust. 'Shall we hang him, John Dog?'

'No,' Crandal shouted. 'Give him the chicken run.'

Before Randy could fire in protest Crandal's carbine barked out and Newbolt recoiled, dropping his Greener, clutching his bleeding right arm.

'Aw, hail,' the older man groaned. 'You lousy snakes.'

He watched as his friend was dragged away

13

through the dust, rocks and scrub at a gallop on a tour at ground level of his homestead. When the rider came charging back he saw the strained look on the bloody face of Logan as he gripped the rawhide rope trying to ride the bumps and bounces.

'OK, that's enough,' John Dog shouted. 'We don't want to kill him, do we? Maybe these two fools have learned their lesson. Next time we call they should be more co-operative. Maybe then we will let them keep half of their stock. But this time we take it all.'

'Yee-hagh!' A boot thudded into Logan's ribs and a voice drawled, as his wallet was ripped from his back pocket. 'You hear that, pal?'

'Hey, thassall I got,' Randy protested, as he too was pummelled by two Mexicans, who leapt on to the porch and snatched his billfold from his shirt. He tried to swing a haymaker with his good arm, but a carbine smashed into his jaw and he fell to his knees. 'Now look what you done,' he wailed, as he spat out blood and a tooth.

'A few lousy dollars,' John Dog said, counting the proceeds. 'Fourteen sixty, in fact. We're wasting our time with these losers. What's in the cabin?'

'Nuthin' worth havin',' another Mexican grinned. 'A nice big can of kerosene, John Dog. Should make a tidy blaze.'

14

'Aw, come on, boys, be sports,' Randy groaned. 'Leave us the cabin. We ain't done nuthin' to you.'

'This'll be a lesson for you,' Crandal said. 'Next time you pay cash.'

'Are you joking?' Bloody and bruised, Logan staggered to his feet to face him. 'You scum of the earth won't get another nickel from me, so I wouldn't count on it. You leave them hosses and cattle where they are or it's you who'll pay. I'm warning *you*, Crandal.'

'He sure is lippy, John Dog,' one of his gang yelled, kicking Logan again. 'Shall we break his arms for him, make him see sense?'

'No, not yet. He jest don't understand.' John Dog smiled, magnanimously. 'Listen hard, you two no-accounts. We are offering all the ranchers around here protection. The smaller ones, that is. You pay up and we let you operate in peace. You don't.' He snapped his fingers 'Pouf!'

'Yeah, pouf to you, too, pal,' Randy jeered.

'You listen to me,' Josh Logan gritted out. 'I've told you once. I'll tell you twice. You won't get a cent more outa me. I'm not a man who changes his mind.'

'All right, boys,' Crandal shouted, 'get them longhorns and hosses outa the corrals. There'll be a full moon tonight. It'll be as easy as taking candy from a baby to drive 'em down the crik. Should make a tidy price.'

Yipping and hallooing the gang rode away, kicking down the makeshift corral, herding the cattle out in a bellowing billow of dust, and heading away through Alamosa Creek.

Logan watched them go, watched bitterly as a lariat went spinning over Satan's head, and, biting, kicking, and whinnying he was dragged away after the gang followed by the mares and foals.

John Dog had remained with half a dozen of his swarthy Mexican *compadres* to keep them covered. '*Muchas gracias* for your co-operation, *señors*,' he mockingly called, producing a stick of dynamite from his saddle-bag. He struck a match on his nail and lit the fuse, brandishing it to set it sparking and hissing. 'Let's git outa here, boys.'

His men jeered and hooted, but quickly hauled on their reins, whipping their mounts away. They knew how crazy John Dog Crandal was. The gunman grinned and hurled the dynamite at the cabin.

Josh grabbed hold of Randy by his shirt, pulled him from the veranda and went with him, rolling across the dirt. Then he got to his feet and dragged his partner on with him, to dive for the cover of a horse trough.

Whoompf! The kerosene fed the almighty blast, flames shooting into the air. The heat and power hit them as they ducked down, shielding their faces. Parts of cabin planks which they had labori-

16

ously hauled from the sawmill to their chosen site showered down about them. The roaring flames died down a bit, but when the two men took a peek there was little to be seen of their cabin or camp except smouldering remains.

'Just look at that burn,' Randy mumbled. 'All that hard work gone to waste.'

'Yeah.' Logan got to his feet. 'That's another get-rich-quick scheme come to an end. You OK?'

'Yeah.' Randy examined his arm wound. 'Ain't nuthin' to worry about.'

'Yep. At least they didn't kill us. We gotta count small mercies.' Josh picked up his Stetson, dusted himself down. 'Just as well we hitched the saddle hosses up along the valley to graze. We won't have to walk back to town.'

'True. But I'm beginning to wonder if I did right ridin' along of you. It's started to strike me you're jinxed, Logan.'

'It's this territory that's jinxed. It's time honest folk started to fight back.'

TWO

The notorious outlaw, Billy Bonney, might have been gunned down there the previous summer, but Fort Sumner was still the haunt of criminals in 1882. Abandoned by the military in '68 it had been bought by the Maxwell family. They had been joined there not only by law-abiding Mexican sheepherders, but a ripe selection of bandits, traders, whoremongers, gamblers, whiskey-peddlers, and hardcore fugitives.

John Chisum still ruled his cattle empire, the biggest on the Pecos. Settlers were recovering from the internecine feuding of the Lincoln County War. But it had not brought an end to the shootings. Rustlers found a ready market for their stolen beeves.

The nationwide publicity given to the Kid had stirred many a young rowdy to emulate his pistol-spinning deeds. The proliferation of weapons, the thirst for whiskey, the arrival on the new railroad to Las Vegas of criminals on the lam from Eastern law-enforcement agencies, made New Mexico a hotbed of crime. Many drifted a hundred miles down the Pecos to the rumbustious fort. Lawmen were reluctant to visit or interfere, for the violence of the gun still ruled this wild land.

'How's y'arm?' Josh Logan enquired of Randy Newbolt as they saddled their broncs in the early dawn beside the still smouldering ashes of their cabin.

'Buzzin'. But it ain' no worse than I've had afore.' Randy had washed the flesh wound in a horse trough and bound it tight with his sweaty bandanna. 'If there'd been half a dozen, you an' me could've taken 'em, but a score is too many for two men.'

'Yep.' Josh had found his Colt Lightning amid the rubble and stuck it back in his holster. 'Maybe there'll be a reckoning one day. What riles me is the thought of Satan. He'll suffer under whip and spur and other tortures men call breaking a critter. He'll turn bad, that's fer sure. I'd jest reached some kinda bond with that horse.'

'You know, I think you're right. All those bastards will do is turn him outlaw. Let's hope he kicks the daylights outa one or two.'

It was a fifteen-mile ride down Alamosa Creek to

19

the nearest outpost of so-called civilization, Stinking Springs, a smattering of ruddy adobes and narrow lanes at the apex of three streams. Originally a Mexican outpost, it had been invaded by a few wandering Americans hoping to make money selling goods, women and whiskey to the cowboys of the Wilcox-Brazil and Yerby ranches.

But it looked much as it was described by one Eastern traveller: 'the dirtiest and filthiest place I have yet visited. The people lack life and energy. The most industrious creatures are the hogs rooting day and night around the houses, creating an intolerable noise and stench.'

'Gawd!' Randy moaned, as they loped in. 'It sure is aptly named! Stinkin' Springs. You can say that agin.'

They let their broncs sup at a filthy waterhole and wandered over to the general store. Amos Adams was leaning on his counter staring into space. 'Give you a loan? You must be crazy. Those gunmen descended on me like a cloud of locusts. Cleaned me out. Food, clothing, boots, barley-sugars. Just helped 'emselves to anything they fancied and rifled my cash drawer.'

It was the same in the cantina run by Manuel Lopez. The cattle and horses had left their calling-cards in the street and so had their herders in his bar. It was wrecked. Tables, chairs overturned, bottles smashed. 'Si', they had high old time. They say unless I pay they be back to do the same again. No, forgive me, *señors*, I cannot give you credit. I have my family to feed.'

One of the Yerby cowboys swaggered into the cantina, unsteady on his legs. 'You'll find the action along in Peg Leg Fanny's place. They missed her!' he yelled, pointing down a lane. 'Knock three times. But she don't open up to nobody she don't like the look of.'

Randy's nose was twitching as the scent of liquor led them towards the establishment. It was just a plain adobe block, with shuttered windows and a locked iron door facing on to the street. Round the back was another door with a small iron grille. Muffled sounds of voices and music wafted through. Logan hammered three times with the butt of his revolver. No response. He tried again. *Bang, bang, bang!*

Two red-rimmed eyes about a rosily veined nose beneath a tangle of grey hair peered out. 'You with that mob who passed through early on?'

'No.'

'You lawmen?'

'Who us? No way.'

'Come on in.'

The door was unlocked and a scrawny woman puffing on a curved pipe admitted them. They were hit by a blast of noise from a room jam-packed with humanity. A black banjoist in a checked suit and bow tie was plucking his strings, two doxies were screaming with excitement, and cowboys were lined up along a makeshift bar, or crowded around a roulette table. Most had tankards of beer or whiskey in their paws and some looked like they might have been there from the night before.

Fanny shoved through them, her peg leg making her hip swivel beneath her long grey dress. She went behind the bar and shouted to them above the din,' What's it to be, gents?'

Logan disliked asking favours, but needs must. He stroked his unshaven jaw, leaned over the plank counter and beckoned her closer. 'It's like this,' he said. 'We're down on our luck. To tell the truth, we've been robbed. Lost everything.'

'Aw, no,' the lady wailed. 'Not another coupla deadbeats. Mister, I've had enough of panhandlers. Do I look like a soft touch? On your way. Git outa here. Beat it.'

'My pal here's purty handy with a dishmop. You got an axe I'll split logs. All we want is a pint of whiskey and a plate of supper.'

Peg Leg Fanny assessed him. 'OK, git out in the yard. I'll call you when you've done enough. Here, you.' She tossed an apron at Randy. 'Put that on. Clear the tables. Get them plates washed.'

Two hours passed before she decreed that they had done enough. In her cramped back kitchen

22

she slopped out venison stew and potatoes into wooden bowls. They filled their bellies and returned to the crowded bar. Peg Leg plonked two large clay pots of home-brewed liquor on the counter. 'Don't hang around long,' she ordered. 'You're occupying valuable space.'

'You're an angel, madam,' Randy crooned. 'A drop of the prairie lightning I bin dreamin' of.'

But when he took a glug he shook his bald head like a stunned dog. 'Hay-zoose!'he cried. 'It blows your damn head off.'

Josh treated it more circumspectly. 'Kicks like a mule. But who's complaining?'

Due to the low ceiling he had to stoop his shoulders, but his eyes lingered on a young brunette perched on a stool at the roulette table. She was attired in the modest manner of the times in a long dress of green silk, pinned by a cameo brooch at the throat. Her cheeks had a natural bloom and needed no powder and rouge, but her full lips were painted crimson and from them drooped a cigarette. 'Place your bets, gents,' she called, as she scooped piles of coloured chips towards her and set the wheel spinning again. As the ivory ball scampered around to its final slot she sang out, 'Twenty-six. *Vingt-six*.'

Glancing around she met Logan's pale-blue eyes and for moments her own dark ones sparkled, warmly, in the candlelight glow. But she quickly returned her attention to her customers. 'Here we go, gents. Who's gonna hit lucky tonight?

Maybe, Logan thought, with his unshaven jowls, scratches, cuts, dusty and bloodstained garb, his hair badly in need of a cut, he didn't look a very promising proposition. Or maybe she didn't hobnob with the clientele. She had a remarkably innocent, well-scrubbed look for a girl of her profession. But appearances could be deceptive.

'Ain't no point you fallin' for them pair of laughing eyes,' Randy butted in, reading his thoughts. 'We're broke. You need plenty in your poke to afford that hussy.'

There was a clamour and commotion from the far end of the adobe shack. Through the throng, Logan glimpsed a strongly built man, his three-piece suit tucked into tall boots, whirling one of the *nymphes-de-prairie* in an exaggerated waltz. He was bumping drunkenly into other men spilling their drinks, and it looked like a brawl was about to begin.

'Aw, no,' Josh growled. 'Quinn! Why did we have to bump into him?'

'If there's trouble,' Randy grinned, 'Quinn's bound to be there.'

Quinn had handsome, if brutal, Mexican looks. His black hair flopped over his brow as he pushed men aside like skittles, roaring, 'Git outa my path.' He waltzed with great abandon their way. Suddenly

24

he saw them and abruptly dropped the dance girl. He staggered forward to slap both hands to the Texan's shoulders, hugging him. 'Josh Logan!'

'That's me. See you're still fond of the ladies and the liquor, Quinn.'

'So, you ain't? Come on, have a drink.'

'Nope,' Logan protested. 'We're just leaving.'

'What? Don't talk crazy. You wouldn't refuse a drink with an ol' *compañero*.' He hauled them both to the bar. 'Gimme a bottle, Peg Leg.'

'How about me, sweetie?' The goodtime gal's chubby face was perspiring freely under its coating of paint. 'You owe me.'

'Aw, git lost.' Quinn shoved a hand into her face. 'This is my old pal, Josh. I ain't seen him in six months. Why'd ya walk out like that, Josh, without even a goodbye?'

'Bottoms up.' Randy hastily filled his tumbler from the bottle. 'I gotta tell ya, Quinn, we cain't buy ya one back.'

'I don't expect you to buy me one,' Quinn yelled. He tossed greenbacks at the beseeching girl. 'I'm loaded. See?'

'What he means is we're temporarily outa funds. The fact is we got robbed at our ranch by a miserable gang of toerags led by John Dog Crandal. He took our hosses, our cows, our last few dollars. Cleaned us out.'

'Crandal?' Quinn suddenly seemed to sober up.

'What did he want?'

'Cash for protection,' Josh scowled. 'When I told him I didn't have nuthin', nor would I give it him if I had, he blew us to smithereens.'

'Dynamite? Yeah, that's Crandal. A little trick of his. Well, at least you stood up to him. Good for you, pal.' Quinn slapped his shoulder and mock-punched him. 'That's the way to deal with Crandal. So, you're stony-broke? Well, that's a laugh. You shoulda stayed with me. I've hit it rich.'

'I'm glad to hear it, Quinn. You allus was a lucky sonuvagun.'

'Yeah,' Quinn growled in his racous voice, still hanging on to Josh, waving the bottle of liquor about. 'I'm loaded. That stage agency we started, I've got the gov'ment contract for the mail. Big income, believe me. Me an' the governor, the state governor at Santa Fe, we're like that.' He grinned widely, holding up two intertwined fingers. 'They're all on the take.'

'You don't say?' Logan shrugged off his arm and took a quaff of the whiskey. 'Kate still with you?'

'Of course she's still with me. Why shouldn't she be? I've bought into a gold mine up at White Oaks. A third interest. Boy, I cain't stop making money. Kate's living like a lady. You should see our new spread. You shoulda stayed with us.'

'Yep. Maybe.' The last time Logan had seen Kate she had been naked beneath him in Quinn's mari-

26

tal bed while he was away in Las Vegas. When he told her he'd had enough, he couldn't go on like that, she had started spittin' and snarling threats like a wild cat.

'I prefer to be my own boss. We gotta be gettin' along now, Quinn.'

'Don't be stupid. You ain't goin' nowhere. You're down and out. Where else you gonna go?'

'We'll get by. Somethang'll turn up.'

'You're coming back with me, *amigo*. No argument. Kate will love to see you. I need you, Josh. I need a good right-hand man I can trust. Tell him, Randy. He can't turn down a chance like this.'

Newbolt shrugged uncomfortably. He was more aware than Quinn, it seemed, of Kate's carryings-on. He glanced at Logan. 'He's the boss. But we could sure do with a leg-up.'

'I've told you,' Logan insisted. 'I like to work for myself.'

'I'll make you a partner. Look, pal' – Quinn pulled a fat wallet from his inside pocket, brandished it under Josh's nose, ruffling a thumb across a wad of notes – 'with you alongside us we can't fail. We need a man who knows what he's doing, a good head on his shoulders, who ain't afraid of hard work. You can run the stage line all on your own.'

Logan noticed a couple of rough *hombres* watching them through the fug of tobacco smoke. 'Put that away, Quinn. You shouldn't flash your cash. It ain't wise. Good to see ya. We'll be on our way now.'

'Allus movin' on,' Quinn roared, hanging on to him. 'You know why you never get anywhere? You're a born drifter. You got the wanderlust. You'll never be a winner like me.'

Logan broke his grip, tossing him away. 'Take it easy on the juice, Quinn. You've had too much. So long.'

'Yeah, go and sleep under a damn cactus amid the ants and pariah dogs, you loser,' Quinn slurred. 'Thass where you belong.'

'Come on, Randy,' Logan said. 'Let's git outa here.'

It was already getting dark outside. 'We musta been in there longer than I thought.'

'Well, where *are* we gonna sleep?' Randy asked. 'He's got a point.'

'We'll mosey on down the Pecos. Chisum's allus lookin' fer hired hands.'

'What, for thirty a month? Put your life on the line?'

Logan stood at the end of the alley, hesitating, deep in thought, stroking his jaw.

'You having second thoughts?'

'Nope,' he smiled. 'I'm thinking of that li'l croupier gal. I didn't say goodbye.'

'So? You didn't say hello, either.'

28

'There was somethang about that gal . . .'

'Aw, Logan, don't go gettin' romantic notions. She's just a whore.'

'Yeah, I guess.'

They were about to turn away when they saw Quinn lurch out of Fanny's and stagger away along the alley in the opposite direction, hanging on to the wall to steady himself.

'He's sure had a skinful.'

But then the shadowy shapes of two men emerged from the booze joint and followed him. One was swinging what looked like a sock full of lead shot. . . .

Sure enough, they set about the stage owner, one buffaloing him across the back of the neck with the butt of a revolver. Quinn roared defiance and swung at them, but the other footpad's weapon caught him across the temple, knocking him to the floor. They hammered blows into him, pinning him down.

'Hey.' Logan set off at a run, followed by Randy. He caught the sock-swinger by the shoulder as he struggled to get Quinn's wallet, and smashed a hard right into his face. His nose split like a ripe tomato. Logan's left hammered into his ribs and he followed up with another straight right to the jaw. Meanwhile Randy was piling into the other thief, twisting his gun from his grasp.

The mughunters stared at them with horror.

Then took to their heels. 'Yeah, you better run, pal,' Logan shouted.

Randy kneeled beside Quinn, examining a bloody gash at the base of his skull. 'He don't look too good,' he said. Quinn groaned, rolling over, looking up at them. 'Josh, where did you come from? Did they get my cash?'

'No, I got it here.'

'Thanks, Josh,' Quinn mumbled. 'I knew you wouldn't run out on me this time.' He tried to get up but collapsed, falling back, seemingly unconscious. A nasty patch of blood was pooling under his head.

'I'll see if Peg Leg Fanny's got a bowl of water and a bandage,' Randy said.

'Yeah?' Logan stared at Quinn. 'I ain't so sure he ain't just dead drunk.'

There was a bit of a commotion as rubbernecking cowboys came from the drinking joint to take a look. 'Damn fool was asking for trouble,' Fanny said, examining the wallet. 'Carrying this wad around. Which reminds me' – her slick fingers deftly extracted several dollar bills – 'he didn't settle up with me.'

The croupier girl was kneeling, washing the blood away. 'He ought to have stitches in this cut,' she said.

'Just bandage him up, Dawn,' Peg Leg curtly replied. 'He's got a two-horse rig down in the square. We'll put him in it.'

'How's he going to get home?' the girl asked.

Logan had an overwhelming desire to stroke her soft, dark waves of hair as she knelt knee-height. What's a gal like you doing in a place like this? he wanted to ask. But knew it would be a foolish, hackneyed question. Instead, he felt an urge to make a crazy, noble gesture to impress her. 'I'll take him back,' he said.

The croupier girl turned her black, soulful eyes up to him. 'Mr Quinn's lucky he's got a good friend like you.'

He put an arm around her waist as she rose to her feet and for moments she faced him, intimately. 'Aw, it's the least we can do. He's an old pal. The handle's Josh Logan,' he drawled, offering his hand. 'Maybe we'll meet again.'

She met his eyes with a quizzical smile, as he gently caressed her palm. 'Dawn Adamson,' she said. 'Who knows? Perhaps we will.'

'Hey,' Peg Leg Fanny snapped. 'Come on, gals. Everybody back inside. I'm losing business. They'll take care of him.'

'Hey, hang on. Where's he live?' called Logan.

'Down at Roswell,' Fanny sang out. 'It's only a forty-mile drive. You should be there by dawn.'

'Shee-it!' Randy gave an exasperated sigh when they were alone. 'What you playing the good Samaritan fer? I thought you didn't want nuthin' to do with him.'

Logan shrugged. 'We cain't just leave him here.'
He didn't notice Quinn open one eye, give a smile
of catlike satisfaction, and close it again.

'Gimme a hand to hoist him up, Randy. He's a
dead weight.'

A full moon had risen high by the time they
reached the Pecos and it was plain from the deep
rutted prints of cloven hoofs in the river mud that
their stolen cattle had been herded north towards
old Fort Sumner. There was little point in following. What could two men do against twenty *viciosos*
in that outpost of outlaws? In his mind Logan
vowed vengeance one day, but he would have to
work out just how to wreak it.

Anyways, they needed to turn south, downriver,
to deliver their passenger, Quinn. This was true
cattle country, carpeted with grama grass as far as
the eye could see, the Pecos plains shimmering in
the moonlight. This was the domain of John
Chisum who had arrived from Texas in '67 trailing
a herd of longhorns. Now his stock had multiplied
to 80,000 head and ranged for 150 miles down
towards the Texas line. Interlopers on to these
public lands were not welcome. But they came,
anyway, often with violent results.

The little community of Roswell was an oasis in
the heart of the plains at the meeting of the Pecos
and the Rio Hondo which flowed down from the

dark mass of mountains to the west where the Apaches lurked, through the small township of Lincoln to Roswell. There it was joined by two spring streams. The resulting network of life-giving *acequias* nourished cornfields, fruit orchards and shady cottonwoods.

'Quinn's sure found himself a swell place to have a house,' Randy remarked as they surveyed the settlement under the dawn light. 'This guy musta been born under a lucky star.'

'Yeah,' Logan grunted, non-commitally, as they hauled Quinn into his luxurious – for those parts – residence. 'Let's dump him here.'

THREE

'Say, look what the cat's brought in!'

Logan wasn't sure whether she was referring to him or Quinn. 'Hi, Kate. He's got a bit of a bad head.'

'I bet he has.'

'No,' Randy explained. 'He got jumped in an alley. Lost a lot of blood. He's been out cold on the back of the rig all night. Better put a blanket over him.'

'What, mollycuddle the hard head?' She went across, grabbed Quinn by his thick black hair, twisted his head and took a look at the cut. 'Too bad they didn't make a better job of it. What you two looking for – a reward?'

'Nope, we ain't lookin' fer nuthin',' Logan replied, angrily.

She was a woman older than he but well-preserved, slim, high-browed, with an arrogant

34

sort of beauty. Her auburn hair was coiffed and curled, and she wore a white silk blouse, a split leather riding-skirt, and neat boots on her shapely legs. She tossed Quinn's head away with a fastidious sniff of her neat nostrils. 'Get a whiff of the whiskey.'

Suddenly her husband came back to life with a roar like a mountain lion. He grabbed her backside and pulled her to him. 'Gimme a kiss, darlin'. Ain'tcha missed me?'

'Like a hole in the head.' She fought away from his rough clutches. 'Stay where y'are. I guess I gotta dose you with black coffee.'

'Look who's here. Josh Logan. And ol' Randy. Ain'tcha pleased I brought 'em back? Get some vittles on, woman. These boys are starvin'. Where's your hospitality? They saved my life. Saved my wallet. Saved my bacon.'

'You don't say?' Kate eyed him sardonically. 'What am I s'posed to play? The devoted li'l wife waiting at home while you go out whoring?'

'I mighta downed some whiskey last night,' Quinn shouted, hoisting himself out of the rocker. 'But I swear to you I never looked at another woman. Never have. Why should I when I got a woman like you?'

He started stumbling about, clattering a frying-pan, knocking over a can of milk. 'Come on, boys, I'm gonna make you coffee and breakfast. Where's the eggs? Where you keep stuff in this house?'

'Oh, get out of the way, I'll do it.' She avoided his embrace, pushing him away. 'You cause more trouble than you're worth.'

'Yeah, she didn't say that when I bought her that magnificent white thoroughbred for her birthday.' Quinn winked at them and sat down at the table. 'Oh, no, she was mighty grateful that night, I can tell you. She ain't allus like this. A very loving lady is my wife, Kate. Sit down, boys, relax.'

Logan sighed but did as he was bid. 'All we did was bring you home, Quinn. I ain't planning on stayin'.'

'Come on, partner. Don't start that again,' the Mexican growled. 'I need you to run the stage line. I'm too busy up at the mine. To tell the truth I've been having trouble from Crandal, too. I need a coupla guys like you who ain't scared of him.'

'Now he tells us,' Randy exclaimed. 'Mighta known there was a catch to it.'

'Come on.' Quinn caught Logan's arm. 'Some of us have gotta stand up to the likes of him. We can't allow 'em to run us out of the territory. Tell Josh, Kate. We need him.'

'Speak for yourself.' She gave a downturned grimace as she broke eggs into a pan. 'Me, I don't need any man.'

'Come off it,' Quinn shouted. 'You know you were cut up when he walked out on us. You were like a bear with a sore head moping about for days. Tell him all's forgiven, he's welcome back, Kate.'

'Is that what you really want?' She turned to her husband and met his dark, smouldering eyes. Then Logan's more pacific-blue ones, and gave a scoffing smile. 'Welcome back, Josh yoo-ah!'

Quinn made a remarkable recovery and, after breakfast, proudly showed them how the *casa* had been converted from a terrace of three sturdy adobes. There were his work office, his gun racks, his billiards den, the dining-room with polished table and leather upholstered chairs, and he gave a throaty guffaw as he led them into the master bedroom. 'This is where the action happens!'

'Yeah,' Logan drawled, swallowing bile as he glanced at the satin-covered bed. He was already wishing he hadn't agreed to stay.

He turned to meet Kate's twinkling eyes as she leaned against the doorway. 'What's the big lunk bragging about now?' she asked.

'Guess,' he growled, as the heavy odour of the French perfume she favoured reminded him of times past. He squeezed past her and was shown the stables, outhouses and fields where Quinn's Mexicans laboured. Quinn kicked open the door of a dark, musty shack and said, 'Here's where you two can bunk.'

'Well, thanks,' Randy replied, not without sarcasm, 'but afore we settle in hadn't you better

37

tell us just what you're expecting and how much we git paid?'

'Plenty of time for that. All I want is for you two to run the stage service from the White Oaks mines down through Lincoln to here, then north to Las Vegas. Then back again. The stage and hosses are at White Oaks. We'll ride up and you can get started.'

'What about your regular driver?' Logan asked.

'He walked out on me,' Quinn muttered. 'Just like you. You can't trust nobody these days.'

'*Why* did he walk out?' Josh asked. 'That's what I'd like to know.'

'Aw, he had a bit of trouble from stage robbers. Nuthin' you two cain't handle?'

'You think?' Logan grunted. 'What makes you so sure of that?'

'Because you're good guys,' Quinn roared, swinging his arms around their shoulders and hugging them. 'Here, you need some spending money?' He dug out his wallet, stuffed twenty dollars each into their hands. 'We'll work out the details later.'

'What about the so-called partnership you were tellin' me about?' Logan pressed.

'Doncha worry, Josh. I'll discuss that with Kate. Then we'll go see a lawyer, have it drawn up nice and legal.'

Suddenly Kate burst out of the stable aboard a

fine spirited grey mare. 'Ain't you boys ready to head for Lincoln yet? I'm gonna give Blanche a gallop. You can catch up with me.'

She went careering away, heading out of the homestead and up along the bank of the Hondo, kicking up dust.

Quinn watched her go. 'That woman of mine's crazy,' he laughed. 'Come on, boys, we'd better git after her.'

'Aw, no, we been driving your rig all night,' Randy groaned. 'When we gonna have us some shut-eye?'

'There ain't much time for sleep when Kate an' Quinn are around,' Logan said, as they ambled away to unhitch their saddle broncs. 'Now maybe you see why I wasn't so eager to return to these fireworks.'

'Cheer up, pardner.' Randy gave a whoop of glee as he swung into his saddle. 'Jest think what we can do with twenty dollars each in Lincoln.'

'You can fergit the wine an' women,' Josh hollered as he rode after him. 'Quinn's expectin' us to drive his damn stage two hundred and fifty miles to Las Vegas. What fer? Peanuts? I don't trust him. Nor that two-timin' wife of his.'

When they reached Lincoln after a fifty-mile ride Quinn booked himself and Kate into the best front room at the Wortley Hotel. Randy and Logan shared a smaller room at the back. They dined together, but in a subdued way, Quinn still suffering either from the crack to his head or a heavy hangover. Logan stayed cool and non-commital to them both. About ten o'clock. Quinn said he was turning in and lurched off upstairs. Kate decided she wanted to take a look at the stars, get a breath of fresh air out on the veranda. There was no mistaking that come-hither look as she stepped out into the night.

'I ain't dancing to her tune no more,' Logan muttered. 'Come on, pal, let's git some sleep. I wanna find the sheriff in the morning 'fore we head out.'

FOUR

'So you lost some cattle and hosses?' Pat Garrett looked a bit of a dude in his four-button brown tweed suit, celluloid collar and tie, as he lounged in his swivel-chair, long legs up on his desk. 'What you expect me to do about it?'

'You're sheriff of Lincoln County, ain'tcha?' Logan said. 'I'm registering a formal complaint. Or do you only look after them who pay you well, like John Chisum?'

Garrett gave a scoffing laugh, his green eyes twinkling, but there was a vicious twist to his thin lips beneath his moustache. 'You got any proof the stock was yourn? Or did you come by it in the usual manner?'

'Our proof was the brands on those critters,' Randy howled at him. 'Our brand, the Leaning Ladder outfit. John Dog Crandal and that scum he rides with stole 'em from under our noses.'

41

'Anybody killed?'

'Nope,' Josh drawled. 'They got the drop on us.'

'In that case there ain't much I can do. For a start, I never heard of the Leaning Ladder. And for second, I'm too damn busy. I got more important things to do.' The former buffalo hunter stood and stretched, at six feet four towering over Randy, and four inches taller than Logan, too. 'Time for my morning tipple.'

Garrett had been living on his laurels as the killer of Billy the Kid the previous summer, albeit he had ambushed him in a darkened room at Fort Sumner.

'I got news for you, Garrett,' Josh drawled. 'You got an even worse band than the Kid's on your hands now. Crandal and his thugs.'

'The name does ring a bell,' Garrett said with a grin. 'But we've no reports of killings by him in this territory. Killings are what I'm interested in.'

'And reward money?'

Garrett reached for his hat. 'I got an election coming up. I ain't got time for your worries. Crandal's just small fry to me.'

'Mighta known that'd be all the help we would get,' Logan muttered, unhitching his pinto. 'We better git movin', Randy. They're waiting.'

The Quinns were coming from the Wortley Hotel, looking across the road at them as they mounted their own horses.

42

'You boys working for Quinn?' Garrett asked.

'Nope, we're partners,' Randy put in. 'We're reorganizing the stage line.'

'Best of luck to you,' Garrett smiled. 'Tell you what, boys, I could swear you in as deputies, then you could legally gun down this Crandal if you cross paths again. That's iffen he don't kill you first.'

'No thanks,' Logan gritted out. 'We've got enough on our hands driving the damn stage.'

Garret gave a hoarse laugh. 'Well, don't expect me to do your killing for you.'

'I won't,' Logan replied.

They had to ride another forty-five miles by wagon road, which wound up into the mountains beneath the flat hump of the 3,000-feet El Capitan peak, before they reached the bustling mining camp.

White Oaks had boomed after gold was discovered there in 1869. Pitch-roofed cabins climbed up the mountainsides and the town's ten saloons and gambling houses vibrated with life day and night.

As soon as they arrived in the late afternoon Quinn strode off to attend to his mining interests, while Josh and Randy took a look at the sturdy Concord coach and horses in the corral at Quinn's livery stables.

'Everything seems OK this end,' Logan said. 'I wonder what the catch is?'

All four met up for a dinner of Porterhouse steaks and pumpkin pie, washed down with California wine, in the back room of the town's top hotel, the Golden Garter.

'Before you get pie-eyed,' Logan said, 'I'm gonna need some ready cash to cover expenses on this trip. We may well need to buy extra horses for the way stations.'

'Sure, you get everything organized, Josh,' Quinn replied. 'How much you want?'

'Two hundred should do. I'll get receipts for any purchases.'

Quinn dug out his wallet and slapped the cash on the table for him. 'Drink up, pardner,' he shouted, splashing the wine about. 'Say, while you're gone I'll get the sign repainted. Quinn and Logan Express Stage Lines. How's that sound? *Salud*! to us, *amigo*.'

Through narrowed eyes Kate watched her husband getting more and more inebriated, her gaze switching from him to Logan and back again. Sometimes she reminded Josh of a wildcat up a tree waiting to pounce.

Quinn beckoned him closer, speaking in a husky whisper. 'You got a ver' important strongbox to carry in the morning. Bars of gold bullion. Five thousand dollars' worth for delivery to the railroad at Las Vegas. I'm putting my trust in you to get it there, Josh.'

'Oh, yeah? I mighta known. That's a helluva responsibility, Quinn.'

'Wassa matter? Can't you handle it?'

'We can only try. Anybody else got wind of this?'

''Course not. Top secret. Look, do you wanna be my partner or not?'

'I said we'll give it a try.' Logan got to his feet looking slightly disgruntled. 'I'm gonna stretch my legs, see the town, maybe sit in a game of monte.'

'Sure, we'll come, too.'

'No thanks, I prefer my own company tonight. See y'all in the morning.'

'What's the matter with him?' Quinn growled. 'I've rescued him from the gutter, given him my cash, set him up in business, bought him dinner. What's the chip on his shoulder? Does he think he's too good for us?'

'Oh, you,' Kate scolded. 'You and your bluster. You'd scare anybody off.'

Randy made a downturned grimace. 'You don't wanna worry about Josh. He's jest a bit of a lone wolf at times.'

When Logan got back to the livery where he and Randy were bedding down above the horses it must have been about two in the morning. 'Hi, Josh,' a voice purred, as he stepped through the door.

'Kate!' She took him by surprise as she caught hold of him, pulled him into her perfumed

45

embrace. 'What you doing here?'

'What you think I'm doing here?'

'Where's Quinn?'

'That lunkhead. Forget about him.' Kate held on to him, peering expectantly up into his face, her lips half-open, waiting to be kissed. 'It's you I want, darling. I knew you'd come back.'

Logan tried to restrain her, but she hung on tight, her eyes glinting feverishly in the moonlight.

'It's over, Kate. I'm just here to do a job.'

'Over? It's never over.' Her nails clawed into his arms through his shirt. 'I'm the one who says it's over. You still love me, Josh. You know you do.'

'You're married, Kate. Don't that mean anything to you?'

'No, it don't. I don't care. He doesn't know anything. There's no need to be worried about him, darling. He was drunk again, snoring like a pig in bed when I left him. Kiss me, Josh. I'm longing for you. It's been so long. I want it to be like it was before.'

'No, Kate, don't start.' He turned his head away as she desperately sought his lips. Then he thrust her away, at arm's length. 'I said it's over, Kate.'

'Why?' she cried. 'Why do you hate me?'

'I don't hate you, Kate. But I don't love you, neither. I don't want another man's wife. I got principles. It ain't right.'

'Principles!' she scoffed. 'You didn't have principles six months ago when you took advantage of me.'

'I didn't? Well, maybe I did. It was a two-way thing, Kate. A crazy thing. I'm sorry, I ain't getting involved in it again.'

'What's the matter, cowboy? You scared of Paco?' It was not often she, or anyone else, called her husband by his Christian name. 'You frightened he might come gunning for you? Is it true what he says, you've turned yellow? Gave your herd away?'

'It's over,' he said, thrusting her away. 'He's your man. You've made your bed, you've gotta lie in it.'

'I'll leave him. We'll go away together, Josh.' She held on to him, frantically. 'I'll never give you up. I'm sorry, darling. I've made you angry.'

'Who's thar?' Randy mumbled from the hayloft, raising himself on one elbow, grabbing his gun. 'Is that you, Josh?'

'*Is that you, Josh*?' she mimicked. 'Oh, go to hell, both of you.'

Logan watched her hurry away down the street and was half-impelled to follow. But he knew that was what she wanted.

'What's wrong?' Randy called.

'Nuthin',' he muttered, still watching her body moving with a feline grace. 'Nuthin' at all.' He climbed up to the loft, hauled off his boots, stretched out on his soogans a few feet away. 'I

47

wanna make an early start with the stage in the morning. The sooner we git outa this town the better.'

FIVE

John Dog Crandal was feeling mighty pleased with himself as he rode at the head of his bunch. They loped along following the Pecos south. Any man would feel pleased with $2,000 in greenbacks stuffed in his jacket pockets. 'We're gonna paint Fort Sumner red, boys,' he yelled. 'We're gonna live like kings.'

'Yee-hah!' The lanky Luke Clay, who cantered beside him, gave a wild whoop of glee. 'You durn tootin', John Dog. All I want is a bucket of whiskey and three purty gals in bed with me.'

'Three? I'm gonna have me a dozen of them flouncy frails every which-a-way. They won't know what hit 'em. I was born in a tornado,' Crandal whooped. 'That's the way I am.'

Instead of trying to sell the longhorns in Fort Sumner they had herded them up to the railroad town of Las Vegas and got a good price, twelve dollars a head. They hadn't even had to bother changing the Leaning Ladder brand. Just said they were theirs. No more questions asked.

John Dog had paid his men $200 each. That kept them happy. The mares and foals had fetched a pretty price, too. Why reveal that he had pocketed the $2,000? He was the brains of the outfit, wasn't he?

The black stallion had taken some taming, but Crandal's vicious spurs and knotted quirt soon made him see sense.

'Yeah, you bastard,' he snarled, as the beast pranced along beneath him and he kept a firm hold. 'You just try any tricks and I'll rake your ribs 'til the blood flows.'

But John Dog knew better than to beat all spirit out of the stallion. Although Satan tossed his head and chafed at the cruel bit, he sensed the man's domination, and that was the way the man liked it to be.

The same applied to Crandal's domination of men, too. They had to be kept scared of you. Long gone were the days when he had been the pariah of a frontier town, scoffed at by the other boys for being the bastard of a whore. He had learned the only way to get respect was to fight, gouge, kick, knife, to best them with fists and guns. He had naturally drifted into nefarious company until soon he was running his own bunch.

In Texas, before the Rangers made it too hot for him, he had had no hesitation in killing anyone who stood in his way. But here in New Mexico he had, he prided himself, learned more guile. If he could get what he wanted by threat, by promise of terror, it would be best. He didn't want the authorities on their tail. He had instructed his men there would be no more murders. Not just for fun. Not unless it was necessary. Yes, no wonder he felt on top of the world!

A dozen girls in black stockings, calico drawers, embroidered bodices, and little else but bangles and beads, stuck their painted faces through the canvas cover of their wagon and screeched like Comanches as Peg Leg Fanny rattled into Fort Sumner and hauled on the reins of the two horses. 'Howdy, boys,' she yelled. 'Here we are! Come and git us!'

Peg Leg Fanny had shut up shop in Stinking Springs as most of the cowboys had ridden back to their ranches for a big round-up. She had decided to try her luck back in this notorious outpost of outlaws. 'Come on, gals,' she yelled, as she unharnessed the nags and let them drink at the big water tank in the centre of the former parade ground. 'Git ya butts down here an' git organized.'

More modestly attired Mexican women were kneeling, washing clothes at the well. They gawped with awe at the new arrivals, these wild, wanton, white women, who were seemingly prepared to sell their bodies and souls to perdition for handfuls of silver.

The Mexicans, with their families, like a few other more law-abiding Americans, had moved into the adobe barracks, officers' quarters, cook-house, armoury, stables and so forth which had been left vacant inside the fort's crumbling walls.

Peg Leg soon found a spare hut, conveniently close to Beaver Jones's saloon, and quickly moved in her cots and bedding, slinging up a curtain to provide space on the other side for her battered roulette table. A makeshift bar of planks on empty barrels was soon improvized, and she had the girls roll in barrels of her own home-brewed corn liquor. 'Hurry it up, Pearl,' she snapped. 'Get them bottles set up. We ain't come here to stand gossip-ing.'

She went outside and called to a couple of Mexicans sitting in the shade under their sombreros. 'Hey, you dagos! Any of you handy with a gee-tar? I need musicians.'

It so happened that Peg Leg's wandering red-light district had arrived at the same time as John Dog Crandal's score of *bandidos* galloped in from Las Vegas, money to burn in their pockets and whooping like coyotes when they saw the girls. Soon Fanny's new joint had become a veritable orgy of drunken men, screaming girls, and thrashing limbs behind the curtain.

Fanny had never been so busy; in between snatching two dollars a time for the favours of her calico queens from these evil, lusty *hombres*, she was kept busy filling bottles with coffin varnish to pass across to eager hands. She stood, wiping sweat from her brow and stuffing greenbacks into her capacious underwear. 'What you hanging about fer?' she snarled at Pearl. 'Tell the gals it's shorter-than-short times. We're gonna make a fortune tonight. I'm putting my prices up.'

The wildest, horniest, and thirstiest of the sweaty bunch was some black-haired galoot who had stripped off his buckskin coat to reveal a magnificent physique, a gold necklace around his muscled throat. He was tossing dollars about like confetti, and seemed to have an unending thirst for women and whiskey.

Peg Leg kept her shotgun handy under the counter. She didn't like the look of that razor-sharp machete hanging on his belt. Things might easily turn nasty. But suddenly John Dog was hit by the hard liquor. One moment he was standing tall, a cigar stuck between his gleaming gold teeth, a bottle in his hand, the next he was passed out flat on his face.

'Sling him out,' Peg Leg Fanny roared. 'He's had his fun. Come on, what's it to be, boys?'

While young, slatternly Pearl frantically served the shouting men, Fanny found Crandal's coat, secretively slipped a good portion of the greenbacks that she found in its pockets into her own, then went outside and tossed it on his semiconscious form. She hurried back to get the roulette wheel spinning. 'That bitch, Dawn,' she snarled, cursing the croupier girl. 'She picked a fine time to quit on me.'

'Yee-hagh!' Josh Logan cracked his bullwhip over the backs of the six-horse team the next morning and set the stagecoach, overloaded with passengers, swaying out of White Oaks along the rough, rutted trail. 'First stop Lincoln.'

Due to the fact that the service had been suspended there had been a queue of folks waiting to board so they had six crammed inside and four more on top. The passengers included miners who had made their pile and were heading back East, a farmer's wife in a poke bonnet cackling like the chicken under her arm, a preacher-man in sober garb and black hat and a rouged and beribboned lady of the night. In other words, a mixed bunch.

Kate had planned to travel back with them as far as Roswell but when she saw the company she would have to keep she quickly changed her mind. That was a relief to the Texan. She had insisted on presenting him with a pink-and-purple polka-dot bandanna and a pair of tanned leather gloves. He could hardly refuse. Still, the scarf would be handy keeping the dust out of his throat.

'So long, Josh,' she called, blowing him a kiss as they pulled out. 'Hurry back. I'll be waiting for you.'

He had given her a grudging grin and a wave as he gathered the reins in his new gloves and pulled out. 'She ain't gonna give up on me,' he said. 'She's a lady who likes to git her own way.'

'Why worry?' Randy hooted, clutching his Greener across his chest. 'Love 'em and leave 'em, that was allus my motto.'

'Yeah, sometimes it ain't as easy as that.'

The woman with the chicken hopped off at Lincoln, as well as a couple of other farmers, but they were replaced by a Mexican, his fat wife and two brats.

'Pulling out in half an hour, folks, after we've changed hosses,' Randy shouted as he headed for Rosie's saloon to wet his whistle. 'Don't be late, 'cause we cain't wait. Strict schedule to keep.'

'See you in a minute,' Logan called. 'Git me a beer.'

He stepped into the gun shop and studied several weapons on the rack. He chose a large-frame, slide-action Thunderer. 'How much?'

'Seventy-five dollars to you, my friend. You know that takes the largest calibre cartridge there is?'

'Yep. Gimme two dozen.'

The owner slid over two boxes of .50-.95s. 'Going hunting?'

'You could say.' Josh grabbed the heavy rifle and joined Randy at the saloon. 'I been spending some of Quinn's expenses cash. We may need extra protection. It's a valuable strongbox we're carrying. There's one of our passengers I don't much like the look of.'

'That shifty-eyed gallows-bird with the scar on his cheek? Aw, don't worry. I'll keep my eye on him.'

'Yeah, well, I don't much like him sitting behind me breathing down my neck.'

There were so many hard-looking characters around it was difficult to judge whom to be most wary of. This one was obviously toting iron beneath the ragged macinaw he wore. But, all men carried guns in these parts. He had, that moment, clattered into the bar, the floorboards thundering under his heavy, spurred boots. He ordered whiskey and ignored them. 'Bit of a mystery, ain't he?' Randy muttered.

It had taken them three hours to get to Lincoln, bouncing up and down on the rough wagon road. Now, high noon, the sun was baking down. Next change of horses would be at Roswell about five in the afternoon. It would be easier once they got to the flatlands of the Pecos valley. But they then had

56

a 170-mile drive before them to reach Las Vegas in the north.

Logan lowered his voice. 'I'm gonna bypass Fort Sumner. Too many lowlifes hang around there for my liking. We'll head right on to Puerto de Luna. We'll get a change of horses at Conejos Springs. With any luck.'

'That's a hell of a long haul without a break.'

'Yep. Don't worry, pard. We can do it.'

'Time to go.' Randy checked his tin watch. 'All aboard, folks.'

The sun was getting low in the sky by the time they'd covered the fifty miles to Roswell. But it wouldn't get dark until about nine and they'd be well on their way by then. The hard character jumped down when he heard they were bypassing Fort Sumner. 'I'm gonna buy myself a bronc,' he said. 'You're too damn slow for me.'

'Good riddance,' Randy commented, as they watched the *hombre* ride out.

'I ain't so sure,' Josh replied.

They helped sort out a new team and headed for the cantina. The nearby stream was teeming with fish and three fried trout each in their bellies and a pile of black-eye beans made them feel like new men. Logan dunked his head in a horse trough and shouted, 'Lets go, lady and gents. We ain't got no time to lose.'

The Mexican family had descended, too, at

Roswell, so they were lighter as they went wheeling out, taking a dusty trail across the waving yellow grasses of the plain. 'It ain't such a bad life,' Randy sang out, enjoying the wind breezing through his bandanna and admiring the way the sun streaked the clouds crimson.

'Yep. You could say.'

Ephraim 'Scarface' Entwistle came charging into Conejos Springs on his new bronco. 'Am I glad to see you here,' he shouted, slithering out of the saddle. 'Thought I'd have to ride up to Sumner to find you. I got great news.'

A scrawny youth in a silk plug hat and a worn overcoat was perched on the corral bar of the staging station. 'I'm here, there an' everywhere these days, Ephraim,' he called. 'I slip into Sumner and out again. It ain't safe to rest no place long. So, what you found out? Spill it.'

'There's five thousand dollars in gold bullion comin' our way, just waitin' to be grabbed.' Scarface smirked proudly. 'Quinn's stage. It'll be along in half an hour or so.'

'Who's driving?' Charley Billings was a hard frontiersman in range leathers. He snorted baccy smoke through his fierce-nostrilled nose. 'Anyone we know?'

'Ain't never seen 'em afore. Jest a coupla dead-beats Quinn's raked up. A tall guy and some old-timer. Won't pose no problem.'

'Five thousand dollars?' Tom Pickles, a former young lawman gone outlaw, gave a whistle of awe. 'That's a thousand each.'

The third man was shaggy, stocky, with a balloon of a beergut. 'Ugly Dave' Richards was wanted for a string of cowardly rapes, stage and train robberies, and killings. He looked what he was: dyed-in-the-wool evil. 'Howja git this info'? he growled.

'A mining office guy got drunk in the Golden Garter, shootin' his mouth off. Doncha worry, it's true. The tall one's got the strongbox under his seat. He's carrying a Thunderer. T'other's got a Greener. Them two's mighty edgy, that's fer sure.'

'That don't sound good.' The young one, Seth Smith, scratched at a red rash of acne on his face. 'What you say, boys?'

'Aw, come on,' Scarface urged. 'It's a godsend. We can head down to old Mexico, have a helluva time with gold like that in our saddle-bags.'

'True. I sure am tired of gettin' hunted from pillar to post, rustlin' a few of Chisum's lousy cows fer a handout.' Seth jumped down from the fence and unhitched his horse. 'Five against two. Not an offer we can rightly refuse.'

'Yeah,' Scarface insisted. 'We can easy take 'em when they pull in here.'

'No, we'll go on ahead, hide out up by Coyote

Rocks. We'll take 'em by surprise with the settin' sun at our backs.'

'Good thinking, Seth.' Charley Billings worked at the Yerby ranch, off and on, but thieving was his prime occupation. 'Anybody else on board likely to give us trouble?'

'Nope,' Scarface said. 'There's just some old hoo-er, a coupla miners, an' a preacher-man. We can have what they got, too. Let's move, shall we? They'll be here soon.'

Seth sprang on to his mustang and cantered over to Vittorio Alvaro, who manned the station. 'We'd appreciate it if you don't mention seein' us, Vittorio.' He flicked him a silver dollar. 'OK?'

'*Sí*, you can trust me, *amigo. Adios.*'

The Mexican watched them go until they were just a spiral of dust on the northern plain. Then he heard Randy giving a fanfare on his battered trumpet and turned to see a stagecoach coming in from the south.

Logan wheeled in in a cloud of dust, hauled up and hitched the reins. 'Howdy,' he said, climbing wearily from the box. 'You got a change of horses for us?'

'Ah, *señor*.' Vittorio stroked the grey stubble of his jaw. 'I have horses but Señor Quinn has not paid me. He owe me seexty dollar.'

'Sixty? You don't say? OK.' The Texan dug out

his billfold and peeled off the greenbacks. 'Seen anybody around?'

'No, *señor*. Nobody.' He hastily helped Randy unharness the sweat-streaming team. 'Not a soul in days.'

'Yeah?' Logan picked up a cigar stogie that had been stubbed out on top of a corral post. He sniffed at it. Freshly smoked. His keen eye noticed hoofmarks leading away across the grass. Fresh ones, too. 'You sure about that?'

'Ah, *sí.*' The Mexican saw his disbelief. 'Just a handful of cowboys from the Chisum spread passing by, thass all.'

'Ain't got time to hang around, folks,' Logan shouted, when the new team were in the traces. 'We're rarin' to go.'

'I don't like it,' he gritted out to Randy as they cantered the horses along at a steady jog, leaving Vittorio Alvaro's lonesome outpost far behind. 'Why should he lie? I got a funny feelin' down my spine. Keep that Greener cocked, old-timer.'

SIX

They came out of the blood-red sunset from behind a stark butte, dark silhouettes charging towards them like five horsemen of the Apocalypse.

'I ain't stopping for 'em, if that's what they think,' Logan shouted, snapping the rawhide snake across the horses' backs, sending them into a pounding gallop, their ears flattened back.

He could hear the cracking of revolvers as they drew near. *Tzit!* A bullet ripped through the sleeve of his shirt. The horsemen were riding in line, trying to cut the stagecoach off, bring it to a halt.

He glimpsed a vivid rash on a youngster's face as he cut across on his mustang, tried to grab hold of the leader's head-harness, slow him down. Logan leaned forward sending the sixteen-foot whip cracking again. It snapped around Seth Smith's wrist, sending his revolver spinning in the dust.

'Ouch!' he cried out, like some boy who'd been caned, and fell back, shaking his smarting hand.

Randy fired the Greener and the slug whistled out, hitting Tom Pickles in the shoulder, spinning him from his saddle. Amid a hail of bullets from the other three the coach went charging through and on up the trail.

It was a wild, hectic chase for half a mile or so. Luckily they reached a slight downward gradient and could get up full speed as Logan sent his whip whistling over the terrified team's heads and Randy hung on, looking back, reloading the single-shot Greener. The gunmen had fallen back, but had got over their surprise, and were charging after them, shortening the distance between them as they quirted their mustangs.

'They ain't gonna give up,' Randy shouted, as he took aim and fired, but he was being bounced about so much the shot went wide.

'We'll see about that,' Logan gritted out, hauling on his left-hand rein to pull the horses in a groaning semicircle off the trail and on to the prairie. When they hit an ant-hill he thought for seconds that they would overturn. But the Concord was back on its four sturdy wheels and he was pulling it to a halt. 'Time to take a stand,' he shouted. 'Stay inside, folks.'

He scrambled back to lie flat, Randy beside him, resting their rifles on a box of peaches due to be delivered to Las Vegas. 'Take aim, pardner. Here they come. Let 'em have it.'

The gunmen were grimly charging towards them. Logan's first shot took off Ugly Dave's hat. Randy's sent Charley Billings's mount tumbling and kicking, blood fountaining from its chest.

Boom! Logan's powerful Thunderer reverberated again, and the heavy slug removed Ephraim 'Scarface' Entwistle's head from his shoulders, brains and bone flying away in a stream of scarlet. His headless body rode on until it eventually tumbled from the saddle.

Seth, bringing up the rear, suddenly had second thoughts about this operation and leapt for cover, cowering in the grass as his mustang shied riderless away.

The youth fired a rapid volley from his Winchester carbine, but at seventy yards range he could not do much damage to the men on top of the coach. 'Jeez!' he cried, as another whistling sizzler from Logan's Thunderer ploughed into the ground and showered him with earth. 'They've turned the damn tables on us. That's for sure.'

To make matters worse, the sun was now in Seth's eyes, and the two miners were leaning from the stage, pistols in their hands, blamming away at him. One however, got too cocky, jumping from the coach to get a better look at the outlaws. Little did he know he was signing his own death warrant.

The last slug from Seth's Winchester hit the man right between the eyes.

Charley Billings was down in the grass, too, hiding behind his dead horse, grimly firing at the two on top of the coach, whom he could barely see. One of his slugs ploughed through peaches and splattered Logan with a face full of fruit. At first, Josh thought it was Randy's flesh. But no, it was sweet and tasty.

Like the bullying braggart he was, Ugly Dave was the first to turn tail. He never liked a taste of his own medicine. He quirted his horse away as fast as its hoofs would go.

'Look at 'em run,' Logan yelled, the excitement of battle coursing through his veins.

'Yeah, the lousy polecats,' Randy hollered, sending another bullet whistling past Seth, who had followed Richards's example and was chasing his own runaway mustang across the prairie. 'We sure showed 'em.'

'We sure did, pal.'

Billings was made of sterner stuff, but even he was unmanned by their onslaught, and by the memory of the headless horseman galloping past him. He jumped up from behind his dead horse and ran off after Seth, desperate to get out of range.

When Seth caught his mount he cantered back to Billings and hoisted him up behind him.

'Who were those guys?' Charley asked.

65

'I seen 'em afore,' Seth mused. 'Used to drive for Quinn up to six months ago. Had some sorta fallin' out. Never seen 'em in action before. You gotta give it to them. They sure can handle 'emselves.'

Tom Pickles was sitting peering at the bloody hole through his shoulder. Tears coursed down his cheeks as he moaned, 'I'm dyin', boys. I'm done fer.'

'Aw, quit whinin',' Richards growled. 'It's only a damn flesh wound. Slug's gawn straight through. Get on your hoss. If you ain't with us by the time we reach Fort Sumner we'll assume you musta dropped off dead.'

They set off trailing disconsolately towards the old fort, while back at the coach the hysterical 'painted lady' was being revived with smelling-salts. She got hysterical again when they hauled the dead miner in to sit beside her.

Randy led the men over to peer at the headless Entwistle. 'Aren't you going to bury him?' the Bible-thumper quavered.

'You jokin'?' Randy spat on the corpse. 'Coyote gotta eat, ain't they?'

The preacher made the sign of the cross. 'At least he's freed of his earthly troubles.'

'Yeah.' Logan patted the trusty Thunderer. 'You could say we sent him to happy oblivion. But I ain't sure what the Good Lord will make of him.'

'He sure looks better dead than he did alive,' Randy chuckled. 'I never did take to that feller.'

It was past midnight by the time the exhausted team had covered another thirty-five miles and rattled the stage into Puerto de Luna. But there was a lamp still burning in the cantina and store of the former priest, Padre 'Polaco'.

Polish by birth, his true name was Alexander Grzelachowski, but the local Latinos couldn't get their tongues around that. 'What's happened?' he cried, as they dragged the dead miner in. Randy, the lady, the other miner, all began babbling at once about the attack.

'It must have been Seth Smith, him and that scum he rides with,' the Pole conjectured. 'You say a buck-toothed scrawny youth in a Lincoln top hat with a rash across his face? That's him. He used to pretend he was my friend, then stole my horses behind my back.'

'You can't trust that li'l weasel an inch,' a gruff voice butted in. 'He's only nineteen but musta killed half a dozen men. Kills without provocation, without reason. Mind you, he's fast.'

The owner of the voice was Whiskey Jim Greathouse, a big man made taller by his white Stetson. He was seated in a corner of the cantina with his sidekick, named Brad. That accounted for the wagon loaded with barrels outside, which they were probably hauling from Las Vegas to White Oaks.

Logan had heard that he was a man renowned for selling whiskey to the Indians and was generally a dark operator, so he merely grunted a reply. 'Yeah? You think so?'

When a Mexican ostler had been roused to go change the horses, rub them down and water them, Logan, Randy and the passengers from the stage sat down to plates of boiled beef and chillied beans.

'The same old thang,' Randy groaned, 'but it sure tastes good tonight. There were moments back there when I thought it was goodbye. Them were tight papers, that's fer sure. Reminds me of that time the Messys attacked us at Shirt Tail Crossing . . .'

'What you got to drink?' Logan asked.

'Whiskey,' Polaco said. 'Jim's just delivered me three barrels.'

Randy guffawed. 'We ain't plannin' on drinkin' that much.'

'Whiskey's the stuff to put lead in your pencil,' Jim said with a laugh. 'Seein' as you're such brave boys and saved the lady's life, I bet she could be mighty grateful.'

The painted sinner in her rustling skirts fluttered her eyelashes. 'We'll have to see about that when we get to Vegas.'

But she suddenly screamed as an eight-inch centipede dropped from the ceiling into her soup and splashed about wiggling its toxic mandibles. Logan scooped it out with a spoon and flicked it through the open door. 'All adds to the flavour, ma'am.'

'She'll be more'n grateful now,' Whiskey Jim growled. 'You might even git it cut price.'

'We'll drink to that.' Logan took a swig from the bottle by the neck. 'Yeah, that's better.'

'So, you're Quinn's new driver, are ya?' Brad McNulty, the hunky young assistant to Whiskey Jim asked. 'Kinda stepped into my shoes?'

'Why, are *you* the one who jacked it in?'

'Too true. I couldn't stand the pace. I guess you know what kinda pace I'm speakin' of? The attentions of a certain lady.'

'Kate?' The word came out involuntarily, such was Logan's surprise. 'You mean you . . . she?'

'Whew? That woman's insatiable, ain't she? A reg'lar meat-mincer.'

Logan frowned, and took another swig of the throat-rasping liquor. 'I don't know what you're talking about.'

'So, it's true.' Jim laughed. 'I'd heard rumours to that effect, that Kate likes to keep herself a handsome stud on the side.' He slapped Logan's knee. 'Come on, mister. Don't play coy.'

'She's sure some gal,' Brad said. 'But it ain't all

69

clover. Someone tittle-tattled to Quinn. That's why I got out, 'fore he came gunnin' for me.'

Logan got to his feet. 'I'd ask you to shut your mouth about this, you blabbermouth. It ain't gentlemanly.' He eased the Lightning on his hip. 'The Quinns are friends of mine.'

'Aw, no need to git riled up,' the young man protested. 'I'm only telling it like it is. You'll find out.'

Logan turned on his heel. 'Come on, folks. Ain't got time to hang around. We got fresh horses and we're ready to go.'

He spotted a shovel in a corner and tossed it hard at the lover boy. 'Here, if you got so much energy, maybe you could bury the stiff?' He flipped a quarter at him contemptuously. 'That should cover it.'

SEVEN

The walls of Fort Sumner glowed a ruddy red as the rays of the rising sun flickered in the east. John Dog Crandal groaned as he stirred, flat on his face in the dust. He sat up and looked around. He wasn't the only one. Several of his *compañeros* lay where they had fallen, thrown from Peg Leg Fanny's whorehouse. They had snored away the night in drunken stupor.

The gaunt and lanky Luke Clay came to his senses at the same time. 'Gawd, my guts,' he moaned. 'There's a gang of snakes writhing in my belly. What's she put in that stuff?'

Crandal retrieved his stained buckskin jacket. 'I feel like I've been run over by an elephant,' he said. In fact, in the darkness men had stamped their boots on his prostrate form as they went in and out of the brothel. Some might have

71

urinated on him, judging by the sticky smell of his coat.

'Shee-it! What's happened to me cash?' he asked, searching the coat pockets. 'I couldn't have spent all that.'

Of the $1,000 in greenbacks that had been in his pocket all he had left was a measly fifty or so dollars and a handful of cents. 'I've been damn well robbed.'

'So?' Luke grinned. 'The way you were whoopin' it up, whatja expect?'

John Dog's band had made camp underneath the nearby wall and were brewing up coffee. He went across, helped himself to a tin mug of the scalding brew, and checked his saddle-bags. At least, the other $1,000 was still intact.

He found his faded pink vest and pulled it on for he had got cold lying out half-naked all night. He checked his big Remington revolver, stuffed it into his belt and strode across to Peg Leg Fanny's hut. He grabbed her by the neck of her flannel nightdress and dragged her from her cot. 'Where's my cash, you thievin' haybag?' He slapped her. 'Give it back you, lousy witch.'

Fanny shrieked like a banshee, rousing the girls, who came from behind the suspended sheet looking like they'd crawled through a hedge backwards. They scrambled, screaming and grabbing hold of John Dog.

'All we've got is what you owed us,' Pearl whined, loyally protecting her mistress as he beat them off. 'You practic'ly drank the place dry.'

Crandal backed off. 'Listen, you harpies,' he screeched. 'Nobody could have spent that much.'

'Now you mention it,' Peg Leg said,' I did notice four fellers ride in late. One was stooped over you, rifling your pockets, that's who it was.'

'Who was he?' John Dog demanded.

'A skinny young sonuvagun in a plug hat. Looked to me like that Seth Smith.'

'Who's he?' Crandal asked.

'Aw, some no-good rustler. Comes and goes like most of you.' Fanny hitched up her nightie to adjust her peg leg. 'Fancy attacking a poor lady like this. I've a good mind to report you to the sheriff.'

'Arr, shut up. Where can I find this Smith?'

'In Beaver's saloon, I guess. Why?' Fanny taunted. 'You gonna call him out?'

'I wouldn't, if I were you.' Pearl gave a wide-eyed, fearful look. 'He's some gunslinger.'

'Get stuffed, you bitches.' John Dog turned on his heel and went back to his men.

'I got a job for you, Luke,' he said. 'I need some-body killed.'

'Sure.' Luke Clay grinned. 'I ain't killed nobody since we left Texas. You said not to.'

'Yeah, well, I've changed my mind. We'll go

73

halves on whatever's in his pockets. OK?'

'Who is he?'

'Just some gutter trash called Smith. Don't worry. He's nobody special. We'll back you if there's trouble.'

It was about noon when Seth in his stove pipe hat and worn brocade vest, strolled into Beaver's saloon followed by Charley, Ugly Dave and the shoulder-bandaged Tom Pickles.

'That's him,' Crandal muttered. 'That spotty-faced li'l creep.'

He, and about fifteen of his *viciosos* were sprawled on one side of the saloon, recovering from the excesses of the night before.

'That li'l punk.' The lanky Luke got to his feet. 'He looks about as useless as a flea on a dawg's dick.' Luke had already been hitting the whiskey and, as he stood centre floor, was bristling for a fight, secure in the knowledge that Crandal's gang could blow Smith and his boys to hell.

'Hey, pint-size,' he jeered at Seth, who was seated at a table on the other side of the saloon dealing from a greasy pack of cards. 'Has your mammy let you out to play with the big boys?'

'Somethun' botherin' you, mister?' Seth peered at Luke, then whipped out his Smith & Wesson revolver, whirling it on one finger, before slipping it back into a holster pig-stringed to his thigh. 'If so, spit it out.'

John Dog gave a roar of laughter. 'You don't impress us with those fancy tricks, sonny boy. Maybe you didn't appreciate who you were sneak-thievin' from last night. My name's Crandal, these are my boys, and Luke there's my first lieutenant. He's requested the honour of killin' you.'

'What you talking about?' Seth scratched at his rash that had intensified in colour. 'I ain't no thief.'

'Well, we say you are.' Luke turned to wink at the men to make sure they appreciated his wit. 'I say he must be one of them molly boys, don't you, fellas? That's where he picked up that rash – from selling his backside.'

'Don't push it, pal,' Charley snarled, stroking his jaw, staring hard.

'Yeah? What's the li'l darlin' gonna do about it?' Luke sauntered, unsteadily, across to Seth's table. 'So, mammy lets you play cards, does she?'

Seth looked up, apprehensively, but deftly dealt the deck. 'You're making a mistake, friend,' he said.

'Listen to him.' Luke lurched back to his own side and took another swig from the whiskey bottle. 'You ever seen such a miserable li'l shit?'

While his back was turned Seth eased out the Smith & Wesson and moved the cylinder forward three notches. When fired the hammer would now hit three spent cases that he hadn't removed. 'What's your handle, feller?' he called.

'Luke Clay. You better remember it.' Clay spun around, his hand covering his own six-gun. 'You better hand back that money you stole.'

Charley looked across uneasily at the grinning gang of badmen. He didn't like the look of them or the odds. 'He's calling you out, Seth. What you gonna do?'

'You're on your own,' Ugly Dave growled. 'This ain't nuthin' to do with me.'

Seth stood and smiled nervously. 'Seems like I got an advantage over you, Luke. It wouldn't be fair. This is a hundred-dollar piece.' He offered it by its barrel for inspection. 'It's deadly accurate. Not like that worn-out ol' Colt of yourn. But, even if we swapped guns, I figure I could still beat you.'

'Yeah?' Luke, surprised, grinned. 'You think? Right!' He grabbed the Smith & Wesson and handed his own Colt across. 'Let's just see about that.'

'It's up to you, Luke,' John Dog growled, beckoning to his men to keep out of it. 'You sure you can take him now?'

'Yeah.' Clay suddenly had the look of a furtive ferret, but it was too late to back down. He examined the revolver. 'Nice piece. Don't need cocking, do it? Let's go for it.'

Seth called out, 'Thirty paces, OK?' He turned his back on Luke and paced towards the door. 'I'll take my stand over here.'

Mad-eyed, Clay didn't wait for him to turn, aiming the fancy shooter, hastily squeezing the trigger. Once, twice, three times the hammer clicked and nothing occurred. 'Shee-it!'

Seth didn't wait for him to try a fourth. He spun around, took careful aim and the old Colt crashed out. Once, twice, three times, too.

Clay went flying backwards and hit the bar, sliding to a sitting position, glassy-eyed. Blood pumped from three holes in his shirt. Seth tossed the Colt away and went to retrieve his own revolver. 'Sorry, Luke. I was just too clever for you. You should beware taking gifts from a stranger.'

John Dog stared, bemused. 'What a crafty li'l mutha! Maybe you and me should join forces. Between us we could carve up this territory.'

Seth grinned as he returned to his card game. 'I'll think about it,' he sang out.

Mandolins, guitars, drums and trumpets rang out in a pounding, raucous chorus as the Mexican population at Fort Sumner enjoyed a *bailie* in one of the old barrack halls. Cotton-clad men shrilled their voices in harmony as laughter and curses rang like silver pesos.

One of the dandiest dancers on the floor was young Seth Smith, who had ingratiated himself with the Mexican sheepherders as a way of getting to know their daughters.

His partner and sweetheart that night was Paulita Jennings, a mixed-race girl. Like many settlers in these parts her father, Jack Jennings, a storekeeper, had taken a Mexican wife.

The buck-toothed Seth could afford to be merry in spite of the setback of the aborted stage robbery. He had spent the day playing poker with whiskey-soaked John Dog and had fleeced him of a good many dollars.

'I do not like that John Dog and his *bandidos*,' Paulita said, as they took a break from the dancing outside under the stars. 'They are not the sort we want here.'

'Aw, he's OK,' Seth grinned. 'Just a tad crazy. He's got this idea about running some sort of protection scheme. He wants me to join him. I told him gamblin's more my scene. He's gone off in a huff, says he's gonna put the screws on Quinn.'

When the army had moved out of the fort about thirty Latino families had moved in, mostly running herds of sheep in the hills. The Spanish-speaking Seth was popular as he spread his ill-gotten gains around in return for safe-hiding at their camps. But neither the Latinos nor the white settlers had expected the fort to become the stomping ground of so much riff-raff.

'Hey,' Seth whispered to Paulita, tickling her ear. 'How about you sneak me into your room? I gotta ride out in the morning.'

'You *are* going to marry me, aren't you, Seth?' the girl murmured, as she unglued her lips from his. 'We *will* go to live in Mexico, like you said?'

'True, we'll settle down there and have lots of little ones. I sure am tired of running.'

'How many other girls have you said that to?'

Seth grinned, for he had said it to quite a few in order to get his wicked way. 'It's you I love best,' he sang out, putting an arm around her waist and swinging her across the former parade ground towards the Jennings's store. 'Believe me, honey, that's the truth.'

It was a warm summer's night, the stars and moon glowed in the heavens above, and Pauilita was easily convinced.

'I'm getting some cash put by,' Seth said. 'Jest need a lucky break. Don't worry, darlin'. We'll head for the border purty soon.'

'When I heard those shots coming from the saloon today my heart was in my mouth. I just knew it was you,' the girl said. 'You worry me, Seth. Won't the sheriff come after you?'

'Nah. Why should he. I'm doin' his job for him. If anyone deserved killin' it was that Luke

Clay. I feel real good tonight for putting that dog down. Nobody's gonna put me in the hoosegow,' the youth boasted. 'I'm a boy who'll allus ride free.'

EIGHT

Josh Logan and Randy had not lingered long amid the railyards, hotels and saloons of bustling Las Vegas. Long enough to hand over the strongbox of bullion to two Wells Fargo guards in the armoured caboose of a locomotive headed back East to New York. A banker's draft would be paid into Quinn's account for the gold.

'That guy jest cain't lose,' Randy opined. 'He'll be a millionaire in a year or two.'

'Yep,' Logan half-agreed, 'if his luck holds out.'

He headed the crowded stage back down the Pecos, the six-horse team eating up the miles through Villa Nueva, Anton Chico, Santa Rosa, Puerto de Luna, until they rolled into Fort Sumner.

'Just a short stay, folks,' Logan sang out. 'We'll be on our way again in an hour.'

That was if there was no trouble. Logan was on edge at the possibility of running into John Dog Crandal and his villainous crew, or the youthful Seth Smith and the gang who had attacked the coach. What could he do against such men except face them down? He loosened the Colt' Lightning in its holster as he stepped warily into Beaver's saloon.

But it seemed the birds had flown. So it was not without a sense of relief that he slapped the white dust from his clothes and downed a beer and a dish of tripe.

Before leaving, he checked his .38. It was Colt's first double-action that had come out in '76. He had sent fifteen dollars for it, mail order, when he read an advertisement saying, 'This pistol exceeds in accuracy and penetration any other of its class.' However, any man who used it would need to be good to beat, in close combat, John Dog or his professional killers. And Smith was said to be fast.

'Can you take the mail pouch along to Pete Maxwell's?' he asked Randy. 'I'm gonna call in on Peg Leg Fanny. Seems she's moved in along the street.'

'Oh, yeah,' Randy guffawed. 'Still got that li'l piece of muslin on your mind?'

'Maybe.' First, he cooled off over at the tank, combing back his long flaxen hair. Yes, it was true, he had Dawn Adamson on his mind. Funny, the thought of seeing her made his heart thump more than the prospect of bumping into Crandal.

'Howdy,' he called, as he entered the brothel. 'How's it going?'

Half-dressed, the girls were sitting idly around, and Fanny was stocking the bar. 'Well, if it ain't the handsome stranger. You lookin' fer a good time?'

'I . . . er . . .' He glanced around. 'Is that croupier girl, Dawn, here?'

'No, she damn well ain't. She lit out.'

'Why so?' He lit a cheroot and paid for drinks all round.

'Because all she wanted to do was be a croupier. To put it frankly, mister, she refused to go horizontal with the customers. What makes her think herself so precious? Snooty li'l cow. You don't open your legs, I tol' her, you can hightail it. Thass what she done. Went off with my banjo man, the coloured boy.'

'Where to?'

'Who cares? Why you worryin'? There's plenty lovely gals here. Take your pick.'

'Ain't got time. I'm driving stage for Quinn. Gotta be moving out. Got a strict schedule.'

'Yeah, same old story.'

'Any sign of a Fort Worth roughneck called John Dog?'

'Crandal? Don't ask. He was behaving like Casanova gone berserk. Then had the nerve to say I robbed him. He and his boys – minus one who gotten killed – moved out a coupla days ago. Unlike you, my friend, he was no gen'l'man. Me and my girls are still recovering. Plus the fact that them greenbacks of his look to me like crude forgeries.'

Logan grinned. 'Yeah, I can guess. So long, y'all. Take it easy.'

The girls came to the door to wave as he and Randy, with their assorted passengers, moved out of the fort and set the horses cantering across the baking prairie. A hundred miles to go to Roswell.

Kate Quinn sat before her bedroom mirror in Roswell and brushed back her crackling auburn hair as her maid cinched tight her corset. The sun's setting rays filtered through her window as she stepped into a flouncy silk dress, with a plunging front, very *décolletée*.She didn't normally dress so elegantly for dinner with Quinn, but if Josh Logan was keeping to timetable he should be bringing in the stage from Vegas in an hour or so. 'He's gonna git the full treatment,' she murmured, smiling at her image. 'See if he can resist me.'

Suddenly, however, the calm of their oasis in the prairie was rudely broken by the clatter of gunfire and shouting and hooting as if they were under attack by Apaches.

But no. These were no Mescaleros. As she peered out she saw that the house was surrounded by a band of horsemen, Mexicans and white gutter trash, all firing off with abandon the carbines in their hands, bullets whining through windows, smashing vases, ricocheting off the adobe walls.

'What the hell's happening?' she screamed, as Quinn came rushing in.

'Get down,' he yelled. 'Keep outa sight. I'll deal with this.'

But Kate could see the fear in the whites of his eyes. And in a way she couldn't blame him. These killer scum were enough to frighten anybody.

'I'm coming out.' Quinn poked a white shirt tied to a rifle through the bead curtain of the house doorway. 'Don't shoot me.'

The fusillade gradually ceased. John Dog Crandal urged Satan closer and waited expectantly. 'Come out, then.'

Quinn showed himself, holding the rifle to the ground. 'What do you want?'

'Cash.' John Dog gave a throaty laugh and shouted, 'We know you got plenty of it. We want two thousand dollars in golden eagles. No paper dollars. There are too many forged greenbacks in circulation. Two thousand in gold. Hand it over and we go, leave you in peace.'

'You're crazy.' Quinn uttered the words in his hoarse whiskey voice. 'I don't keep that sorta cash in the house. My money is in the bank at Vegas. Or in my safe at the White Oaks mine.'

Kate suddenly pushed through the doorway beside him, her green eyes flashing with anger. She, too, had a rifle in her hand, but hers was aimed at Crandal. 'What are you parleying with these scum of the earth for? Tell them to get off of our property.'

'Get back inside.' Quinn put an arm across her. 'I'll handle this.'

'You!' Kate hissed, scornfully. 'Give them a taste of lead. That's the only talk these devil's spawn understand.'

Crandal shrugged black hair from his face and his lips curled back in a leering grin as he peered at her partly bared bosom, the dipping neckline of her skimpy dress. 'This your wife? Hey, I like what I see.'

Others of his men gave shrill catcalls, making obscene suggestions as they laughed at her.

'Where you find your wife?' John Dog asked. 'In a bordello? Tell you what: I will have the whore in part payment. So then you only owe me one thousand nine hundred dollars in gold. That is a generous offer.'

'I'm not for barter,' Kate shrilled. 'Don't think I

86

am. I spit in the face of a cur like you. You lay a finger on me and you'll have a posse of decent white men in this county after you so fast you won't know what hit you.'

John Dog grinned. 'She's sure got a lot of sass, ain't she, boys? She's just the sorta fancy lady who needs takin' down a peg or two. How about we give her a good—?'

'Look,' Quinn interrupted, pulling out his wallet, thumbing the notes. 'I swear this is all I got here. Two hundred dollars or so. It's yours.' He tossed it to John Dog who deftly caught it in one hand. 'I'll get you the rest in gold. Just give me a few days.'

'We don't want trouble,' John Dog cajoled. 'There is no need for any bloodshed. We will be back in four days. You have our two thousand in gold ready and waiting, OK? Otherwise, I will have that woman in front of your eyes, while my men hold you with a noose round your neck. Then – *boom* – we will blow your house to hell.'

'All right, I'll have it ready here.'

'And don't go blabbing to the army or the sheriff, neither. If I suspect double dealing' – John Dog pointed a finger at Kate – 'she dies.'

He gave a yell, hauled the prancing Satan around, and spurred him away, followed by his men.

Quinn watched them go, his hair over his eyes,

his face tense, then he pushed Kate back inside. 'What you dressed up like a two-bit whore for? Cain't you see you've given him ideas? What for you walking around like some half-naked hussy. Where's that whiskey gone?'

When he had found the bottle and filled a glass tumbler with an unsteady hand, tipping it back with a gasp, he stared at her and groaned, 'Ah, I get it. You're expectin' Logan back tonight. You're half-crazy about that guy.'

'Why don't you talk some sense,' Kate replied, laying the rifle aside. 'And go get the sheriff. Tell him we need protection. Why are you so scared of that bunch of ragtails?'

'Admit it!' Quinn caught her by the throat. 'You got eyes for Josh Logan, ain'tcha?' He increased pressure as she struggled like a bird caught in a net and forced her back over a table. 'That's why he left before. It's true, isn't it?' He laughed harshly in her face. 'That's a joke 'cause he don't want you. He's too decent a feller to want a whore like you. See, so you're stuck with me and where you are. You do what I say or—'

'Or what?' she cried defiantly, trying to make him loosen his grip.

'Or,' Quinn shouted, 'I'll toss you to Crandal and his dogs like the piece of trash that you are.'

'Brave words,' she sneered, as he released her. 'You're afraid of them so you pick on me. What sort of man are you?'

'You behave,' Quinn shouted. 'I can take so much and no more. That's a warning.'

NINE

'What was that shooting?' Randy shouted, as Logan drove the stagecoach on along the white dusty trail that gleamed in the moonlight. 'It sounded like it was coming from Roswell.'

'Keep your Greener primed, old-timer,' Josh gritted out. 'There might be more trouble.'

When he hauled in outside Quinn's place he saw in the lanternlight estate workers scurrying around, throwing out shattered mirrors and vases. 'Looks like they been under siege.'

'Oh, Josh!' Kate Quinn met him at the kitchen door, raising her arms as if she wanted him to hug her to him. 'Why didn't you come sooner? We could have done with a real man around here.'

Logan tried to evade her embrace as best he could. 'What's happened?'

'It's John Dog Crandal,' she cried. 'He's been shooting up the place, making horrible threats to me. Disgusting things he said. He wants two thousand dollars. Or me. What can we do?'

'Why are you asking *him?*' Quinn roared, hanging on to the kitchen table, waving the bottle around.

Logan pushed past her as gently as he could and asked Quinn, 'You're not going to pay, are you?'

'My whole life's wrapped up in this place, in the mine, in the stage company. I've got to pay,' Quinn whined. 'What else can I do? That cur Crandal means what he says. Look what he did to you.'

'Look how white Paco's gone. His hand's shaking,' Kate cried. 'What kind of husband is he? You're a wise man, Josh. Tell him what we should do.'

'You shut your mouth,' Quinn shouted. 'What's it to do with him?'

'I would like to ask his opinion, do you mind? He is going to be our partner, after all. I'd like his advice.'

'Some partner,' Quinn snorted. 'A sleepin' partner is what you'd like him to be.'

'My advice would be you all calm down. But if you really want to know, I wouldn't give Crandal a peso. If you pay him now, he'll be back and he'll want double or triple next time.'

'Yeah, that's easy for you to say, pal. It ain't your house he's gonna put to the flames, your woman he's gonna rape.' Quinn held his glass aloft and stared at them both. 'Or is she? Mine?'

'Take no notice of him, Josh,' Kate put in. 'He's drunk. He's talking rot.'

'Yeah, so *you* go fight him.'

'Ach,' she sneered. 'You make me sick.'

'Those sorta words don't help none,' Logan said, moving away from her to help himself to a drink. 'But I figure you gotta fight him, Paco. There ain't nuthin' else you can do.'

'Pah!' Quinn spat out. 'I got a bandit sittin' on my back and what am I surrounded by – a crazy wife and a lousy hero.'

Suddenly, Quinn lurched forward, pushing Logan away. 'Clear off. Get outa my house. You're the lousy snake in the grass. Not Crandal.'

Randy, who had been watering and unharnessing the horses, burst in. 'What's going on? Shall I rig up a new team? Or are we staying here? We've been on that box eighteen hours. I'm just about stoved in.'

'We'll go on to Lincoln,' Logan replied, his face grim. 'I knew we should have never taken on this job again.'

He was in the stables putting the finishing touches to the harness of the fresh horses in the traces when Kate caught hold of him in the semi-darkness. She held him close, pressing her breasts tight to his chest, her face entreating him. 'Josh, take me with you,' she cried. 'I can't stand it here

92

another minute. Take me with you tonight.'

Her perfume was almost overpowering and he was tempted, he had to admit, to kiss her, to have her one last time. But he firmly placed her aside and swung up on to the box. 'We got a full passenger complement,' he drawled, moving the team out. 'Ain't got room for another.'

The coach loaded, six squashed inside, and four on top, he snaked his whip cracking over the fresh horses' ears and they lumbered away into the night on the fifty-mile climb to Lincoln.

Bounced about inside the coach like a pea in a bucket, Azariah Wilde groaned and peered through the buckskin curtain at the moon-streaked barren crags. How much further would he have to travel through this godforsaken country before his mission was completed?

Wilde was a Pinkerton detective, seconded to the federal secret service. He had been to see the state governor in Santa Fe. A forgery ring had been churning out dud greenbacks. It was believed to be operating out of this area. He would be expected to rake through this rugged terrain seeking their hideout.

It was five in the morning by the time they rolled into Lincoln. Wilde, in his dark suit and derby, climbed stiffly down and called, 'Where's the sheriff's office?'

'Across the road,' Logan said.

'Who's that pasty-faced dude?' Randy asked. 'What's he want?'

'Beats me.' Logan rubbed at his tired eyes. It had been a long trail. There would be no sleep until they reached White Oaks. He banged on the door of Rosie's saloon. 'Breakfast here for half an hour,' he called out to the passengers. 'Then we go the last forty-five miles up through the hills. Don't know about y'all, but I'll be damned glad to get to White Oaks.'

TEN

'Tomorrow we'll raid Chisum's herd,' Seth Smith called out to Charley, Ugly Dave and Tom Pickles as they sprawled around their campfire. 'We need to raise some hard cash.'

'Yeah, we can sell 'em to old Pat Murphy,' Charley hooted. 'He'll give us a good price. Old Pat'll buy anythang. He's no love for Chisum, neither.'

In fact, the Irishman had grabbed some land to ranch further down the valley, on the edge of the cattle baron's empire. He had also built a saloon and hotel for passing travellers. 'Him and Old John are like two hounds with teeth bared,' Charley said.

'I don't like it, Seth. Things aren't going well. The raid on the stage was a disaster.' Tom had been silent all night, laid out in his blanket by the fire, nursing his wounded shoulder. 'I think we should leave Chisum alone, head for the border now while we got the chance.'

'You ain't losing your nerve, are you, Tom?'

Seth grinned. 'We can't head for Mexico stony-broke. I promise you this'll be our last raid, then we'll go.'

Tom's wound had been patched up at the fort by one of the Mexican women, but the bullet hole was raw-edged and pounding painfully. There was an eerie feel about the dark, eroded rocks around this hideout, the flickering firelight, and the lugubri-ous screeching of owls. 'I just got the feelin' our luck's running out,' he whispered.

'Aw, quit whining,' Ugly Dave retorted. 'Why'd you bring this cowardly whelp along fer, Smith? He ain't no use to us in that state.'

'Tom's my pal,' Seth said, and asked Charley, 'You sure Murphy will pay?'

'Yeah, Pat'll give us eight dollars a head,' Charley said. 'He'll sell 'em to gov'ment contrac-tors for double that. He'll be glad to have 'em. Old Pat's a pretty hard thief. He's stealing every which way he can.'

'Sounds like us, eh, boys?' Seth cried, setting them off laughing. 'Only thang Ol' Pat won't steal's a red-hot stove. We sure ain't gonna git our fingers burned stealing a few old cows.'

They woke at first light and set off down the Pecos

valley. After a couple of hours they came across a nice little herd of about 200 beeves in fine fettle. 'These'll do, boys,' Seth shouted. It was an easy matter to round them up and send them skittering.

Or, it would have been. But, suddenly, two of Chisum's cowboys appeared riding fast across the rustling grass towards them. One had a revolver in his fist and fired a warning shot as he approached. 'Hey!' he yelled. 'What you doing with them cattle?'

Seth jerked his mustang around, jacked a shell into his Winchester and hit the cowboy square on, knocking him back off his saddle. 'What you think, dummy?'

The cowboy's companion reined in, gawped down at the body in the grass, then croaked, 'You done killed him.'

'Yeah. You lookin' fer the same treatment?'

As the cowboy jerked his reins with an expression of terror and spurred his mustang away, Seth put a bullet in his back, rolling him into the grass. He cantered across and put another in to make sure. 'Don't do to have witnessess,' he grinned. 'Dead men tell no tales. Ain't that what they say?'

It didn't take long to herd the longhorns at a fast clip towards the Irishman's lonesome hotel on the prairie.

'Jasus, boys,' Murphy roared. 'You ain't even

changed the brands on 'em. Never mind, get 'em in the corral, then come and cut the dust from your throats.'

In the bar he poured them all a stiff whiskey and counted out $1,000. 'That's the best I can do for stolen beeves. Now be off widja. It ain't advisable for me to be seen doin' business wid the likes of youse.'

They split the cash and got back on their mustangs. 'See, I told ya it would be OK, Tom,' said Seth. 'You and Dave go back to the hideout. Me an' Charley have business at the fort. We'll see ya in a coupla days, then head for the border.'

'Why you got to go to Sumner for?' Tom called out. 'It ain't safe there. Chisum's gonna be on the warpath.'

'Aw, you worry too much, Tom. Truth is I wanna see Paulita. I gotta say goodbye. Or, who knows, I might even bring her along.'

Tom shook his head as he watched Seth go. 'He's crazy.'

'Yeah,' Ugly Dave muttered, darkly. 'A man's prick has oft been his undoin'.'

ELEVEN

The Four Aces was the best-run gambling den in White Oaks. The curtains were kept drawn night and day and there was no clock on the wall so, unless you consulted your own pocket watch, you had no idea what time it was. Most men were so busy concentrating on their cards they paid time little heed. Sometimes a poker game could go on for three days and nights as the chips piled up. The whale-oil lanterns were kept low and any rowdiness was quickly taken care of by the casino-minders. All the tables, monte, blackjack, keno, would generally be packed and miners stood three deep around the roulette tables, but conversation was subdued unless somebody had a big win and was celebrating. Or a loser had to be thrown out of the joint, protesting vociferously. The miners had gold to burn, but they were greedy for more. Or was it just a compulsion, a heart-thumping, intensified form of risk-taking that made them flock there?

Josh Logan had slept for twelve hours, then soaked in a tub at the bathhouse. After a shave and trim at the barbershop, he bought himself a new wool check shirt and cavalry twill tight pants, and felt like a new man. He handed in his gun as he stepped inside the casino and found a place at the bar.

'Whiskey straight,' he said, and glanced around at the tables, the bearded, scruffy miners, the tradesmen in dark suits, and the nattily attired professional gambling men puffing on cheroots and contemplating their cards.

'Hi.' The slim brunette, Dawn Adamson, slipped on to a bar stool beside him. 'What's your game?'

'Oh, hiya.' She had taken him by surprise, appearing as if out of nowhere. 'What's yours?'

'Blackjack. But I can't do you any favours. Nuthin's rigged here, I'm glad to say.'

'I ain't asking for none. But I guess blackjack'll be my game, too. Not that I'm one of your big spenders. I only got fifty dollars to risk.'

'A gambler ought to know how much he can lose. A pity more don't.' She smiled at him, her cheek dimpling, mischievously. 'If they all did, however, I'd probably be out of a job.'

'No fear of that with this crowd. Fancy a drink?'

'No. I'm just going on duty. I've been asleep

upstairs.' She was in a dress of rustling turquoise silk, a little less severe tonight, revealing her pale throat. A gold crucifix on a chain dangled on her chest. 'Maybe, if you're still around at midnight, we could.'

'I'll be here.'

'Just a drink. I ain't promisin' nuthin' else.'

'I wasn't expecting nuthin'. It'd be nice to talk.'

'Just as long as that's understood. There's so many heavy gropers around.' She grinned at him, showing neat white teeth between her crimson-painted lips. 'You look quite the dude tonight.'

'Yep.' He took a swig of his whiskey and met her eyes. 'Back in Stinking Springs I guess I looked beat up. Which was what I was. We'd had a spot of bother. But I've just drawn what's owed me for taking the stage to Las Vegas and back. So, I'm enjoying a bit of rest and recreation.'

'Which means hitting the hot spots?'

'To tell the truth I was half-hoping you'd be here.'

'That's funny,' she laughed,' because I'd been rather hoping to see you again.'

'That's good news.' He flicked his hair out of his eyes and asked, 'So how did you get to be a gambling lady?'

'My daddy taught me. What else is a gal to do?'

'I guess it pays well.'

'You get tips. Last night some old galoot was

shooting chips at me like bullets from a gun. He couldn't believe he'd spent a thousand dollars when he dropped out. But he was generous. He tucked a fifty-dollar bill in my garter.'

Logan didn't much like the sound of that. But it was the custom. If a gal hoicked up her dress to show a silk-stockinged leg it was much appreciated by some lonesome old miner. He assumed that that was all she had showed.

'Blackjack ain't really my game,' he said, to take his mind off it. 'Kinda complicated.'

'People play a lot of systems. There's a lot of unspoken rules. But usually the most skilled person wins. I'll have to show you sometime. Uhuh, here comes the pit boss. I can't hang around. See you later, perhaps?'

'I'll hold you to that,' he said, and watched her sashay away.

The Quinns were riding on their fine thorough-breds up towards Lincoln when they ran into Sheriff Pat Garrett and Azariah Wilde coming fast their way.

'Just the man I wanted to see,' Quinn roared. 'We've had our house under attack by a gang of thugs led by John Dog Crandal. We need protection.'

'Anybody killed?'

'Not yet,' Kate screeched. 'But what do I have to

do? Get raped and slaughtered before you act?'

'I'll call in on my way back. I'm looking into another matter. Top priority from Washington.'

'That's enough, Garrett. No need to tell the whole damned territory,' Wilde butted in. 'Come on. We haven't got time to hang around.'

When they reached White Oaks the Quinns booked into the Golden Garter. As they freshened up in the hotel's best room Quinn couldn't resist taunting his wife. 'So, you're still in love with your precious Logan, are ya?'

Kate ignored him but he could see her claws tense, her nails scratching the surface of the dressing-table. So he went on: 'It looks like we're gonna have to cut him in as a partner, then, don't it? You don't wanna lose him. And I ain't gonna find another feller who can run a stage line like him. Looks like we both need him. So, I'd better go sweeten him.'

'Where is he?' Kate asked sharply.

'I dunno. One of the saloons, I guess.'

First Quinn had to do business at the mine, then draw out $2,000 in gold from the bank. He deposited this for the night in the stage line office safe. He found Logan propping up the bar at the Four Aces, chatting to the croupier girl, Dawn Adamson.

'So this is how you waste your time,' Quinn

chuckled, slapping him on the back. 'Tryin' to get in the pants of this dinky li'l darlin'?'

Logan groaned. 'What do you want, Quinn?'

'We've got an appointment at the lawyer's office. You and me. I'm making you a full partner in the stage company. You'll be in charge, run it the way you like. Come on, pal, let's go.'

'I ain't so sure I wanna be a partner,' Logan drawled, shaking Quinn's hand off his shoulder. 'You ain't even heard how we got attacked by that lousy gang of road agents.'

'Sure I have. Old Randy tol' me all about it. You'll both be gettin' a big bonus for getting the gold through. And you can name your own remuneration. Whatever the line will stand. Come on, Josh, no hard feelin's. Kate's told me all about your li'l, how shall I say, get-together, last summer. You played the white man and called a halt. Time to forgive an' forget. I'll see she don't bother you no more.'

'That's easier said than done.' Logan glanced uneasily at the girl. Then turned to Quinn. 'OK, from now on I'll play straight with you if you play straight with me. Kate and me . . . I'm sorry about it, Paco. It's a long time ago. It's over now.'

'Don't worry about it, Josh,' Quinn said. 'You can reorganize the line, buy another coach, hire relief drivers, whatever you like. Come on, I wanna head back tomorrow. I gotta meet Crandal.'

'You're gonna pay?'

'Yeah,' Quinn growled. 'But I'd like you along in case of trouble.'

'OK,' Logan sighed. 'It's a deal. Partners, it is.'

'Let's go over to the Golden Garter and celebrate,' Quinn suggested, when the contract was all signed and sealed.

Logan could hardly refuse to raise a glass to their success. 'You're not a saddle bum any more,' Kate said, in her husky tones. 'You'll be a man of standing in the community.'

'Listen to her,' Quinn roared, the whiskey already getting to him, not caring if everybody else in the bar heard. 'She married me for my money, because I provide her with everything she wants. And what gratitude do I get? She tells me she's in love with this other guy. Yeah, *him*. He looks like butter wouldn't melt in his mouth, don't he? So, I say, OK, go and live with him like some tramp.'

Quinn got to his feet and stumbled to the bar for a refill. He caught hold of a drinker's arm and laughed uproariously in his face. 'The big joke is he don't want her no more. He's fallen for some other gal. So Kate can't have him. She's stuck with me whether she likes it or not. She married me and I got her.'

'Is that right?' Kate hissed, staring at Josh. 'Who is she?'

'Ach, take no notice.' Logan got to his feet and shrugged. 'It's just Quinn. Drunk talk.'

'Where you goin', partner?' Quinn had returned to the table. 'I was gonna order supper.'

'I got someplace to go. Don't drink too much, Paco, we've all got an early start in the morning.' He stuck his Stetson on his head. 'Have a nice evening, folks.'

Kate watched him leave the hotel. Quinn could see she was seething. 'Aw, gee, now look what I done,' he grinned. 'Frightened him off again.'

'Where's he gone?'

'Who cares?'

'I said where?'

'The casino. The Four Aces. He's got some young dame who runs the blackjack game. Strikes me he's crazy about her. Now, what are we gonna eat, darlin'?'

It was midnight. Kate, a hooded shawl around her, was in the shadows watching the casino. Eventually the tall figure of Josh Logan emerged. He strolled off back up the street to the livery where he was bunking. Kate Quinn watched him go. She opened her bag and checked the small Cloverleaf house pistol. It was an improvement on a derringer, lying snugly compact in her purse, its snubnose, two-inch barrel hardly discernible. And it packed a lot more power.

'Good evening, Mrs Quinn,' the bartender greeted her. 'Your husband's not here.'

'No. I'll have a glass of white wine.'

She examined the crowded gambling tables and spotted the girl croupier in a far corner. 'Good,' she whispered. She bought some chips and strolled over.

Dawn Adamson eyed her astutely. A bunch of gents around the table were just giving up the game, going to cash up. 'You lookin' to play, Mrs Quinn?'

Kate faced her and tossed down some chips. Dawn flipped cards, scooped the chips in. Kate tried again.

'I'm glad I've caught you alone,' she said, and took the Cloverleaf from her purse, concealing it in the wide sleeve of her coat. 'I need to ask you a question.'

Dawn looked into the deadly hole of the small gun that was pointed at her breast. Nobody else was aware of what was going on. She tried to catch the eye of the pit boss, but he had his back to her.

'Yes,' she said. 'What do you want to know?'

'Is Josh Logan in love with you?'

'I don't know.' Dawn hesitated, rattled. 'I don't mind admitting I'm in love with him.'

'You can forget him. Fast. I oughta kill you now, but I'm gonna give you a chance. I want you out of town, out of this territory. By tomorrow. If I ever see you again I'll kill you.'

'Why?' Dawn protested. 'What have I ever done to you?'

'He's not in love with you. He just imagines he is. How can he be in love with a cheap little saloon chiseller? That's all you are. What can he see in you?'

'Maybe I should ask him next time I see him?'

'Don't try to be funny. There won't be any next time,' Kate sneered. 'Remember there's four bullets in this. If I don't kill you with the first, I'll finish you with the next three. You better remember that the next time time you walk along a darkened street.'

The two women eyed each other coldly for moments, then Kate tossed her chips down, stuffed the Cloverleaf away in her bag, turned and walked out.

TWELVE

Early the next morning Randy and Logan stocked up with shells for their rifles and revolvers, and made some purchases in the mining store, before driving the Concord coach along to meet Quinn. 'So, OK?' he called. 'Are we ready for a fight? Or are you going to pay the weasels?'

Quinn threw his hands into the air as he had them load a strongbox into the stage. 'Twenty *desperadoes*? We can't take them all on, Josh. There's only three of us.'

'Don't forget me,' Kate shrilled, joining them. 'I'm gonna be there to make sure they don't ride roughshod over you.'

'Ain't I told you it's too dangerous for you to be there?' Quinn growled. 'I said you're to stay here.'

'It's my house,' Kate insisted. 'And I'm gonna be there come hell or high water.'

'Be it on your own head. I ain't arguin' with you.

Come on, let's move. We gotta be there by tomorrow. *Domingo*, Crandal said. Sunday at noon.'

'Sorry, men, ain't taking no passengers today,' Logan told two miners who wanted to get on board. 'This is a private excursion. Just Mr and Mrs Quinn, the owners, riding inside.'

Logan climbed on to the box, cracked his whip to set the team moving, and gritted out to Randy, 'Whatever Quinn decides, I'm ready to play John Dog at his own game. Who knows, we might have a surprise for him.'

'Yeah,' Randy drawled. 'I cain't wait.'

When they got to Roswell they rose early and told the Mexicans to stay in their houses. Then they waited. That was what got to them, not knowing when Crandal would appear.

Kate had donned her split leather riding-skirt and hard-brimmed hat. She clomped about in high-button boots, a lightweight Pearson sporting rifle in her hands. 'What are you gonna do?' she asked her husband for the umpteenth time.

'Aw, I dunno. Leave me alone.' He had dragged his casket of gold pieces from the coach and dumped it on the parlour floor. 'What else can I do but pay 'em off?'

But Quinn was like a parrot with a sore head, talking constantly to himself, switching from one idea to the next, forever changing his mind.

110

'Why should I give them all my hard-earned cash?' he asked Logan. 'It ain't right. But I think I got to.'

Josh had checked his Colt Lightning revolver and was oiling his high-powered Thunderer rifle. He shrugged, peering out of the window. 'If it ain't right, why you got to?'

'Because he's a coward, that's why,' Kate sniped. 'He's terrified they'll blow us to kingdom come.'

'I ain't sceered. Tell her, Josh, it's the only sensible option.'

'Fear is a bad enemy. You gotta pull yourself together, Paco. Make your mind up. It's your cash. But you know my opinion.'

'Yes, Josh is a *man*,' Kate snapped. 'He's ready to fight.'

'I ain't no braver than the next man, I gave into 'em once,' Logan replied. 'Sometimes there ain't nuthin' else to do but stand up for your rights.'

'Good on you, Josh.' Randy was kneeling at the window, his Greener resting on the ledge. 'I smell gun-fightin' weather!'

They hung around glumly most of the day, trying to kill time. 'Maybe they won't turn up after all,' Kate remarked, as she made coffee.

Quinn tipped whiskey into his mug. He was already half-soused. He stood to go to peer from a window for the hundredth time. '*Christ*!' he growled. 'Here they come!'

111

They sprang to the windows. Logan knelt but did not show himself. 'Pull your rifle back, Randy,' he called. 'Let's surprise 'em.'

The line of bandits, all with rifles or carbines in their fists, came pounding towards them on their fiery mustangs, splashing across the streams, through the allotments, leaping over peasant carts, hauling in a snorting, stamping, menacing line before the house.

John Dog spurred Satan forward. 'We're here for what we're owed, Quinn. Bring it out an' there'll be no trouble.'

'He ain't havin' my money.' Quinn lurched to the door, his rifle in his hands. 'You lousy packrats can go play with yourselves. Get off my land.'

Quinn raised his rifle and snapped off a shot, grinning as John Dog's hat went spinning. He backed into the house. 'That showed him, eh, Josh? Who's yeller now?'

John Dog had swirled Satan around and scattered his men in all directions. At a safer distance he turned, his long black hair blowing across his face. 'That's the way you want it, Quinn?' He gave a shrill scream. 'Blast 'em outa there, boys.'

Suddenly they were all shooting at once, Kate, Quinn, Randy and Logan, giving the *viciosos* a fusillade of rattling gunfire. One man was catapulted backwards off his bronco. Another caught a bullet in his back as he spurred to move away. 'Got

112

him!' Logan cried, as his lead shattered a bandit's jaw in a spray of blood and bone.

The outlaws were galloping backwards and forwards, before and around the house. 'Cover the back, Randy,' Logan yelled. 'Don't let any of them jump on the roof.'

Everybody was yelling and blazing away, for he who hesitates is lost. Snap-shooting, ducking back, those inside had no time to think as bullets screamed and smashed into the walls, just to scramble up again, try to take aim as a rider thundered past, and shoot.

John Dog came pounding towards them on Satan, the lit fuse of a stick of dynamite fizzing in his fist. Josh, reluctant to bring down the fine beast, tried a split-second shot at his head. Crandal swerved away, hurling the stick. But Logan's reaction had made the throw go awry. A bedroom at the end of the house was blasted apart, instead.

'Two can play at that game,' Logan gritted out.

When he had visited the mining store in White Oaks he had bought a box of dynamite. While they waited he had rigged up booby traps at strategic points, running long fuses back to the house covered over by sand to disguise them. He leaned back and lit the first. He watched it go fizzing across to the foot of an old cart which several bandits were using as a vantage point from which to hammer bullets their way.

'*Boom!*' The cart went up and so did the bandits, limbs torn apart in a mess of rocks and splinters.

Others ran for cover as he set yet more fuses off, horses somersaulting as more explosions crashed out, men throwing up their hands and rolling away as the ground fountained beneath them.

Kate fired at one on the ground, making sure that he was dead. Logan glanced at her. Like them all, she had the killer instinct in her eyes, the bloodlust that comes when the enemy comes in sight. She gritted her teeth and sent a Mexican *hombre* bowling over like a shot jackrabbit.

Logan grabbed for another dynamite stick, lit it, and when he saw John Dog galloping towards them again, hurled it towards him. But Crandal veered clear as it exploded in the air.

'Damn him,' Logan said. 'I'm going after him.'

Suddenly, he heard Randy, at the back window, cry out. He dashed in and saw him lying on the floor holding his abdomen. 'They got me,' he groaned.

'Hold on, old-timer,' Logan dragged him to one side. He whipped off his bandanna and tried plugging the wound. But it didn't look good.

The face of a moustachioed man, probably the one who had shot Randy, appeared at the window. He was trying to climb up, a pistol in his hand. Quinn blasted him on to his back and roared, '*Hijo*

114

de puta! Try to kill me, would you? That's the only treatment you understand.'

'Cover me,' Logan said, and vaulted out of the window, his Lightning in his hand. He edged his way around the house and sprinted across the yard. A Mexican in a sombrero, carbine in hand, rose up from behind a pile of rubble caused by one of Logan's mines, and spat out a shot. Logan put a slug between his eyes. There was nothing to do but try to stay calm, ready to react. He took aim, fired at another who presented himself. There were bodies all over the place. But where was John Dog?

He prowled forward through the stream and trees, shooting twice more at adversaries, without success. Suddenly Satan was charging down upon him, John Dog swinging his machete. Logan rolled aside, got John Dog in his sights, but there was a dull click when he squeezed the trigger. He was out of lead.

It seemed Crandal was, too, for he had stuffed his Remington in his belt. He had the razor-sharp machete in his hand and swung it viciously at Logan. It could have severed his head if it connected. But he dodged and dived as the blade swished back and forth. A chunk of his hair was trimmed as he was forced backwards into a deeper stream. Crandal spurred Satan at him. The stallion lost his footing on the muddy bank, slithering and

115

kicking, and keeled over on to his side, pitching John Dog into the stream.

It gave Logan a chance to snatch up a discarded rifle to use it as a club as Satan floundered away and Crandal struggled to his feet, the machete still in his grip. Then they were locked in combat like two warriors of old, slashing and blocking and parrying, their weapons clanging against each other. . . .

Quinn had lurched out in front of the building. firing wildly. 'We've won, Kate!' he shouted, elated by the heat of battle. 'We're gonna be OK.' He turned back to the house doorway where his wife stood. 'Just you and me, baby. We'll start anew.'

'You think so?' She was pointing the rifle at his chest. Snakily her eyes switched back and forth to make sure nobody was watching, but amid the drifting black powder fumes, the general mayhem, who would notice? 'Think again.'

A blank look came into Quinn's dark eyes, like a dog about to be whipped. He reached a hand out to her, pleading, 'Honey, don't do this. I'll make us rich.'

Kate squeezed the trigger, once, twice, three times and her husband stumbled from side to side, groaning, 'No!' He collapsed at her feet. She quickly retreated back into the house as the sulphurous gunsmoke billowed.

Down at the stream the two men were still

locked in a struggle. Logan jumped back as the machete cut across his abdomen. He grimaced with the effort and caught the outlaw a mighty crack across his cranium with the rifle stock. 'Unh!' Crandal rolled his eyes and dropped the machete. Logan snatched it up and with all his strength sliced the blade into the outlaw's jugular. Blood fountained as John Dog screamed, and rolled back into the water.

Logan collapsed to one knee, gasping for breath, and watched his enemy's blood colour the sunlit whorls of the stream. John Dog was quite dead. 'Waal,' he drawled, as he got up, 'you can't say you didn't ask for it, pal.'

He waded across and tried to catch hold of Satan, but the stallion showed his teeth, whinnying and going up on his back legs, kicking out. 'Steady, boy,' Josh soothed, hanging on to him, seeing the deep spur scars in his sides. 'You remember me, doncha? Nobody ain't gonna hurt ya no more.'

Most of Crandal's mob lay in attitudes of death, others were moaning with their injuries, and yet others were climbing on to mustangs, making their escape, heading away across the prairie as though all the devils in hell were after them.

Logan led the stallion back and stopped, surprised to find Quinn, too, laid out dead.

'He should never have showed himself outside,'

Kate cried, pointing to the running men. 'One of those bastards pumped three bullets into him.'

She hugged the tall Texan to her. 'Oh, Josh, thank God you're safe.'

'Yeah, I'm safe enough,' he muttered, somewhat puzzled by Quinn's position, and easing himself from her. 'How's Randy?'

'You don't ask about *me*, if I'm all right. All you worry about is Randy. You and he are like an old married couple.'

'We been partners a long time, Kate.' He strode into the house but was glad to find Newbolt sitting up. 'How ya doin', fella?'

Randy forced a grin to his hard face. 'Guess I'll pull through.' He was still holding the blood-soaked bandanna to his belly. 'I been gut-shot afore.'

'Quinn ain't been so lucky. He's lying out there dead. So's John Dog. I'm gonna send a Mex'can fer the doc to attend to you. We need to get that bullet out. And, maybe, those outa Quinn, too.'

The villagers had crept from their adobes and were looting the bodies of boots, belts, whatever valuables they possessed. Crandal's gold teeth were prised out, an extra lucky find! The corpses would be hauled over to a communal grave and buried without ceremony.

Logan pulled Quinn into the shade so he didn't

118

get ripe in the sun. He would, at least, get a head-stone in the local cemetery. On an impulse he used his knife to dig out the slugs from him. Three smallish ones. Twenty-eights. The same calibre as Kate's lightweight lady's rifle.

She had brushed her hair and tidied up a bit, and was pouring them drinks when he went back inside. They had helped Randy into a bed in another room and were alone.

'Have some of Quinn's corn whiskey,' she said. 'He won't be needing it no more.'

'Nope, I guess not.' He took a swig from the tumbler and glanced her way. She looked so cool and confident. 'It was quite a fight. How did you say he got it?'

'Why worry about Quinn any more? He's gone. We're alive, Josh.' She raised her glass and gave him a dazzling smile. 'Now we're alone you know what I have to say.'

'Don't say it.'

'We have got everything, darling. Everything we ever wanted. We're rich.' Kate put the glass aside and stepped across the kitchen to hug herself into him. 'Oh, Josh. We can start to live again. Just like last summer.'

'What about Brad?'

'Brad?' The question flurried her. 'What do you mean?'

'Your winter driver. He's got a lot to say about

you, Kate. It kinda surprised me.'

'Brad? You haven't been listening to him? He's jealous. It's all lies. Yes, he tried to come on to me. That's why we had to get rid of him. Who do you believe, him or me?'

'I'm inclined to say him.'

'Don't be like this, Josh.' She stared into his face as if in anguish. 'This is our chance. Don't throw it away. I'm desperate, Josh. I need you. Help me.'

'This time I'm helping myself.'

'You mean that croupier girl?'

'Now I think about it, yes.'

'Don't be absurd. She's nobody. Just a cheap little saloon trollop. Have you gone out of your mind? What can she give you?'

'I dunno. But one thing I do know – I can trust her.'

'I can't let you go now. Not after what I've done for you.'

'What have you done, Kate?' He showed her the three bullets in his palm. 'Would these have anything to do with it?'

'Where did you find those?'

'Where do you think – in Quinn. You shot him, Kate.'

'Sure I killed him. I did it for us.'

'You're crazy, Kate. I never wanted you to do that. I told you a long time ago it was over 'tween us.'

'It ain't over,' she cried. 'I'll kill that bitch. She's not having you. I'll kill you, too, if you try to stop me.'

The lanky Pat Garrett stepped into the kitchen at that point, surprising them both. 'You won't be killing nobody, Kate. Not any more.'

Azariah Wilde joined him, officious-looking in his suit and derby. 'We heard everything. I am a lawman, too. Your words amount to a full confession. You will be charged with the premeditated murder of your husband.'

'Yeah, I'll gladly be a witness,' Randy called from the other room.

The law officers had heard the shooting as they rode towards the village. When they arrived, seeing all the carnage, they had proceeded on foot cautiously towards the house. When they heard voices coming from the open kitchen window Garrett had beckoned Wilde to pause and listen.

'I didn't say I murdered anybody,' Kate snarled, backing away, and pointing to Josh. 'It was him, Logan. He murdered him. He wanted our money. Don't you see? I'm the grieving widow here.'

'Save all that for the judge, Kate,' Garrett drawled. 'You'll git the chance to say a few more last words on the scaffold.'

'You lousy filth.' Kate pulled the Cloverleaf snubnose from a kitchen drawer and aimed it at Logan. 'You're the cause of this. You an' your *prin-*

121

ciples. If I can't have you, that bitch you fancy certainly ain't going to.'

She squeezed the trigger and the .28 razored Logan's cheek as he turned his body instinctively away. She fired again, her face contorted with anger, but as she did so Garrett reached out a long arm of the law, grabbed her wrist and twisted her arm up. The slug splintered the ceiling. Garrett held her by her throat with his left hand, and disarmed her by superior strength.

'Hot damn, Kate,' he drawled. 'Take it easy. I'm gonna have to cuff ya.'

'Take your hands off me,' she screamed. 'I'll break you, Garrett. How dare you touch me?'

'Calm down, for God's sake.' Garrett snapped manacles on her wrists behind her. 'I reckon I'd better read you your rights to make this legal. Then I'm taking you up to Lincoln.'

Kate Quinn was snapping, snarling, spitting, luridly cursing and threatening them with hell. 'Let me go,' she screamed. 'You've no right to do this.'

'Sweetheart,' Garrett shouted. 'I got every right. You better get used to your new lodging. It's gonna be my jailhouse.'

THIRTEEN

When Josh Logan drove the stage into White Oaks, alone on the box and with no passengers, Dawn Adamson hurried over from the Four Aces, along with curious bystanders. Logan climbed wearily down and winced, holding his abdomen as a line of blood dampened his shirt.

'Josh,' she cried. 'What's happened?'

'A helluva lot,' he said. 'No need to worry. This is just a machete cut, courtesy of John Dog Crandal. It'll heal.'

'What's that burn on your cheek?'

'Aw, a present from Kate.'

He tried to push through the crowd but they demanded to know what was going on.

'John Dog's dead. Quinn's dead. Kate Quinn has been charged with her husband's murder,' he shouted. 'That's all I'm gonna say 'til the trial.'

Of course, they were screaming and shouting,

wanting to know more. He put an arm around Dawn's waist, more or less scooping her up, and pushed through to the Golden Garter. He clanged the bell for the manager. 'I wanna room,' he said, turning to her. 'Just want to git outa the way. You wanna come up with me?'

She hesitated, then nodded. 'OK.'

'What's your favourite tipple?'

'California white.'

'Right, that'll do. Make sure it's iced, mister.'

'You want a double room?'

His brow furrowed, questioning, as he met her warm brown eyes. 'I dunno.'

She shrugged and smiled. 'Why not?'

'Right,' he smiled. 'Make that two for dinner tonight.'

When she slipped off the rustling silk dress and underwear she revealed a body that was neat-waisted and curvaceous, soft, warm and white as fresh milk. 'You're like an oasis in the desert to me,' Logan said, drawing her to him. She stood, naked but for her black stockings and gold crucifix on its necklace.

'You're not the first,' she murmured, as they kissed and caressed, 'but you're the first in a long, long time.'

And, as they rolled over on to the bed and made love, in spite of his wound, it struck him how easy

124

and natural it was with her. They fitted together like two halves of a black-eye bean, as if they were made for each other. . . .

'I was born into a world gone mad,' she told him over their candlelit dinner. 'The Siege of Corinth. My mother had brought me in when I was three years old from our place in the country for protection from the invading northern hordes. All I remember is the booming and whistling of cannon fire, collapsing walls, screams and shouts of terror. When the city finally surrendered we were starving and in rags and that's how it was for the rest of the war. Somehow my mother kept us alive.'

Her daddy, too, had survived as the Rebs retreated, fighting desperately with the South Louisiana Cavalry to the inevitable end. He had returned, limbs and body intact, but somehow shattered in his soul. 'He had always been a gambling man, working the riverboats, from N'awleans up to Corinth, Memphis aad St Louis and back again,' she said. 'When he had a big win we lived in clover. But when he lost we were back on the breadline.'

Dawn's mother died of a fever, and her father took her along with him on his trips after that. 'I was brought up in smoky, chandeliered salons, listening to the clicking of dice, sitting behind him, watching every card he played. It was a bit of a shock when I realized that the moves he made weren't exactly legal as he rooked the wealthy ladies and gents. Even more of a shock when they banned us from the paddle steamers along the whole of the Mississippi.'

'So, that's when you headed West?'

'He tried Dodge, Denver, Santa Fe. I was growing up by then, sixteen or seventeen, and an expert blackjack and poker player myself. Then there was some sort of trouble a month or so ago and we were moving south again. He had heard that White Oaks would be lucrative, but he made the mistake of stopping off at Fort Sumner.'

'Not a wise move,' Logan said. 'Those boys play rough.'

'Yes, and they sure don't like to lose. Two men, Charley Billings and Seth Smith, accused him of cheating and he was gunned down before my eyes. He's buried in the cemetery there.'

'Gambling ain't a healthy life style,' Josh mused. 'The dice are loaded against livin' long, 'specially in these parts.'

'He had that terrible addiction. He had to play on and on to the last throw. Me, I love to play the cards, but he certainly put me off cheatin' or losing my cash on 'em.'

'So,' Logan enquired, as he lit her cigarette and a cheroot for himself, 'who was the first one you mentioned? If it ain't ungentlemanly to enquire?'

126

'A mistake.' She smoothed back her thick black tresses and trickled smoke from her crimson lips. 'The spittin' image of my daddy, a handsome gambler man, but twenty years younger. I was head over heels with the two-timin' twister. But that was back on the boats.'

'I get the picture,' Logan smiled. 'So you ended up at Fort Sumner, down and out, with no place to go, and Peg Leg Fanny and her travellin' circus came along.'

'What was I to do? She said she was opening a casino at Stinking Springs and needed a croupier. Call me crazy, but I imagined that was all the job entailed. I soon found out it wasn't. Some casino!'

'Yeah, Peg Leg told me you lit out and why.'

'On the back of Clarence's mule. That black banjoist. He's with the orchestra at the Four Aces. A nice guy. For a former slave he don't have no chip on his shoulder, just lets the world roll along.'

They were interrupted by a reporter from the *White Oaks Advertiser* wanting to find out what he knew about the deaths of Quinn and Crandal. 'All I know is that Kate's been accused,' Logan drawled, getting to his feet. He glanced at Dawn and took her arm. 'C'm on, honey. Maybe we should have an early night.'

'That,' she smiled, 'sounds like a good idea.'

'We got a problem,' Pat Garrett told Logan when

he rode in to White Oaks. 'Kate Quinn is looking for the sympathy vote.'

He handed Logan a copy of the *Las Vegas Gazette* with the banner headline: 'Quinn's Widow Hounded by Garrett.'

Mr Hieronymous Epstein, Kate's attorney, was reported to have stated at her preliminary appearance at Lincoln Court, 'This was a tragic accident, nothing more, nothing less.'

He described the incident when 'the Quinns had been gallantly defending their home from attack by Crandal's merciless killers against overwhelming odds' and said, 'In the noise and confusion, amid the rolling clouds of gunsmoke, Mrs Quinn, not realizing that her husband had ventured outside, pointed her lady's rifle at a figure coming towards her. Before she could ascertain who it was the rifle accidentally discharged,' he said. 'She was appalled to see her beloved husband had been killed by her own hand.'

Mr Epstein proposed that the 'rridiulous and insulting' charge of first degree homicide be summarily dismissed. 'Surely this lady should be left in peace to mourn beside her husband's grave?'

Sheriff Garrett, who, it was said, had brought the charge against the widow of one of the territory's most prominent citizens, asked at this point, 'How does Mr Epstein account for the fact that I have three bullets taken from Quinn's body, fired by Kate Quinn's rifle?'

'We have only your word for that,' Epstein replied. 'The word of a gunman notorious for ambushing his victims, like Charley Bowdre and William Bonney, who might well have been reha-bilitated into the community, and killing them without warning, in Bonney's case in a darkened room, without giving him the chance to surrender. What kind of man is that?'

He added, 'In my opinion the sheriff is trying to cash in on his current, sensational publicity nationwide by bringing yet another attention-grab-bing charge in his self-promoting bids for higher office.'

When Garrett objected to this, Epstein told the judge, 'This case has a very unsavoury smell about it. The sheriff's only other witness to back his claim that this poor woman – in a state of shock – admit-ted to the alleged crime is some ne'er-do-well drifter, a former employee, a stage-driver with a grudge against her.'

Making an application for bail, the attorney pleaded that the widow should be allowed to attend her husband's funeral and arrange his affairs, which she could not do in the confines of prison. 'This lady is of the highest moral character, has worked tirelessly beside her husband to build up this territory and to bring a civilizing influence to the rugged ways of southern New Mexico. There would not be the slightest risk that she would abscond.'

'District Judge George Beaney said that for the present, while investigations were concluded, the charge would stand, but granted Mrs Quinn bail until the trial in the sum of two thousand dollars,' the report concluded.

'I see what you mean,' Logan said, giving a scoffing grunt of dismay as he laid the *Gazette* aside. 'Kate's painting us two as the villains of the piece. The violins are certainly being played on her behalf.'

'You're not kidding.' They were in the bar of the Golden Garter and the tall lawman tipped them both a slug of whiskey from the bottle. 'In the past, judges and jurors round here have been frightened to bring in guilty verdicts due to threats of violence. Now they'll be sceered folk'll say they're hounding a poor innocent widder-lady. You can't win.'

'What about your pal in the derby? Ain't he giving evidence?'

'No, he's had to back out.' Garrett lowered his voice. 'Secret service. It would blow his cover. He's working around here on unearthing whoever it is has been forging them dollar bills.'

'Well,' Logan replied, savouring the liquor. 'Epstein's right in one thing. This whole case *has* an unsavoury ring to it. Maybe you should bury it?'

'What, and let that murdering bitch get away scot free? Don't you go backing out on me, Logan. You're my main witness.'

'Yeah? Well, Kate ain't gonna give up easy. She'll hit us with every underhand trick she can conjure.' Logan slammed down his glass and headed for the door. 'So long, sheriff. I got work to do.'

There was no way he could go on working as stage driver for Kate Quinn, so he had tied up the loose ends, paid out the last of Quinn's expenses cash on hay at the livery for the horses, and suspended the service.

He had found himself a job attending to the broncos along at the Martinez corral. It didn't pay much but it would keep him alive.

Meantime, he had sent a letter with the fast rider, care of Ash Upson, postmaster at Roswell, for Randy, telling him to take it easy, and come on up to White Oaks when he had recovered from the gunshot wound.

Logan had had to move out of the hotel and lodge above the stables, which was where, later that night, Dawn Adamson found him.

'Looks like I'm down and out agin, don't it?' he muttered. 'I had hopes I might make somethang of myself with the stage line.'

'You're young. You've plenty of time. We both have.' As she lay in his arms on his blanket on the

131

straw, and listened to horses shuffling below, she asked, 'What are you apologizing for? I don't mind.'

'What, the smell of a man who shovels horse shit?'

Dawn laughed and kissed him. 'I like you for who you are. Anyway, this is quite romantic.'

'Well,' he muttered, 'I had planned on asking you to marry me.'

'But' – she looked up at him, mischievously – 'you don't need to now?'

'No, it ain't that. A man needs some sorta steady future, somethang to offer a gal if he's gonna git wed. I ain't got nuthin' to offer you right now.'

'If you're offerin' yourself that's all I need. So when's the happy day gonna be?'

Josh suddenly smiled, forgetting his troubles. 'Let's say a week. How's that suit you?'

'Suits me fine. And don't worry about cash problems. I got a good job and income. We can make do until you find your feet again, Josh.'

'I ain't got no intention of being a kept man. I been thinking, when this business with Kate is over, of heading up to Colorado. They call it God's own country. We could homestead some land, build up our own ranch.'

'We could even,' she smiled, 'run our own hotel and casino, before the kids come along.'

'That's the last thing we need right now,' he

132

muttered. 'Maybe one day.'

'In that case, if you're gonna make love to me, you better be careful,' she smiled, as he rolled her over into the hay.

But their troubles, for the moment, were not to be little ones. 'I've lost my job,' Dawn told him, a week later. 'The pit boss called me into his office, showed me two peculiar letters, one supposedly in the hand of Peg Leg Fanny, saying I worked as a croupier for her and absconded with a large sum of the takings.'

'And the other?'

'From somebody in Santa Fe I'd never heard of, claiming that I worked with my father as a gambling team, that we'd both been caught cheating and banned from the riverboats. And that more recently we'd been run out of Santa Fe.'

'It's Kate,' he said. 'She musta hired a private eye to dig up dirt. Those letters are obviously fakes. Whoever heard of Peg Leg Fanny puttin' pen to paper? She's trying to ruin us.'

'Unfortunately, the pit boss didn't think so. He said I was a security risk. He *did* offer me a job as a so-called waitress. Maybe I'll have to take him up on it.'

'No way,' Logan growled. 'You ain't doing that.'

'So, what shall we do, Josh?'

'I sure don't know. Guess what? Kate's accused me of stealing cash from Quinn and her. The two-hundred-dollar expenses cash. Garrett says she aims to haul *me* up in court.'

'She's crazy.'

'You're right. Mentally unhinged might be more accurate. But she's gunnin' for us in a very poisonous way, that's for sure. You got any savings?'

'Yes,' Dawn replied. 'Why?'

'I think you better take them out and go. We gotta split up for a while. Go someplace she won't find you. Back East. That's all she wants. To get rid of you.'

'But that would be giving in to her.'

'It ain't right you should suffer 'cause of me. I'll find you when this is all through.'

'No, I ain't going. There's only one way I'm leaving, that's as your wife.'

'It's you who's crazy.' He hugged her to him. 'But I love ya for it. I can't leave 'til I've faced down this charge of theft agin' me. I gotta clear my name. But you gotta git outa the firin' line, doncha see?'

'But how can I go? There's no stage out any more.'

'I'll hire a rig. We'll drive to Las Vegas. We'll git hitched there. Then you can catch the train someplace safe.'

'I *have* got an aunt in Kansas City. I *could* stay. But you make sure you write me.'

'It's a deal. It's you I'm worried about. But don't

worry. Everythang'll be OK. I'll meet you in a month or so an' we'll be together again.'

'Good.' Dawn linked her arms around his neck, holding tight. 'I can't give you up, Josh. I love you too much.'

FOURTEEN

It would take them a good five days to drive the 250 miles to Las Vegas in the hired lightweight rig, even if they kept up a steady clip. It was wild, rough country and travellers were few and far between.

They reached Lincoln the first night and Logan called in the sheriff's office. Garrett told him Kate was pressing the charge of theft of expenses cash. 'I'm gonna grant you a bail bond in the sum of fifty dollars to appear at court here in ten days' time,' the lawman drawled. 'I'll trust you not to abscond. Kate's telling everybody who'll listen that it was you killed her husband, not her. There were no direct witnesses, of course, but when her trial comes up I'll stick by what I overheard. The trouble is the more she repeats them lies the more likely folks are to believe her.'

They had a few drinks in Rosie's saloon and bedded down overnight in Garrett's empty jail. When they trotted their pair of horses into Roswell

136

the next afternoon Logan located Randy at the 'dobe of a Mexican family. He was sitting outside beneath a bamboo canopy, tugging thoughtfully at his moustache danglers.

'You're gittin' wed?' he beamed, when they told him the news. 'I'd sure like to be your best man, but I ain't sure I'm up to riding to Vegas just yet.' He had eased himself painfully out of his chair. 'This hole in my side's taking a while to heal.'

Logan slipped ten dollars into Randy's palm to cover his keep as they left. By then it was getting dark and he was keen to slip away without being seen by Kate, if she was home. 'Take it easy, old-timer,' he called out. 'See ya on my way back.'

They pressed on north along the Pecos as the moon showed. 'I feel like a fugitive,' Dawn said, as she slipped an arm through his. 'Like it's me who's to blame, not Kate.'

When he deemed the horses needed to rest they laid out on their blankets on the riverbank. Logan didn't light a fire for it was dangerous country. There were still plenty of ne'er-do-wells about who might not think twice about trying to rob them, or worse.

With the dawn they went clipping on, following the narrow trail across the prairie. He had planned to give Fort Sumner a wide berth, but when one of the horses lost a shoe Logan changed his mind. 'We'll have to call in at the blacksmith's there,' he said. 'We can't risk her going lame.'

He didn't like the idea, but what else could he do?

Paulita's pantalettes were dangling from one ankle as her bedsprings creaked and she hung on to Seth Smith. '*Mi amor*,' she groaned. 'That was beautiful.'

'Yeah?' Smith raised himself above her, sweat streaming from him, and grinned toothily in the half-darkness. 'I allus aim to please.'

'Don't worry,' the girl said, as they paused, listening intently for any sounds from her parents' room. 'Papa still snores.'

Seth extricated himself from her, dragging on his trousers and shirt. 'All that action's given me a thirst. I'm goin' over to Beaver's for a beer.'

'Darling, don't leave me,' Paulita pleaded.

'I'll be back.' Seth grinned. 'For seconds.'

'Please don't be long,' she moaned. 'Hurry back to me.'

The youth jammed his plug hat on his head at a jaunty angle and climbed out of the open window, not bothering to put on his boots, just picking up his Smith & Wesson, letting it hang from one finger as he strolled across the parade ground barefoot. He looked as if he didn't have a care in the world.

'Hi,' he called to Charley Billings as he sauntered into the saloon, bought a beer, and joined him. 'Wimmin'! Don't they cling?'

'Yeah.' Charley grinned. 'Funny how once ye've done it they don't seem so int'restin' no more. At least, 'til next time.'

'Ugly Dave' Richards had left Tom at the hide-out and come into the fort to find out where they had got to. He glowered at them. 'No woman ever got me tied to her apron strings,' he muttered. 'You're crazy hanging round here. When we going to Mexico?'

'*Mañana, amigo.*' Seth gave him a reckless grin, raising his glass. 'Relax.'

'*Mañana!*' Ugly Dave spat the word with contempt. 'You're gittin' like the damn Mex'cuns, Smith. It's allus *mañana.*'

'What's the hurry?' Charley stretched out his long, leather-clad legs and eased the revolver stuck in his belt. He poured them whiskeys from the bottle. 'Nobody ain't gonna bother us. We left no witnesses.'

It was about midnight and the saloon was remarkably quiet, just a bunch of Mexicans swapping stories in one corner, another gently strumming a guitar, and three Anglos, harmless characters with whom they were familiar, sharing a bottle in another corner.

'True,' Seth said, placing his revolver on the table. 'Think I'll git me another beer.'

Logan drove the high-wheeled buggy through the gates of Fort Sumner in the moonlight, past the Maxwell house, and across the dusty parade ground to the smithy. The stable doors were closed so he roused the blacksmith from his living quarters. 'I'll pay double if you'll put a shoe on tonight,' he said. 'We're in a kinda hurry to get to Vegas.'

'It would mean rekindling my coals,' the blacksmith protested. 'It'll take an age. Aw, OK. You'll have to hang about.'

Maybe the sight of Dawn's proferred dollars made him agreeable. 'I'm starving,' she said. 'Is there anywhere we can eat?'

'Only Beaver's saloon this time of night.'

Logan frowned, pursing his lips. He didn't like it. Not the thought of going in there. Not with the girl in tow. But his stomach rumbled too, at the prospect of the sonuvabitch stew – bits of all sorts of offal chucked in – that Beaver kept bubbling on his stove.

'Guess we can give it a try,' he drawled, sticking his thumbs in his trousers' pockets and setting off across the parade ground. Dawn swung along beside him, hooking her arm into his. 'But the sooner we git outa here the better it'll be.'

Moths fluttered around a hurricane lamp and

the air inside Beaver's saloon was warm from the pot-belly stove and murky with tobacco smoke. 'What kinda vittles you got?' Logan asked at the bar.

The old saloon-keeper slid two bowls towards them and pointed to a cauldron on the stove. 'Help yourselves.'

'What have we got here?' Seth called mockingly from behind him. 'If it ain't the stage driver.'

Logan froze for moments. 'Shee-it,' he gritted out.

'Who's the purty gal?' Charley asked, his fingers playing over the butt of his revolver. 'Tasty, ain't she?'

Logan put his gun hand on her arm and pressed Dawn aside. 'Keep well outa the way,' he muttered. 'This is 'tween me and them.'

He turned to face them, registering each one's position as the men in the room began to scrape their chairs back out of the shooting line. 'I understand you two killed this young lady's father,' he whispered. 'That weren't a nice thang to do.'

'What's he talking about?' Ugly Dave asked.

'The gambling man's daughter,' Seth recalled. 'Yeah, nice of her to come back. And you, too, mister. You got some grievance with us?'

'Walked right into a trap, ain't he? Knows it, too.' Charley Billings stood slowly and stalked away to one side, easing the fingers of his right hand, his

141

eyes fixed on the Texan. 'Ever see a man look so sceered?'

Ugly Dave gave a caustic laugh, and got out of his chair, pulling his six-gun in its holster around from under his beer gut. He hitched up his gunbelt, moving away, preparing to strike. 'Say your prayers, pal. Don't worry, I'll personally attend to the li'l gal for ya. Hey, maybe we could sell her down in Mexico?'

'You cowards,' Dawn shrieked, from her position by the stove. 'Why don't you fight fair? Josh would willingly meet you one at a time.'

'Josh, is it?' Seth crowed. 'Ain't that sweet? Allus like to know who I'm killing.'

But he screamed as Dawn hurled the cauldron at him and the boiling contents hit him in the face. His Smith & Wesson was out as he staggered, but his shot went wild. And he hit the ground as Logan's Lightning thundered, the slug crashing into the youth's chest.

The distraction made Ugly Dave flinch, and blink stupidly, losing valuable moments before he squeezed a bullet from his six-gun. Logan ducked down on one knee and Dave's lead smashed into the woodwork of the bar. Logan made no mistake with his second shot, sending Ugly Dave back-pedalling out of the open door.

But the Lightning was sent skittling from his grasp as Charley fired and his slug hit the steel cylinder of Logan's gun.

'You jest hold it there down on your knees, mister.' Charley grinned through the curling gunsmoke, his spurs jingling as he edged closer, and kicked the Lightning well out of range into a corner. 'And you, sweetheart, come over and jine him where I can keep an eye on you both.'

'You've won,' Dawn replied, her dress rustling as she stepped across. 'Leave us be. We'll go. You can't kill us both in cold blood.'

'Cain't I?' Charley's dark-hued face beneath his hat brim was set in a determined leer as he pointed his gun at Logan's head. 'Down on both knees, you bastard. You've asked for it. You've killed my buddies.'

'No!' Dawn screamed as a gunshot reverberated, jumping with shock, her eyes wide with fear. But it was Charley, the rugged frontiersman and killer, who suddenly twisted his body with a groan of pain, throwing up his hands and pitched to one side to lie prone on the dusty floor. Blood oozed through the back of his shirt.

Young Brad McNulty stepped forward from where he had been sitting with the other men, Logan's smoking Lightning in his hand. 'I wouldn't shoot a man in the back . . . not normally,' he stuttered. 'But it weren't right. Three against one. Is he dead?'

'Better put another slug in him to make sure,'

Beaver said, coming up from behind the bar. 'Charley was a tough old goat.'

As Brad did as he was bid Logan got to his feet and hugged Dawn to him. 'You'd better do the same to that ugly one outside,' he said. 'Me, I could do with a beer.'

Others of the men had made a dive for Seth, the lucky one brandishing his Smith & Wesson.

'Sling the stiffs outside,' Beaver roared, ' 'fore they stink up my establishment.'

He passed a tankard of beer to Logan. 'It's on the house, mister. That's a plucky gal you got there.'

Just then, however, there was the sound of a posse of horsemen drawing up outside. They were led into the saloon by a tall rancher, Old John Chisum. 'What's going on?' he demanded.

'Feller here,' Beaver said, indicating Logan, 'just cleaned out a nest of rats.'

'They're the ones we were looking for,' Chisum replied. 'They gunned down two of my boys, sold the stolen cattle to Murphy. We strung him up from his barn rafter after he told us who they were. Then we followed their trail.' He gripped Logan's hand. 'Much obliged to you, stranger.'

Logan winced, shaking his bleeding knuckles. 'I'd be a dead man,' he groaned, 'if young Brad hadn't intervened.'

The hunky Brad looked elated. 'He's the first

man I ever killed.'

'Yeah? Well,' Logan drawled. 'I'll have my Lightning back now.'

'In that case you'd better share the reward,' Chisum announced, taking a wad of notes from his pocket and counting them out on to the bar. 'I put up a hundred dollars on each of those rats' heads.'

Without further ado he led his men back outside. They mounted their mustangs and rode off into the night.

'Waal, whadda ya know, things are looking up!' Logan split the cash, shoving one pile towards Brad, one wad into his pocket, and passing the third to Dawn, winking at her. 'That's yours, honey. You earned it.'

He finished his beer and settled down with Dawn. 'Looks like we've lost our bowls of stew. What's all that caterwaulin'?'

'Aw, it's that Paulita Jennings,' Beaver told them providing them with plates of ham, instead. 'She was crazy about that spineless snake, Seth Smith. She's out there tearing her hair out. Hey, maybe you should console her, Brad?'

'Not tonight.' The young man grinned, ruefully. 'She'd be likely to crack a branding iron over my head, the mood she's in.'

Logan finished his meal, pushed his plate away, stuck out his long legs, and studied his Lightning. 'That advert of Colt's when I bought this gun said

I'd have six trusty friends in times of trouble,' he mused. 'That's sure proved true these past weeks.'

'It all depends who's firing the gun,' Dawn said. 'That's what counts. And, although Paulita has yet to realize it, your gun has probably done her a good turn.'

FIFTEEN

In Las Vegas Logan smartened up, buying a dark-blue bandanna and light-blue shirt, polishing his boots and giving them a shine. Dawn was radiant in a dress of silver tulle and a mantilla as they stood before the justice of the peace in the city hall. Logan had tipped an old galoot a dollar to act as witness. They treated him to a few drinks in their hotel after the ceremony and he insisted on showering them with a packet of rice.

'It didn't seem much like a wedding,' Dawn said, as they climbed the stairs to their room for a late siesta. 'I always dreamed of a church one with lots of friends around.'

'Maybe we'll do it in style again some day,' Logan said. 'Soon as I've sorted myself out.'

'Still, at least I've got your ring,' she murmured, as she snuggled in the bed by his side and twisted it on her finger. 'It makes me feel good.'

147

'Are you happy now?' he asked, as he kissed her and held her naked body close.

'Of course, I always feel good with you.'

But, to tell the truth, both were saddened by the fact that too soon they would be torn apart.

'I guess it's time to get ready to go,' Dawn sighed, as it grew dark, hardly able to bear the thought of leaving him. But they were both agreed, and her train was due to pull out at 10 p.m.

Randy Newbolt had made a last-minute decision to try to get to Las Vegas for the wedding. But it was his first time back in the saddle, and, with the sun baking down as he rode north along the Pecos, sweat poured from him and he was forced to take several rests, feeling kinda whoozy. It was all over by the time he arrived. At the hotel they told him the newlyweds had left fifteen minutes before for the railroad depot. Well, maybe he could still wish them well.

It was a good walk from the hotel to the rail station and Logan strode along with Dawn in the moonlight as the big engine with its tall stack got up steam. There was a bustle of passengers climbing into the carriages for the journey back East.

Logan handed Dawn's valise to a porter, then they lingered for a final kiss on the track by the steps to her compartment. 'We'll be together soon, honey,' he whispered, huskily.

He still had her fingers in his as she turned away to board. There was the sound of drumming hoofs and at first he thought somebody had left it late to catch the train. A white mare was charging towards them along the side of the track. It was almost upon them before he saw a woman's grinning face beneath a black hat. She wore a billowing cape, and the gleam of a revolver could be seen in her hand. It was aimed point blank at the startled Dawn. Too late Logan tried to intervene. There was the crash and flash of the explosion as Kate Quinn squeezed the trigger, and rode on her way, screeching with witchlike laughter, to disappear into the darkness.

Dawn cried out with shock as she lay, collapsed, half on the train steps. She slowly slid down to the track, staring at him with horror. 'Why?' she pleaded. 'Why us?'

'Dawn, honey, you're going to be OK,' he soothed, as he held her cradled in his arms. 'Hold on.'

But he could see blood flowering on the breast of her tight-bodiced dress as she groaned, 'Josh, don't leave me.'

'I'll never leave you, sweetheart,' he whispered.

As he was riding towards the depot Randy suddenly heard a gunshot, screams, shouts of anger and dismay. Then, galloping towards him along the track away from the scene came a white horse ridden by what appeared to be a man astride, in a black hat and cape, a gun in hand.

'What's this jasper been up to?' Randy muttered, raising his Greener. 'Halt!' he shouted.

But the rider charged straight at him, firing several shots that whistled past his ears. Randy could do nothing but reply. He levelled his piece with an iron grip and, from forty feet, his bullet blasted a hole through Kate Quinn's chest.

'*Hay-zoose!*' he hissed, as he knelt down and met her glittering eyes. 'Kate! I didn't know it was you.'

'You bastard!' She coughed out her blood. But the light in her eyes was fading and she was soon gone.

'Nobody wants to kill a woman,' Randy told the inquest two days later. 'But she looked like some desperado comin' at me in the dark.' He was relieved that the coroner absolved him of all blame.

Logan had sat for several days and nights beside Dawn's bed. It was touch and go. But gradually she pulled round and she could sit up and take some broth. He moved her to the house of a widow lady who would be glad of a few dollars to nurse her back to health. She had lost a lot of blood but was out of danger.

In the meantime Logan had taken a job as a bartender just to make ends meet. It was a bit of a rough house so he had to quell any trouble, too. A right to the jaw generally sufficed. One day a boy gave him a note summoning him to the law office of Hieronymous Epstein. 'What the hell's he want?' he wondered.

'So, you're this character Logan I've been slandering in the courts?' The lawyer beamed at him from among his books and papers. 'No hard feelings. I was acting on Kate's instructions. Now, of course, all charges are dropped.'

Logan shrugged. 'So, what's this all about?'

'I've been sorting out the Quinns' affairs. Relatives popping outa the woodwork from all over the place. Their mining assets made them rich. However, that's nothing to do with you.'

'So, what is? I hope you ain't suggesting I owe 'em—?'

'No, not at all. It seems you were their legal partner in the stage company. It was never dissolved. So you now own the whole caboodle, offices, horses, and there's a new coach that had been ordered by Mr Quinn. You'll find it at your depot. It's been held in escrow. The corrals, the balance in the stage account, it's all yours.'

'Waal,' Josh drawled, 'you could knock me down with feather.'

'I'd be happy to represent you, Mr Logan, take

151

care of all the legal flapdoodle.'

'Sure, why not?' Logan tipped his hat over one eye and scratched the back of his head. 'It ain't the way I would have liked it to happen, but if Quinn's set me up in business I guess I ain't gonna look a gift horse in the mouth.'

Outside, he was still feeling pretty dazed, but he found Randy Newbolt and took him along to Quinn's yard. 'Ain't it a beauty,' he said. 'We're back in business, pal.'

The coach they were admiring was being given a finishing touch by a painter, so Logan gave him some instructions, then when he was done, a team in the traces, they drove the coach through the town.

'What's all the commotion?' Dawn smiled, as she rose from her garden chair.

'How you feelin' today, honey?'

'Fine. I guess I've been lucky. I feel really good.'

'You're gonna feel even better when you take a look outside.'

He blindfolded her and led her out to the garden gate, then whisked the bandanna away. 'Behold.'

'Oh, my golly!' Dawn stared at the spanking new Concord coach. Enscrolled on the door in gold paint was 'Logan Express Stage Lines.'

'I can't believe my eyes!' she cried. 'Does it mean it's yours?'

'Ours,' he said, opening and beckoning her inside. 'Fancy a ride?'

They descended at the town's best hotel, the Golden Garter, and went inside to the bar. A bottle of sparkling wine was ordered and he filled their glasses, raising his in celebration. 'To us,' he said.

'We still got the deeds to the Leaning Ladder?' Randy asked, 'Ain't we?'

'Sure have. So ever we get tired of running a stage line we can go back to herding cows. Or do both.'

'Sounds fine,' Randy said.

Logan put an arm around Dawn's shoulders and gave her a squeeze. 'I got a postponed honeymoon to fulfill. How's that sound to you, sweetheart?'

Dawn hardly needed to reply. The warmth of her kiss said enough. 'I'm ready when you are,' she murmured. 'When's the next Pullman leave?'

'To us!' Dawn took a sip of the bubbly. 'Tell me I'm not dreaming, Josh. This has all happened so sudden-like.'

'You ain't dreaming, honey.' Josh encircled her waist with his free arm and kissed her lips. 'The wheel of fortune's spun lucky for us and that's the way it's gonna be from now on.'

Randy grabbed the bottle by the neck, took a swig, and gave a rip-roaring rebel yell. 'Yes, siree, that sure is the way it's gonna be.'

Just then the lanky Pat Garrett strode into the bar, looking even taller due to his high-heeled boots and Stetson, and called, 'Hi, glad to see you folks. I got some good news.'

He laid out a broadsheet copy of the *Las Vegas Gazette*, fresh from the press, with the front page banner headline, 'Sheriff Garrett vindicated', and the sub-head, 'Kate Quinn's testimony proved to be a pack of lies.'

'Clap your peepers on this,' Pat said. 'We've made 'em all eat their words.'

'New Mexico rejoices today as the popular Sheriff of Lincoln County, Pat Garrett was proved to be the upright, truthful man-of-action we always believed him to be,' the report began. 'Kate Quinn's testimony against him has turned out to be a tissue of lies.'

Written by the editor of the newspaper himself, it stated, 'This loathesome creature, a harlot and liar of the deepest hue, not only murdered her own husband in cold blood, but gunned down Dawn Adamson, the young and pretty newly-wed wife of another hero New Mexico can be proud to have in its midst, stage driver, Josh Logan.

'It would appear that Mrs Quinn had the hots for Josh, but the handsome young Texan stead-fastly refused her lascivious advances. So enraged was Kate that she went around spreading calumnies about the Logans, and even swore out false testimony that Josh had defrauded the stage company of 200 dollars. When such dastardly actions failed, Kate Quinn mounted her fine horse and made an unprovoked gun attack on the lovely and innocent young bride as she was about to board the train East. The evil attacker was shot dead from the saddle by stalwart frontiersman and stage guard, Randy Newbolt, as she tried to make her escape.

'The Governor of New Mexico has spoken out not only in praise of Sheriff Garrett for sticking to his guns and arraigning Kate before the courts, but in praise, too, of Josh Logan and his friend, Randy, who risked their own lives to defend the Quinns' home at Roswell when it was attacked by John Dog Crandal and his gang of 20 murderous thugs.

'Not only did the brave Texan, Logan, kill Crandal in hand-to-hand combat, but he and Randy put paid to one of the worst bands of killers that have terrorized these parts since the demise of Billy the Kid.

'That, dear citizens, is not all. Josh Logan was himself responsible for killing the heinous Ephraim 'Scarface' Entwistle when that notorious ne'er-do-well Seth Smith and his boys tried to hold up his stage. He later faced-out this lowdown pack of rustlers and robbers in Beaver's saloon at

Fort Sumner and shot dead Smith, and 'Ugly Dave' Richards, sending them to a richly deserved fate. The well-known young freight driver, Brad McNulty, came to his aid in the saloon, shooting down another notorious villain, Charley Billings.

'New Mexicans can sleep more easily in their beds tonight knowing that they have such fine, upright citizens as Sheriff Garrett, Josh Logan, Randy Newbolt and Brad McNulty dedicated to finally cleaning up this territory.

'It is understood that Paco Quinn, although subject to bursts of boozism, as we all know, had done much to build up this country and provide his ungrateful, double-crossing wife, Kate, with all the luxuries a woman could expect, unaware that she was secretly a disgrace to the name of woman-hood, and is believed to have lived a wanton lifestyle. It is further understood that he had made Mr Logan a partner in his company, and, on the death of the Quinns, Josh inherits it and will be operating the new stage line under his own name.

'Many will regret that this evil woman, Kate Quinn, could not have been hanged by the neck from a sour apple tree, burned at the stake, or, at least, imprisoned for life in a bastille on bread and water. Meanwhile, we wish the Logans good health and prosperity in running their new venture.'

'Whoo,' Josh yelled, after Garrett had read out the report word for word. 'That's some vindication. How did you get that editor to write such an abject apology after the lies he printed about us before?'

'Aw, them editors are all the same, hiding behind their desks and their highfalutin' words,' Garrett growled. 'I told the snivellin' li'l skunk that if he didn't I'd shoot him down like a dog. Publish or else!'

Garrett ordered another bottle as a photographer from the Gazette bustled in to take their pictures. 'This ain't gonna do me any harm at the polls for re-election,' he said, with his wide, gleaming grin, putting his arm around them to pose. 'What's more, I've heard from Texas that there's a thousand dollars reward due to you for killing Crandal, and five hundred each on the heads of Ugly Dave and Scarface.'

'Things are looking up,' Josh mused. 'You know, you're getting a tad old to be riding shotgun in all weathers, Randy. How about we put that cash to restocking the Leaning Ladder ranch and you run it as your own?'

'You mean it, Josh?' Randy beamed and blinked tears from his eyes. 'That's a dream. To have my own spread.'

'You deserve it and you can do it, pard,' Logan

LOGAN'S GUN

said, giving him a hug. 'Drink up now. It's time to celebrate. Here comes the whiskey.'

He had heard the thud of a barrel being rolled into the bar and it was none other than the strapping Brad McNulty. 'Waal, whadda ya know,' he yelled. 'If it ain't our other hero. Howja fancy driving the stage again, Brad?'

The young man grinned and asked, 'When do I start?'

'Tomorrow. I'm gonna trust you to take care of things while I'm away for a couple of weeks. Can you handle the new rig and take it up to White Oaks?'

'You bet I can, boss.'

'Be sure to tell Señor Martinez to hang on to my hoss, Satan, and not to sell him. We'll be returning his buggy and pair in a coupla weeks time.'

'Why?' Garrett asked. 'Where are you off to?'

Josh pulled Dawn into him and kissed her lips again. 'We'll be kinda busy,' he said. 'We're catching the next Pullman to Kansas City. We've got a delayed honeymoon to catch up on.'

Dawn eyed him, astutely. 'Couldn't we have a proper church wedding first?'

'Sure. Go dig out the preacher, Randy. We ain't got no time to lose.'

By now, folks had read the news and word had got around. There was a big crowd for their wedding in the church and a bigger one when they rolled up in the stage with Brad and Randy on the box to board the express. Logan and Dawn stood on the rear platform as their Pullman pulled out. People called good luck and cheered as the smiling Dawn tossed her bouquet to the girls. Randy fired his Greener in the air and there was a general hullabaloo as Brad drove the new stage and six alongside the track for half-a-mile or so as the train rattled off.

'There goes a couple,' the sheriff said, as he stood among the waving crowds, 'who deserve to do well in this territory.'

Garrett, alas, didn't do so well himself. He lost his job in the ensuing election of sheriff for Lincoln County. He returned to Texas and joined the Rangers. Later in life, as he stepped down from his horse on a lonesome road, he was shot in the back by an unidentified assassin. Such was the Wild West!